PRIORITY QUEUES

This is Volume 50 in
MATHEMATICS IN SCIENCE AND ENGINEERING
A series of monographs and textbooks
Edited by RICHARD BELLMAN, *University of Southern California*

A complete list of the books in this series appears at the end of this volume.

PRIORITY QUEUES

N. K. JAISWAL

1968

ACADEMIC PRESS New York and London

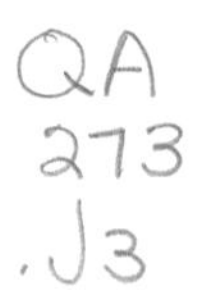

ACADEMIC PRESS, INC.
111 Fifth Avenue, New York, New York 10003

United Kingdom Edition published by
ACADEMIC PRESS, INC. (LONDON) LTD.
Berkeley Square House, London W.1

LIBRARY OF CONGRESS CATALOG CARD NUMBER: 68-14648

PRINTED IN THE UNITED STATES OF AMERICA

To My Parents

PREFACE

This book resulted from an advanced seminar course on priority queues which was given at the Case Institute of Technology, Cleveland, Ohio. The need for such a book was felt immensely by research students, as no unified account of congestion systems under priority disciplines was available. In addition, some recent attempts to apply such results in analyzing congestion behavior in time-sharing computer systems, job-shop scheduling, etc., has led to more research interest in this field. Consequently, the book is addressed primarily to research students interested in studies of congestion systems under priority disciplines or similar stochastic processes. The reader is assumed to have some familiarity with queuing theory, as well as with renewal theory and a general background in stochastic processes. The book may also be used as the basis for a one-semester course for graduate students having the above-mentioned background.

Chapters I and II summarize the results of the basic infinite-source and finite-source queuing models. Chapters III–VI are devoted to the study of priority processes under exogenous priority disciplines, i.e., head-of-the-line, preemptive-resume and preemptive-repeat, and discretionary disciplines. Chapter VII reviews some of the recent work on alternating priorities, round-robin priorities, dynamic priorities, cutoff priorities, etc. The last chapter is devoted to pointing out areas in which further work is needed.

The basic approach adopted here is to conceive of a queuing process as a sequence of busy and idle periods. The entire process is termed a "general process," and the results for the general process are related to those of the busy-period process by renewal-theoretic arguments. The busy-period process can be further subdivided into a sequence of "completion-time" processes for a class of priority disciplines which we term "exogenous." The results for the general process are obtained by studying the completion-time process and then properly "assembling." This assembling method has the obvious advantage of relating the complicated priority process to the simple completion-time process, and makes the priority study much easier for exogenous disciplines.

An effort has been made to maintain uniformity of notation as far as possible. The following points may be noted in this connection: We use the same letter to denote the random variable and its density function. For example, if b denotes the length of the busy period, the busy-period density is denoted by $b(t)$. The general-process probabilities are distinguished from the busy-period process probabilities by placing a (^) over the latter. A glossary of symbols has been appended to the end of the book.

N. K. JAISWAL

ACKNOWLEDGMENTS

The main source of inspiration in writing this book has been the Case Institute of Technology, and in particular, the Operations Research Group of the Division of Organizational Sciences, which provided all the necessary facilities. I am extremely grateful to the Research and Development Organization, Ministry of Defense, Government of India, for granting me a leave of absence. I had the privilege of working with K. Thiruvengadam, S. Subba Rao, and H. C. Jain of the Research and Development Organization, and with A. Benn and M. Estchmaier of Case Institute of Technology as they worked toward their Doctoral and Master's dissertations related to priority queues. Not only do I thank them for helping me in writing this book, but also for the many ideas which resulted from our discussions.

The suggestion to write this book came from Professor Richard V. Evans of Case Institute. I owe him a great deal for his encouragement, suggestions, and help in writing this book, and also for criticizing and suggesting improvements in the original manuscript. Other colleagues and students who helped me in this endeavor and to whom I am grateful are Professor W. Pierskalla, Dr. Peter Mevert, T. S. Chidambaram, Bruce Powell, Stuart H. Mann, and Dr. Boghos Sivazlian, all of whom belong to the Operations Research Group of the Case Institute of Technology.

Thanks are due to Miss Janet Gelb for typing the manuscript and for having helped in all secretarial work. Finally, I thank my wife and children, who had to subsist on less than their rightful share of my attention during the preparation of the manuscript.

TABLE OF CONTENTS

Chapter IV. **Preemptive Disciplines**

Chapter V. **Head-of-the-Line Priority Discipline**

Chapter VI. **Discretionary Priority Discipline**

Chapter VII. **Other Priority Disciplines**

Chapter VIII. **Areas for Further Work**

Chapter I

BASIC INFINITE-SOURCE MODEL

1. Introduction

Waiting lines have become an accepted fact of modern life. In a normal context, they mean to most of us delays which, though somewhat unpleasant, can at least be tolerated. But when congestion occurs—in industry, in transportation, in communication systems—and waiting lines are built up, they result in a blocking up of resources with consequent losses not only in time but in money as well. As such, efforts to reduce congestion are of vital importance, and this has led to the rapid growth of research activity in the mathematical study of waiting-line processes which goes by the name of "queuing theory."

Basically, a queuing or waiting-line phenomenon is described by the following model: Units emanating from a source arrive at a service facility, wait if necessary, and depart after receiving service. A mathematical study of the queuing process needs specification of the following:

(a) *Source*: A source is defined as a device or a group of devices from which units emanate and call for service. The source is said to be infinite or finite depending upon whether the number of units in the source is infinite or finite. If the source is finite but large, it is usually assumed to be infinite; for example, in telephone traffic, the subscribers to a given exchange, although finite in number, are taken to constitute an infinite source.

(b) *Input process*: Units emanating from an infinite source arrive at a service facility at times $t_0 < t_1 < t_2 < \cdots < t_k < \cdots$.

The random variables $\tau_k = t_k - t_{k-1}\,(k \geqslant 1)$ are the interarrival times. We assume that the τ_k form a sequence of independent and identically distributed random variables with the distribution

$$A(x) = \Pr\{\tau_k \leqslant x\}$$

$A(x)$ is called the arrival-time distribution.

A common form of $A(x)$ is the negative exponential distribution defined by

$$A(x) = 1 - \exp(-\lambda x)$$

where $1/\lambda$ is the mean interarrival time. It is easy to prove that in this case, the distribution of $n(t)$, the number of units that arrive in time t, follows the Poisson distribution which is given by

$$\Pr\{n(t) = n\} = \frac{(\lambda t)^n}{n!} \exp(-\lambda t)$$

However, when the source is finite, the input is defined as follows:

Consider a particular unit belonging to the source. This unit, after staying for a time τ_1' in the source, demands service for the first time. After receiving service, it returns to the source and stays for a time τ_2' before making the second demand for service. In general, it stays for a time τ_k' in the source before making the kth demand for service. Let $A(x) = \Pr\{\tau_k' \leqslant x\}$. Instead of specifying the input process through the interarrival-time distribution, which involves both the distribution of τ_k' and the size of the source, we specify the input process through the distribution of τ_k' alone.

As an example, let N be the size of the source and $A(x) = 1 - \exp(-\lambda x)$. Then the arrival process, i.e., the distribution of $n(t)$, the number of arrivals up to time t, is given by

$$\Pr\{n(t) = n\} = \binom{N}{n} [1 - \exp(-\lambda t)]^n \exp[-(N - n)\lambda t] \qquad (1.1)$$

We do not specify the arrival process as in (1.1); instead specify the distribution of τ_k' (which, in this case, is exponential).

(c) *Service process*: Let θ_k be the service time demanded by the kth arriving unit. We assume that θ_k $(k = 1, 2,\ldots)$ are identically and independently distributed random variables with the distribution function

$$F(x) = \Pr\{\theta_k \leqslant x\}$$

$F(x)$ is called the service-time distribution. We assume that the probability density function $S(x) = (d/dx)F(x)$ exists. The mean service time ν is given by

$$\nu = \int_0^\infty xS(x)\,dx = \int_0^\infty F^c(x)\,dx$$

where $F^c(x) = 1 - F(x)$ is the complementary distribution function.

(d) *Number of channels*: The service facility can have one or more channels. Queuing processes with a single channel are called single-channel or single-server queuing processes, while those with more than one channel are called multichannel or multiserver queuing processes.

(e) *Service discipline*: The rules according to which units are selected and serviced constitute the service discipline. The simplest discipline and the one frequently met in practice is the "first-come, first-served" discipline. Several others are possible, such as the random-service, last-come first-served, batch-service, and priority-service disciplines.

The reader may note that every time we wish to describe a queuing process, specifying all the above information can be a lengthy procedure. However, the same information can be conveyed in a compact way by using the abbreviated notation $a/b/c/N$ where a denotes the input distribution, b the service-time distribution, c the number of servers, and N the size of the source. Further, the following symbols are used to denote the various distributions: M—exponential distribution, D—regular distribution, E_k—k-Erlang distribution, and G—general distribution with no specification regarding its form.

Thus, a c server, finite-source (source size N) queuing model with exponential input and general service-time distribution is represented by $M/G/c/N$. If $N = \infty$, i.e., the source is infinite, the source size is not specified, so that $M/G/c$ denotes a c server, infinite-source queuing process with Poisson input and general service-time distribution.

After having specified a queuing process, we will now consider those characteristics of a queuing system which are of operational importance and through which questions pertaining to the efficient operation and control of the system can be answered. These characteristics are:

(a) *Queue length*: Queue length is specified by the number of units in the system waiting and being serviced at any time t. The determination of the distribution of queue length is of importance in any theoretical investigation and is useful in the design of the system.

(b) *Occupation time*: The occupation time of the server at any instant t is the duration of time required to complete the service of all the units which joined the queue before time t. The knowledge of the distribution of the occupation time will be useful in answering questions regarding the delay that a unit experiences either in the queue or the system.

(c) *Busy period*: We say that the server or servers are in the idle state when there are no units to be serviced in the system. The busy period is then defined as that length of time during which the server or servers remain busy servicing the units without entering the idle state. The distribution of the busy-period duration is of interest from the server's point of view.

1-1. Method of Analysis

Before we outline the method of analysis which we use in this book, we point out that a queuing process is basically a stochastic process. A stochastic process is a process in which the state of the system changes with a parameter, usually time, in a probabilistic manner. An interesting class of stochastic processes is the Markov process. A stochastic process is said to be a Markov process if the present state of the system is sufficient to predict the future without a knowledge of the past history of the system. Stochastic processes which do not exhibit the Markovian property are termed non-Markovian.

We may represent the state of the system by $\hat{m}(t)$, the queue length at time t, or by $\hat{\xi}(t)$, the occupation time of the server at time t. Let us consider the stochastic process $\{\hat{m}(t)\}$. This process is, in general, non-Markovian, because the future behavior of the process cannot be predicted with the present knowledge of the system alone, namely the number of units present in the system. For example, for the $G/G/1$ process, the future behavior of the system cannot be predicted from a knowledge of $\hat{m}(t)$ alone unless the time since the last arrival and the elapsed service time are also specified in the present state of the system. An exception is the case where the distributions underlying both the arrival and service processes are exponential, such as $M/M/c$ and $M/M/c/N$. This is because of the characteristic Markovian property of the exponential distribution.

A non-Markovian process can be studied by extracting a set of points at which the Markovian property holds good. Such points are called "regeneration points." A probabilistic definition of a regeneration point is given as follows: A point is said to be a regeneration point for the stochastic process $\{\hat{m}(t)\}$ if and only if for all $t > t_0$, $\Pr\{\hat{m}(t)|\hat{m}(t_0)\} = \Pr\{\hat{m}(t)|\hat{m}(\tau)\}$ for all $\tau \leqslant t_0$. As an example, consider the $M/G/1$ process. The set of points $\{T_n + 0\}$, where the T_n ($n = 0, 1, 2,...$), are epochs at which units depart, constitute a set of regeneration points. Hence, the queue lengths at these points constitute a Markov chain with an enumerable infinity of states and can be studied through the theory of Markov chains. This technique, due to Kendall [50], is called the "imbedded Markov chain technique" because it involves extracting a discrete-time Markov chain imbedded in the continuous-time process. Details of this technique can be found in textbooks on stochastic processes or from Kendall [50].

Another method of making the process Markovian is to incorporate the missing information by adding "supplementary variables" to the state description. The process $M/G/1$ can thus be made Markovian if the state of the system is defined by the pair $[\hat{m}(t), z]$, where z denotes the elapsed service time of the unit under service. This approach was conceived by Kendall [51], but was first used by Cox [20], and is known as the "augmentation technique" or the "supplementary variable technique."

The method of analysis adopted in this book is to conceive of a queuing process, which we refer to as the general process, as comprising alternating busy and idle periods. We discuss the busy-period process using the supplementary variable technique, although one can use the imbedded Markov chain technique as well. The general process is then studied in terms of the busy-period and the idle-period processes through renewal-theoretic arguments. This approach, due to Gaver [28], is more elegant and logical, since the characteristics during the general process can be obtained from the discussion of the corresponding characteristics during the busy-period process.

We close this section with the remark that, although this book is devoted to the study of queuing processes under various priority disciplines, we defer the discussions on priority queues to Chapter III. In the present chapter, we study the basic infinite-source model ($M/G/1$), and in the next, the basic finite-source model ($M/G/1/N$). We call these models basic because the results and the methodology of these models play a basic role in the study of priority-queuing processes.

2. Busy-Period Processes

In this section, the busy-period process of the $M/G/1$ model will be studied, the results of which will be used to study the general process in Section I, 3. We also investigate a closely related process called the initial busy-period process, the results of which will be needed in studying priority processes.

2-1. Busy-Period Process of the $M/G/1$ Model

We mentioned in the previous section that a busy period is initiated by the arrival of a unit which terminates the idle state of the server. However, we now introduce a slightly more general notion of the busy-period process, in the sense that the process need not start with one unit but with any number $i > 0$, and redefine the process as follows: Let, at time $t = 0$, the process start with $i > 0$ units, one of which enters service. During the time, these units are serviced, some more units may arrive and join the queue. Let b^i denote the time, measured from $t = 0$, at which the server becomes free for the first time. The random variable b^i is called the length of the busy period starting with $i > 0$ units. Let $m(t) > 0$ $(0 < t < b^i)$ denote the number of units present at time t during the busy-period process. We investigate the distributions of $m(t)$ and b^i by defining the following probabilities:

(i) $$p^i(m, x, t)\,dx = \Pr[m(t) = m, \quad x < z < x + dx, \quad m(t_1) > 0 \quad \text{for all} \quad t_1\,(0 < t_1 < t) \mid m(0) = i] \qquad (m > 0)$$

This is the joint probability that at time t, the busy period which started at time $t = 0$ with $i > 0$ units, is continuing, and that there are m units waiting and being served, with the elapsed service time of the unit under service lying between x and $x + dx$.

(ii) $$b^i(t)\,dt = \Pr[t < b^i < t + dt \mid m(0) = i]$$

This is the probability that the busy period which started at $t = 0$ with $i > 0$ units terminates between t and $t + dt$.

We further assume that the initial state will not be specified if $i = 1$, so that $p^1(m, x, t)$ and $b^1(t)$ will always be represented by $p(m, x, t)$ and $b(t)$, respectively.

To obtain the differential difference equations connecting these probabilities, we relate the state of the system at time $t + \Delta$ to the state at time t, and obtain

$$\begin{aligned} p^i(m, x + \Delta, t + \Delta) &= p^i(m, x, t)[1 - \{\lambda + \eta(x)\}\Delta] \\ &\quad + (1 - \delta_{m,1})\lambda \Delta p^i(m - 1, x, t) \\ &\quad + o(\Delta) \qquad (m > 0, \quad x > 0) \end{aligned} \tag{2.1}$$

where $o(\Delta)$ means that $o(\Delta)/\Delta$ tends to zero as Δ tends to zero, $\delta_{m,1}$ is the Kronecker's delta function defined as

$$\begin{aligned} \delta_{i,j} &= 1 \qquad \text{if} \quad i = j \\ &= 0 \qquad \text{if} \quad i \neq j \end{aligned}$$

and $\eta(x)\Delta$ is the first-order conditional probability that a unit completes service in the interval $(x, x + \Delta)$ conditional on its not having completed service by time x, so that

$$\eta(x) = \frac{S(x)}{1 - \int_0^x S(u)\, du} \tag{2.2}$$

or

$$S(x) = \eta(x) \exp\left[-\int_0^x \eta(u)\, du\right] \tag{2.3}$$

Taking the limit as $\Delta \to 0$, we obtain

$$\begin{aligned} &\frac{\partial}{\partial t} p^i(m, x, t) + \frac{\partial}{\partial x} p^i(m, x, t) + [\lambda + \eta(x)]p^i(m, x, t) \\ &\quad = (1 - \delta_{m,1})\lambda p^i(m - 1, x, t) \qquad (x > 0, \quad m > 0) \end{aligned} \tag{2.4}$$

To derive the boundary conditions at $x = 0$, we define

$$q^i(m, t) = \int_0^\Delta p^i(m, x, t)\, dx$$

which is the probability that at time t there are m units present, and that the service time of the unit under service lies between 0 and Δ. We obtain the following relation approximate to the first order in Δ:

$$q^i(m, t + \Delta) = \int_0^\infty p^i(m + 1, x, t)\eta(x)\,\Delta\,dx \qquad (m > 0) \tag{2.5}$$

Expanding the left-hand side and taking the limit as $\Delta \to 0$, we obtain

$$p^i(m, 0, t) = \int_0^\infty p^i(m + 1, x, t)\eta(x)\,dx \qquad (m \geqslant 1) \tag{2.6}$$

Also, as the busy-period process terminates, if the completion of service of a unit makes the system empty, we have

$$b^i(t) = \int_0^\infty p^i(1, x, t)\eta(x)\,dx \tag{2.7}$$

Equations (2.4), (2.6), and (2.7) are to be solved subject to the initial condition[†]

$$p^i(m, x, 0) = \delta(x)\,\delta_{i,m} \tag{2.8}$$

where $\delta(x)$ is the Dirac delta function defined as zero for all x other than $x = 0$ and such that $\int_{-\infty}^{\infty} \delta(x)\,dx = 1$.

We introduce the generating function

$$\Pi^i(\alpha, x, t) = \sum_{m=1}^{\infty} p^i(m, x, t)\alpha^m \qquad (|\,\alpha\,| \leqslant 1)$$

and obtain

$$\frac{\partial}{\partial t}\Pi^i(\alpha, x, t) + \frac{\partial}{\partial x}\Pi^i(\alpha, x, t) + [\lambda(1 - \alpha) + \eta(x)]\Pi^i(\alpha, x, t) = 0 \tag{2.9}$$

$$\Pi^i(\alpha, 0, t) = \frac{1}{\alpha}\int_0^\infty \Pi^i(\alpha, x, t)\eta(x)\,dx - b^i(t) \tag{2.10}$$

[†] From physical considerations, one would like to replace the upper limit of the integrals in (2.5) to (2.7) by t. In general the upper limit depends upon the initial condition and may extend to infinity. However, the assumed initial condition (2.8) implies that the integrands in (2.5) to (2.7) vanish for $x > t$ [$a^i(\alpha, t) = 0$ for $t < 0$ and therefore $\Pi^i(\alpha, x, t) = 0$ for $x > t$]. As such, we retain the upper limit in these integrals as infinity.

The solution of (2.9) is given by

$$\Pi^i(\alpha, x, t) = a^i(\alpha, t - x) \exp\left[-\{\lambda(1 - \alpha)\}x - \int_0^x \eta(u)\, du\right] \tag{2.11}$$

where $a^i(\alpha, t)$ is an unknown function which is determined by using the boundary condition at $x = 0$ and the initial condition (2.8). Hence,

$$\begin{aligned} a^i(\alpha, t) &= \Pi^i(\alpha, 0, t) && (t > 0) \\ &= \alpha^i \delta(-t) \exp\left[-\{\lambda(1 - \alpha)\}t + \int_0^{-t} \eta(u)\, du\right] && (t \leqslant 0) \end{aligned}$$

Henceforth, we denote the Laplace transform of any function $f(t)$ by $\bar{f}(s)$, so that

$$\bar{f}(s) = \int_0^\infty f(t) \exp(-st)\, dt \qquad (\mathrm{Re}(s) \geqslant 0)$$

where $\mathrm{Re}(s)$ denotes the real part of s. Substituting (2.11) in (2.10) and taking the Laplace transform, we have, after using (2.3),

$$\bar{\Pi}^i(\alpha, 0, s) = \frac{\alpha^{i-1}\bar{S}[\lambda(1 - \alpha) + s] - \bar{b}^i(s)}{1 - (1/\alpha)\bar{S}[\lambda(1 - \alpha) + s]} \tag{2.12}$$

$$\bar{\Pi}^i(\alpha, x, s) = \frac{\alpha^i - \bar{b}^i(s)}{1 - (1/\alpha)\bar{S}[\lambda(1 - \alpha) + s]} \times \exp\left[-\{\lambda(1 - \alpha) + s\}x - \int_0^x \eta(u)\, du\right] \tag{2.13}$$

To evaluate $\bar{b}^i(s)$, we use the following results:

The equation $\alpha = \bar{S}[\lambda(1 - \alpha) + s]$ has a unique root $\bar{b}(s)$ inside the unit circle $|\alpha| = 1$ if $\mathrm{Re}(s) > 0$ or $\mathrm{Re}(s) = 0$ and $\lambda\nu > 1$, where

$$\nu = \int_0^\infty x S(x)\, dx$$

Specifically, $\bar{b}(0)$ is the smallest positive root of the equation $\alpha = \bar{S}[\lambda(1 - \alpha)]$. If $\lambda\nu > 1$, $\bar{b}(0) < 1$, and if $\lambda\nu \leqslant 1$, $\bar{b}(0) = 1$. For proof, we refer to the proof of a more general lemma by Takács [86, p. 47].

Now, since $\bar{\Pi}^i(\alpha, x, s)$ is the generating function of the Laplace transform of the probabilities, it must be bounded inside and on the unit circle $|\alpha| = 1$. Since the denominator of (2.13) has a zero $\bar{b}(s)$ inside or on the unit circle $|\alpha| = 1$ for $\mathrm{Re}(s) \geqslant 0$, the numerator must vanish at $\alpha = \bar{b}(s)$, so that the Laplace transform of the busy-period density is given by

$$\bar{b}^i(s) = [\bar{b}(s)]^i \tag{2.14}$$

where

$$\bar{b}(s) = \bar{S}[\lambda\{1 - \bar{b}(s)\} + s] \tag{2.15}$$

and

$$\bar{\Pi}^i(\alpha, x, s) = \frac{\alpha^i - [\bar{b}(s)]^i}{1 - (1/\alpha)\bar{S}[\lambda(1-\alpha) + s]} \times \exp\left[-\{\lambda(1-\alpha) + s\}x - \int_0^x \eta(u)\,du\right] \tag{2.16}$$

From the above results, it follows that if $\lambda\nu > 1$, then $\int_0^\infty b(t)\,dt < 1$, i.e., the busy period may never terminate, while if $\lambda\nu < 1$, the busy period will certainly terminate. Also, if $E[b^i]$ represents the mean busy period starting with i units, we have, from (2.14) and (2.15),

$$\begin{aligned} E[b^i] &= \frac{\nu i}{1 - \lambda\nu} && \text{if } \lambda\nu < 1 \\ &= \infty && \text{if } \lambda\nu \geqslant 1 \end{aligned} \tag{2.17}$$

Thus, if $\lambda\nu = 1$, the busy period terminates with probability one but has an infinite mean, while if $\lambda\nu > 1$, the busy period may not terminate. This corresponds to recurrent null and transient cases in Markov chain analysis.

Now, if $\bar{p}_e{}^i(m, s)$ represents the Laplace transform of the probability that at time t a unit enters service during the busy period which was initiated at $t = 0$ with $i > 0$ units, and there are $m - 1$ units waiting in queue, then, from (2.16), we have

$$\bar{\Pi}_e{}^i(\alpha, s) = \sum_{m=1}^{\infty} \alpha^m \bar{p}_e{}^i(m, s) = \frac{\alpha^i - [\bar{b}(s)]^i}{1 - (1/\alpha)\bar{S}[\lambda(1-\alpha) + s]} \tag{2.18}$$

Finally, if $\bar{p}^i(m, s)$ represents the Laplace transform of the probability that there are m units present at time t during the busy period initiated at $t = 0$ with $i > 0$ units, we have, integrating (2.16) and using (2.3),

$$\bar{\Pi}^i(\alpha, s) = \sum_{m=1}^{\infty} \bar{p}^i(m, s)\alpha^m = \bar{\Pi}_e{}^i(\alpha, s) \frac{1 - \bar{S}[\lambda(1-\alpha) + s]}{\lambda(1-\alpha) + s} \tag{2.19}$$

2-2. Initial Busy Period Process of the *M/G/*1 Model

Suppose that at time $t = 0$, the process starts with the server becoming occupied with ancillary duties. The server remains occupied with the ancillary duties for a random length of time having the probability density $\Omega(y)$. We call $\Omega(y)$ the initial occupation-time density. During the initial occupation time, the units may arrive but are not serviced. If there is no unit after the initial occupation time, the process terminates, while if there are $i > 0$ units, the server starts serving, and a busy period, as described above, is initiated. Let the process terminate after a random length of time b^Ω which has the density $b^\Omega(t)$. Such a process is called the initial busy-period process and $b^\Omega(t)$ is called the initial busy-period density. Let the process be defined by the following probabilities:

(i) $q^\Omega(m, t) = \Pr[m(t) = m, \quad t < \Omega \mid m(0) = 0] \qquad (m \geqslant 0)$

(ii) $p^\Omega(m, x, t)\, dx = \Pr[m(t) = m, \quad x < z < x + dx, \quad \Omega < t < b^\Omega \mid m(0) = 0] \qquad (m \geqslant 1)$

(iii) $b^\Omega(t)\, dt = \Pr[t < b^\Omega < t + dt \mid m(0) = 0]$

Then,

$$q^\Omega(m, t) = \frac{(\lambda t)^m}{m!} \exp(-\lambda t) \int_t^\infty \Omega(y)\, dy \tag{2.20}$$

and

$$p^\Omega(m, x, t) = \sum_{i=0}^{\infty} \left[\frac{(\lambda t)^i}{i!} \exp(-\lambda t)\Omega(t)\right] * p^i(m, x, t) \tag{2.21}$$

where $*$ denotes the convolution operation and $p^i(m, x, t)$ is as defined at the beginning of this section.

Thus,

$$\bar{\Pi}^\Omega(\alpha, x, s) = \sum_{m=1}^{\infty} \alpha^m \bar{p}^\Omega(m, x, s)$$

$$= \sum_{m=1}^{\infty} \alpha^m \sum_{i=0}^{\infty} \bar{p}^i(m, x, s) \int_0^\infty \frac{(\lambda\tau)^i}{i!} \exp[-(\lambda + s)\tau]\Omega(\tau)\, d\tau \tag{2.22}$$

Hence, using (2.16), we obtain

$$\bar{\Pi}^{\Omega}(\alpha, x, s) = \sum_{i=0}^{\infty} \frac{\alpha^i - [\bar{b}(s)]^i}{1 - (1/\alpha)\bar{S}[\lambda(1-\alpha)+s]} \times \exp\left[-\{\lambda(1-\alpha)+s\}x - \int_0^x \eta(u)\,du\right] \times \int_0^{\infty} \frac{(\lambda\tau)^i}{i!} \exp[-(\lambda+s)\tau]\Omega(\tau)\,d\tau$$

$$= \frac{\bar{\Omega}[\lambda(1-\alpha)+s] - \bar{\Omega}[\lambda\{1-\bar{b}(s)\}+s]}{1-(1/\alpha)\bar{S}[\lambda(1-\alpha)+s]} \times \exp\left[-\{\lambda(1-\alpha)+s\}x - \int_0^x \eta(u)\,du\right] \qquad (2.23)$$

Similarly,

$$\bar{\Pi}_1^{\Omega}(\alpha, s) = \sum_{m=0}^{\infty} \alpha^m \bar{q}^{\Omega}(m, s) = \sum_{m=0}^{\infty} \alpha^m \int_0^{\infty} \frac{(\lambda t)^m}{m!} \exp[-(\lambda+s)t]\,dt \int_t^{\infty} \Omega(y)\,dy$$

$$= \int_0^{\infty} \exp[-\{\lambda(1-\alpha)+s\}t] \int_t^{\infty} \Omega(y)\,dy\,dt$$

$$= \frac{1-\bar{\Omega}[\lambda(1-\alpha)+s]}{\lambda(1-\alpha)+s} \qquad (2.24)$$

and

$$b^{\Omega}(t) = \sum_{i=0}^{\infty} \left[\frac{(\lambda t)^i}{i!} \exp(-\lambda t)\Omega(t)\right] * b^i(t) \qquad (2.25)$$

so that

$$\bar{b}^{\Omega}(s) = \bar{\Omega}[\lambda\{1-\bar{b}(s)\}+s] \qquad (2.26)$$

If $E[b^{\Omega}]$ represents the expected length of the initial busy period, we have

$$E[b^{\Omega}] = \frac{E(\Omega)}{1-\lambda\nu} \quad \text{if} \quad \lambda\nu < 1, \quad E(\Omega) < \infty$$
$$= \infty \quad \text{otherwise} \qquad (2.27)$$

3. General Process—Stochastic Behavior of the Process $\{\hat{m}(t)\}$

The general process consists of alternating busy and idle periods. Let us assume that the general process starts at time $t = 0$ with

i units ($i \geqslant 0$), and that if $i > 0$, a unit enters service. If $\{\tilde{t}_1, \tilde{t}_2, ...\}$ denotes the sequence at which busy periods start, the sequence $\{\tau_k = \tilde{t}_k - \tilde{t}_{k-1}\}$ ($k \geqslant 2$) is composed of identically and independently distributed random variables each having density $r(t)$ such that

$$r(t) = b(t) * \lambda \exp(-\lambda t) \tag{3.1}$$

since each τ_k ($k \geqslant 2$) is the convolution of a busy period starting with one unit and an idle period. Hence,

$$\bar{r}(s) = \frac{\lambda}{\lambda + s} \bar{b}(s) \tag{3.2}$$

Obviously, τ_1, the time to the first renewal, depends upon the initial condition. If $r_1{}^i(t)$ denotes the density of τ_1 when the process starts with i units ($i \geqslant 0$) we have

$$\begin{aligned} r_1{}^i(t) &= b^i(t) * \lambda \exp(-\lambda t) \qquad (i > 0) \\ &= \lambda \exp(-\lambda t) \qquad (i = 0) \end{aligned} \tag{3.3}$$

Hence

$$\bar{r}_1{}^i(s) = \frac{\lambda}{\lambda + s} \bar{b}^i(s) \qquad (i \geqslant 0) \tag{3.4}$$

where we define $\bar{b}^0(s) = 1$.

From the above, it is obvious that the sequence of random variables τ_k ($k \geqslant 1$) constitutes a modified renewal process. Hence, if $h^i(t)$ denotes the renewal density, i denoting the initial number of units in the system, we have [21, p. 54]:

$$\bar{h}^i(s) = \frac{\lambda \bar{b}^i(s)}{\lambda + s - \lambda \bar{b}(s)} \tag{3.5}$$

Now, let us define the following probabilities for the general process:

(i) $\hat{p}^i(m, x, t)\, dx = \Pr[\hat{m}(t) = m, \quad x < z < x + dx \mid \hat{m}(0) = i]$ $(m > 0)$

(ii) $\hat{e}^i(t) = \Pr[\hat{m}(t) = 0 \mid \hat{m}(0) = i]$

If the general process starts with no unit, i.e., $i = 0$, the superscript (i) denoting the initial condition will be dropped.

These probabilities can be related to the busy-period probabilities obtained in the earlier section in the following way: When the system reaches the specified state, a renewal may or may not have occurred. Since $h^i(t)\,dt$ is the probability of a renewal occurring in the time interval $(t, t + dt)$, we have

$$\hat{p}^i(m, x, t) = p^i(m, x, t) + h^i(t) * p(m, x, t) \qquad (m > 0) \tag{3.6}$$

$$\hat{e}^i(t) = l^i(t) + h^i(t) * l^1(t) \tag{3.7}$$

where

$$l^i(t) = b^i(t) * \exp(-\lambda t) \tag{3.8}$$

These equations hold good for $i = 0$ if we specify $p^0(m, x, t) \equiv 0$ and $b^0(t) = \delta(t)$. Finally, if $\hat{p}^i(m, t)$ represents the probability that there are m units present during the general process, i denoting as usual the initial state of the system, and if

$$\hat{\Pi}^i(\alpha, t) = \hat{e}^i(t) + \sum_{m=1}^{\infty} \alpha^m \hat{p}^i(m, t) \tag{3.9}$$

represents the generating function, we have

$$\bar{\hat{\Pi}}^i(\alpha, s) = \bar{\hat{e}}^i(s)[1 + \lambda\bar{\Pi}(\alpha, s)] + \bar{\Pi}^i(\alpha, s) \tag{3.10}$$

The last term vanishes if $i = 0$, since $p^0(m, x, t) \equiv 0$. Also, from (3.5), (3.7), and (3.8), taking the Laplace transform, we get

$$\bar{\hat{e}}^i(s) = \frac{\bar{b}^i(s)}{\lambda + s} + \frac{\lambda\bar{b}^i(s)}{s + \lambda - \lambda\bar{b}(s)}\,\frac{\bar{b}(s)}{\lambda + s} = \frac{\bar{b}^i(s)}{\lambda + s - \lambda\bar{b}(s)} \tag{3.11}$$

so that

$$\bar{\hat{e}}^i(s) = [\bar{b}(s)]^i/\{\lambda + s - \lambda\bar{b}(s)\} = \frac{1}{\lambda}\,\bar{h}^i(s) \tag{3.12}$$

For $i = 0$, the above relations reduce to

$$\bar{\hat{\Pi}}(\alpha, s) = \bar{\hat{e}}(s)[1 + \lambda\bar{\Pi}(\alpha, s)] \tag{3.13}$$

so that using (2.19), we get

$$\bar{\hat{\Pi}}(\alpha, s) = \bar{\hat{e}}(s)\left[1 + \lambda\bar{\Pi}_e(\alpha, s)\,\frac{1 - \bar{S}\{\lambda(1-\alpha) + s\}}{\lambda(1-\alpha) + s}\right] \tag{3.14}$$

where

$$\bar{\hat{e}}(s) = [\lambda + s - \lambda\bar{b}(s)]^{-1} \tag{3.15}$$

4. Limiting Behavior of the Process $\{\hat{m}(t)\}$

To study the limiting behavior of the random variable $\hat{m}(t)$ as $t \to \infty$, we use the following results due to Smith [79]. If (i) the renewal periods are nonnegative and have expectation $E(\tau)$ such that $E(\tau) \leqslant \infty$, (ii) $r(t)$ is of the class $L_{1+\delta}$ for some $\delta > 0$,† i.e.,

$$\int_0^\infty |r(t)|^{1+\delta}\, dt < \infty$$

and (iii) $r(t) \to 0$ as $t \to \infty$, then

$$\lim_{t\to\infty} h^i(t) = \frac{1}{E(\tau)} \tag{4.1}$$

the limit being taken as zero if $E(\tau)$ is infinite. And, if $f(t)$ is a nonnegative, nonincreasing function of $t \geqslant 0$, integrable over $(0, \infty)$,

$$\lim_{t\to\infty} f(t) * h^i(t) = \frac{1}{E(\tau)} \int_0^\infty f(t)\, dt \tag{4.2}$$

Now, for the process under study

$$\begin{aligned} E(\tau) &= \frac{1}{\lambda} + \frac{\nu}{1-\lambda\nu} = \frac{1}{\lambda(1-\lambda\nu)} && \text{if} \quad \lambda\nu < 1 \\ &= \infty && \text{if} \quad \lambda\nu \geqslant 1 \end{aligned} \tag{4.3}$$

so that $\lim_{t\to\infty} h^i(t) = \lambda(1-\rho)$ if $\rho = \lambda\nu < 1$, and $\lim_{t\to\infty} h^i(t) = 0$ if $\rho \geqslant 1$. ρ is called the traffic intensity.

Using these results in (3.6) and (3.7), we obtain the following steady-state results:

If $\hat{p}(m) = \lim_{t\to\infty} \hat{p}(m, t)$ denotes the steady-state probability that there are $m > 0$ units in the system, and $\hat{e} = \lim_{t\to\infty} \hat{e}(t)$, the probability that the system is empty, then

$$\begin{aligned} \hat{p}(m) &= \frac{1}{E(\tau)} \int_0^\infty p(m, t)\, dt = \lambda(1-\rho) \int_0^\infty p(m, t)\, dt && \text{if} \quad \rho < 1 \\ &= 0 && \text{if} \quad \rho \geqslant 1 \end{aligned} \tag{4.4}$$

† The Lebesgue class L_p denotes the class of functions $f(x)$ such that $f(x)$ is measureable and $|f(x)|^p$ ($p > 0$) is integrable. (See E. C. Titchmarsh, "The Theory of Functions," p. 381. Oxford University Press, New York and London, 1961.)

(observe that the result $\int_0^\infty p(m, t)\, dt = \bar{p}(m, 0)$ can be obtained from (2.19) by putting $s = 0$ and evaluating the coefficient of α^m), and

$$\begin{aligned}\hat{e} = \frac{1}{E(\tau)} \int_0^\infty b(t) * \exp(-\lambda t)\, dt &= 1 - \rho \qquad \text{if} \quad \rho < 1 \\ &= 0 \qquad\quad\;\; \text{if} \quad \rho \geqslant 1 \end{aligned} \tag{4.5}$$

Hence, if $\rho < 1$, the system settles down to the steady state irrespective of the initial conditions, and if

$$\hat{\Pi}(\alpha) = \sum_{m=1}^{\infty} \hat{p}(m)\alpha^m + \hat{e}$$

represents the generating function of the steady state probabilities, we have

$$\hat{\Pi}(\alpha) = \frac{(\alpha - 1)\hat{e}}{\dfrac{\alpha}{\bar{S}[\lambda(1 - \alpha)]} - 1} \tag{4.6}$$

where

$$\hat{e} = 1 - \rho \tag{4.7}$$

The same results are obtained if the limiting behavior of the queue-length distribution is examined by the imbedded Markov chain analysis, in which case we consider the queue lengths only at those points at which customers depart. If t_m $(m = 1, 2,...)$ represents the points at which customers depart, it is obvious that the set $\{\hat{m}(t_m)\ (m = 1, 2,...)\}$ is a subset of the set $\{\hat{m}(t), t \in C\}$, where C is the set of all points on the real line. The limit of a subset need not be the same as the limit of the set; however, it just happens that for the process $M/G/1$, these limits are identical. We will see later that these limits are not the same for finite-source as well as for priority models.

Differentiating (4.6) with respect to α at $\alpha = 1$ yields

$$E(\hat{m}) = \rho + \frac{\lambda^2 E(S^2)}{2(1 - \rho)} \tag{4.8}$$

where $\rho = \lambda\nu$ is the traffic intensity and $E(S^2)$ denotes the second moment of the service-time distribution. From (4.8), it is easy to show that the ratio of the value of $E(\hat{m})$ when the service time is constant to the value of $E(\hat{m})$ when the service-time distribution is

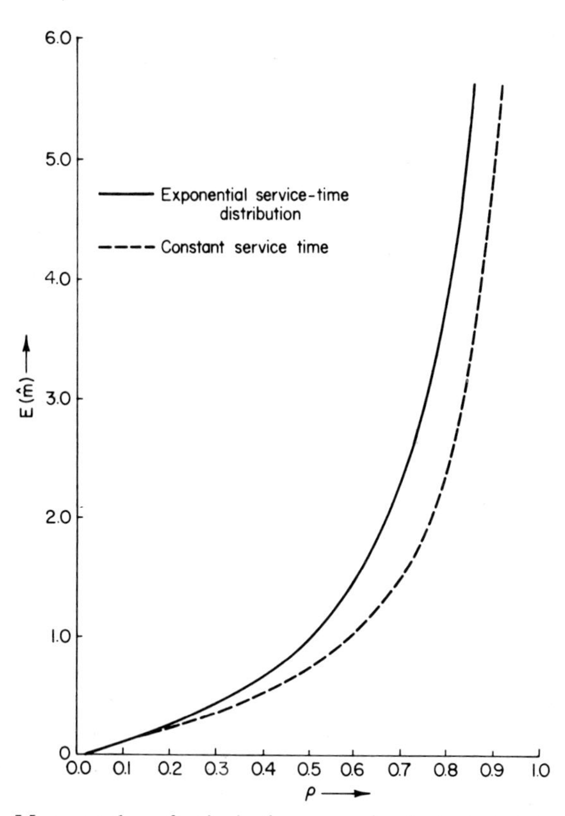

FIG. I.1. Mean number of units in the system for the basic infinite-source model.

exponential but has the same mean, approaches $\frac{1}{2}$ as $\rho \to 1$. Figure I.1 depicts the behavior of $E(\hat{m})$ as ρ varies from 0 to 1. For lower values of ρ, the effect of reducing the service-time variability in diminishing the mean congestion is less, but increases rapidly as $\rho \to 1$.

It may be noted that in (4.4), $\int_0^\infty p(m, t)\, dt$ represents the expected duration of time for which there are $m > 0$ units during a busy period. To show this, let us consider the indicator function defined as follows: if m units are present at time t during a busy period, the indicator function $\alpha_m(t) = 1$, otherwise, $\alpha_m(t) = 0$. Then, T_m, the time for which there are m units during a busy period is given by

$$T_m = \int_0^\infty \alpha_m(t)\, dt$$

so that

$$E(T_m) = E\left(\int_0^\infty \alpha_m(t)\,dt\right) = \int_0^\infty E[\alpha_m(t)]\,dt = \int_0^\infty p(m, t)\,dt \tag{4.9}$$

Hence, (4.4) and (4.5) can be written as

$$\hat{p}(m) = \frac{E(b)}{E(\tau)}\frac{E(T_m)}{E(b)} = \frac{E(b)}{E(\tau)}p(m) \tag{4.10}$$

$$\hat{e} = \frac{E(I)}{E(\tau)} \tag{4.11}$$

where $E(I)$ is the expected duration of an idle period and $p(m)$ represents the conditional probability that there are m units during a busy period, given that the busy period is in progress. The equivalence of $p(m)$ and $E(T_m)/E(b)$ can be easily established as follows:

Let us consider a large number N of such busy periods, and let $T_{m,i}$ be the total time during the ith $(1 \leqslant i \leqslant N)$ busy period that there are m units, and b_i be the length of the ith $(1 \leqslant i \leqslant N)$ busy period. Then, with probability one,

$$p(m) = \lim_{N\to\infty} \frac{\sum_{i=1}^{N} T_{m,i}}{\sum_{i=1}^{N} b_i} = \lim_{N\to\infty} \frac{\frac{1}{N}\sum_{i=1}^{N} T_{m,i}}{\frac{1}{N}\sum_{i=1}^{N} b_i}$$

$$= \frac{E(T_m)}{E(b)} \tag{4.12}$$

by the law of large numbers.

In the following example, we give an alternative interpretation and derivation of the above results.

Example A

The general process considered as a sequence of alternating idle and busy periods is the familiar zero-one renewal process [71, p. 39], and, therefore, if the process has been in operation for a long time, the expected proportion of time $\hat{e}$ the system is in the "zero" cycle (empty) is given by

$$\hat{e} = \frac{E(I)}{E(I) + E(b)} = \frac{E(I)}{E(\tau)} \tag{4.13}$$

and the expected proportion of time the system is in "one" cycle (busy) is given by

$$\sum_{m=1}^{\infty} p(m) = \frac{E(b)}{E(I) + E(b)} = \frac{E(b)}{E(\tau)} \tag{4.14}$$

Since $p(m)$ is the probability that during a busy period there are m units, we have

$$\hat{p}(m) = \frac{E(b)}{E(\tau)} p(m) \tag{4.15}$$

where, from (4.9) and (4.12), $p(m)$ is given by

$$p(m) = \frac{1}{E(b)} \int_0^{\infty} p(m, t)\, dt = \frac{\bar{p}(m, 0)}{E(b)} \tag{4.16}$$

Example B

We may remark that the steady-state probabilities can also be obtained using the Tauberian theorem on the Laplace transform, i.e., $\hat{p}(m) = \lim_{s\to 0} s\bar{\hat{p}}(m, s)$ and $\hat{e} = \lim_{s\to 0} s\bar{\hat{e}}(s)$ provided the limits exist. The above results follow directly from (3.13) and (3.15).

5. Some Generalizations

During the above derivation, we confined our attention to the queue length. However, one can extract more information about the system behavior by making a more comprehensive description of the state of the system. For example, if one also wishes to investigate the distribution of the number of units serviced, one may do so by incorporating information on the number of units serviced in the state description. For the busy period process, we may define

(i) $p^i(m, n, x, t)\, dx = \Pr[m(t) = m, n(t) = n,\ x < z_{n+1} < x + dx \mid m(0) = i,\ m(t_1) > 0 \text{ for all } t_1,\ (0 < t_1 < t)]$

(ii) $b^i(n, t)\, dt = \Pr[t < b^i < t + dt,\ n(t) = n \mid m(0) = i]$

Here, $n(t)$ denotes the number of units serviced, and z_{n+1} the elapsed service time of the $(n + 1)$th unit at time t. The method of solution is the same, except that we use double generating functions and require the more general lemma [86, p. 47]. Several variants of the basic model, such as those noted in the following examples, can also be studied by the above analysis.

Example A. Batch Arrivals

If units arrive in batches instead of arriving singly, but all other assumptions hold good, it can be shown that

$$\sum_{n=1}^{\infty} \alpha^n \bar{b}^i(n, s) = \bar{x}(s, \alpha) \tag{5.1}$$

where $\bar{x}(s, \alpha)$ is the root of the equation $\beta = \alpha \bar{S}[s + \lambda\{1 - \delta(\beta)\}]$, where $\delta(\beta) = \sum_{k=1}^{\infty} \beta^k \delta_k$ and δ_k is the probability that the batch size is k. This model has been studied by Gaver [28].

Example B. Batch Arrivals with Balking

In the above model, if each unit in the batch either joins the queue with probability p or departs immediately with probability $q = 1 - p$, it can be proved that if $\lambda p \nu < 1$, the busy periods end in finite time with probability 1, and if $\lambda p \nu > 1$, the busy periods last indefinitely with probability $1 - \epsilon$, where ϵ is the smallest root of the equation $\beta = \bar{S}[\lambda - \lambda\delta(p\beta + q)]$. This result is due to Gaver [28].

6. Occupation Time of the Server

Let $\hat{\xi}^i(t)$ denote the time at the instant t needed to complete the service of all those units which joined the queue before t in the general process. We call $\hat{\xi}^i(t)$ the occupation time of the server at time t and denote its density by $\hat{w}^i(\tau, t)$. Since the service discipline is "first come, first served," the occupation time is equal to the virtual waiting time, i.e., the time a unit would wait if it happened to arrive at instant t. We proceed to evaluate $\hat{w}^i(\tau, t)$ by studying the stochastic behavior of the random variable $\xi^i(t)$, which denotes the occupation time of the server at time t of the busy period starting with i units, and then use renewal-theoretic arguments, as in Section I, 4.

6-1. Derivation of $w^i(\tau, t)$

Let $w^i(\tau, t)\, d\tau = \Pr[\tau < \xi^i(t) < \tau + d\tau \mid m(0) = i > 0]$ denote the probability that the occupation time of the server at time t of the busy period which started at time $t = 0$ with $i > 0$ units lies between τ and $\tau + d\tau$. Then,

$$w^i(\tau, t) = \sum_{m=1}^{\infty} \int_{x=0}^{\infty} \int_{y=0}^{\tau} p^i(m, x, t) \frac{S(x + y)}{1 - \int_0^x S(u)\, du} S^{(m-1)*}(\tau - y)\, dy\, dx \tag{6.1}$$

This follows because at time t, the busy period process is in the state (m, x) with probability $p^i(m, x, t)$, and in order for the occupation time to lie between τ and $\tau + d\tau$, the unit under service and the remaining $(m - 1)$ units waiting in queue must complete service between τ and $\tau + d\tau$. The $S^{(m-1)*}(\tau)$ denotes the $(m - 1)$-fold convolution of $S(\tau)$ with itself, and we define $S^{0*}(\tau) = \delta(\tau)$. Denoting the double Laplace transform of a function $f(\tau, t)$ by $\bar{f}(\theta, s)$ such that

$$\bar{f}(\theta, s) = \int_{t=0}^{\infty} \int_{\tau=0}^{\infty} \exp[-(st + \theta\tau)] f(\tau, t)\, dt\, d\tau \tag{6.2}$$

we have, using (2.16),

$$\begin{aligned}
\bar{w}^i(\theta, s) &= \sum_{m=1}^{\infty} \int_{x=0}^{\infty} \bar{p}^i(m, x, s)[\bar{S}(\theta)]^{m-1} \\
&\quad \times \int_0^{\infty} \frac{S(x+y)}{1 - \int_0^x S(u)\, du} \exp(-\theta y)\, dy\, dx \\
&= \frac{[\bar{S}(\theta)]^i - [\bar{b}(s)]^i}{\bar{S}(\theta) - \bar{S}[\lambda\{1 - \bar{S}(\theta)\} + s]} \\
&\quad \times \int_0^{\infty} \int_0^{\infty} S(x+y) \exp(-\theta y) \exp - \{[\lambda\{1 - \bar{S}(\theta)\} + s]x\}\, dy\, dx \\
&= \frac{[\bar{S}(\theta)]^i - [\bar{b}(s)]^i}{\bar{S}(\theta) - \bar{S}[\lambda\{1 - \bar{S}(\theta)\} + s]} \, \frac{\bar{S}[\lambda\{1 - \bar{S}(\theta)\} + s] - \bar{S}(\theta)}{\theta - s - \lambda\{1 - \bar{S}(\theta)\}} \\
&= \frac{[\bar{b}(s)]^i - [\bar{S}(\theta)]^i}{\theta - s - \lambda\{1 - \bar{S}(\theta)\}}
\end{aligned} \tag{6.3}$$

We briefly outline the derivation of the occupation time density for the initial busy period process before using (6.3) to derive $\hat{w}^i(\tau, t)$.

Occupation Time Density for the Initial Busy-Period Process

If $w^{\Omega}(\tau, t)\, d\tau$ represents the probability that the occupation time of the server at time t during the initial busy-period process lies between τ and $\tau + d\tau$, it follows that

$$\begin{aligned}
w^{\Omega}(\tau, t) &= \sum_{m=0}^{\infty} \int_{x=0}^{\tau} q^{\Omega}(m, t) \frac{\Omega(t+x)}{1 - \int_0^t \Omega(u)\, du} S^{m*}(\tau - x)\, dx \\
&\quad + \sum_{m=1}^{\infty} \int_{x=0}^{\infty} \int_{y=0}^{\tau} p^{\Omega}(m, x, t) \frac{S(x+y)}{1 - \int_0^x S(u)\, du} S^{(m-1)*}(\tau - y)\, dy\, dx
\end{aligned} \tag{6.4}$$

Using the results of the initial busy-period process of Section I, 2 and proceeding as above, we obtain

$$\bar{w}^{\Omega}(\theta, s) = \frac{\bar{\Omega}[s + \lambda\{1 - \bar{b}(s)\}] - \bar{\Omega}(\theta)}{\theta - s - \lambda\{1 - \bar{S}(\theta)\}} \tag{6.5}$$

The above results will be used in later chapters to study priority processes.

6-2. Derivation of $\hat{w}^i(\tau, t)$

To evaluate $\hat{w}^i(\tau, t)$, the occupation-time density for the general process starting at $t = 0$ with $i \geqslant 0$ units, we observe that if at time t the system is empty, the unit will be immediately taken for service, and if the server is busy, the unit will have to wait for a random time with density specified by (6.3). Hence, following the method of Section I, 3, we get

$$\hat{w}^i(\tau, t) = \hat{e}^i(t)\delta(\tau) + w^i(\tau, t) + h^i(t) * w(\tau, t) \tag{6.6}$$

where we assume, following our general convention, that $w^1(\tau, t) = w(\tau, t)$ and $w^0(\tau, t) = 0$.

Hence, taking the Laplace transform and using (3.12), we obtain

$$\bar{\hat{w}}^i(\theta, s) = \bar{\hat{e}}^i(s) + \bar{w}^i(\theta, s) + \lambda\bar{\hat{e}}^i(s)\bar{w}(\theta, s) \tag{6.7}$$

If $i = 0$, i.e., the system starts with the empty state, we have

$$\bar{\hat{w}}(\theta, s) = \bar{\hat{e}}(s)[1 + \lambda\bar{w}(\theta, s)] \tag{6.8}$$

so that, using (3.15) and (6.3), we get

$$\bar{\hat{w}}(\theta, s) = \frac{\theta\bar{\hat{e}}(s) - 1}{\theta - s - \lambda[1 - \bar{S}(\theta)]} \tag{6.9}$$

6-3. Steady-State Occupation-Time Density

If $\hat{w}$ is the random variable denoting the occupation time of the server under steady state and has the density $\hat{w}(\tau)$, it follows from Section I, 4 that if $\rho < 1$, $\hat{w}(\tau) = \lim_{t\to\infty} \hat{w}(\tau, t)$ exists, and, applying Smith's theorem (see Section I, 4) to (6.6), we get

$$\hat{w}(\tau) = \hat{e}\,\delta(\tau) + \lambda(1 - \rho)\int_0^{\infty} w(\tau, t)\,dt \tag{6.10}$$

It may be noted that $\hat{w}(\tau)$ is the same as the waiting-time density, i.e., the density of the time a unit has to wait in queue under steady state. Taking the Laplace transform and using (6.3), the Laplace transform of the waiting-time density is given by

$$\bar{\hat{w}}(\theta) = \hat{e}\left[1 - \frac{\lambda}{\theta}\{1 - \bar{S}(\theta)\}\right]^{-1} \tag{6.11}$$

Since the limiting behavior of $\hat{\xi}(t)$ follows from the limiting behavior of $\hat{m}(t)$, (6.11) can also be obtained directly from (6.9), using Tauberian arguments.

Finally, if $E(\hat{w})$ denotes the average waiting time of a unit in the queue, we have

$$E(\hat{w}) = \frac{\lambda E(S^2)}{2(1 - \rho)} \tag{6.12}$$

Also, if $E(\hat{d})$ denotes the expected delay time, i.e., the average waiting time of a unit in the system, we have

$$\frac{E(\hat{d})}{\nu} = 1 + \frac{\lambda E(S^2)}{2(1 - \rho)\nu} \tag{6.13}$$

This is known as the Pollaczek–Khintchine formula. A comparison of (4.8) and (6.13) gives the well-known formula $E(\hat{m}) = \lambda E(\hat{d})$ due to Little [58]. Thus, Fig. I.1 also represents $E(\hat{d})$ in terms of the mean interarrival time, and the same conclusions that were drawn for $E(\hat{m})$ can be drawn regarding the behavior of $E(\hat{d})$.

Throughout this chapter and in the subsequent chapters, we assume that the service-time distribution possesses a density. This may appear, at first sight, to be a serious limitation of the method. However, the method extends easily to cases where the density can be regarded as a limiting form of a differentiable function, e.g., a regular distribution can always be considered as a limit of an Erlang distribution. Even if this is not the case, we may regard the densities and the processes of differentiation and integration in the generalized sense of Schwartz [78].

Chapter II

BASIC FINITE-SOURCE MODEL

1. Introduction

In the previous chapter, we considered queuing processes in which the units emanate from an infinite source. However, situations arise where the units arriving at a service mechanism emanate from a finite source (e.g., a finite group of machines being attended by an operator, mechanics arriving at a tool crib, or consoles connected to a time-shared computer processor). All such situations may be described by mathematical models which we term "finite-source queuing models," and define as queuing models in which the units emanate from a finite source, to which they return after getting service.

The simplest model of this type can be defined as follows: Units emanating from a finite source of size N call for service at a single server. Each unit stays in the source for a time which is identically, independently, and exponentially distributed with mean $1/\lambda$ before requiring service. Hence, if n units are present at the service facility, the probability that a unit arrives in time interval $(t, t + \Delta)$ is $(N - n)\lambda\Delta + o(\Delta)$. The service times of the units are identically and independently distributed random variables with density $S(x)$. After completing service, the unit returns to the source. We represent this model by the symbol $M/G/1/N$.

One of the problems to which this model has been largely applied is the "machine interference problem." The problem can be stated as follows: An operator attends a set of N machines. If a machine fails, it will be immediately attended by the operator if he is free;

but if a machine fails while the operator is busy repairing another machine, it must wait until the operator becomes free. This results in a loss of production, which is said to arise due to interference. Obviously, if the number of machines assigned to the operator is large, the loss of production due to interference increases. On the other hand, if fewer machines are assigned to the operator, the operative cost per machine increases. Hence, the problem is to determine the number of machines to be assigned to an operator so as to minimize production cost by balancing the cost of operator per machine against the loss of production due to interference.

The problem was posed in this way by Khintchine [53] and was studied by a large number of workers, e.g., Palm [69, 70], Ashcroft [1], Naor [64–66], and Takács [84–86]. The interest of these workers was mainly centered around evaluating two characteristics—machine availability and server's utilization (also called operative efficiency). These terms will be defined later. Little effort was made to evaluate other characteristics which were not directly useful to the machine interference problem; e.g., the busy period distribution for this model was obtained only recently by Blom [12] and Thiruvengadam and Jaiswal [92, 93].

Since the finite-source model has applications in widely different situations, we will investigate all its characteristics, including those which may have little relevance to its application to the machine interference problem. The method that we adopt here is the same as in the previous chapter, i.e., we obtain the busy-period probabilities and use renewal theory to discuss the general process.

2. Busy-Period Processes

In this section, we study the busy-period and the initial busy-period processes for the basic finite-source model. We also study the busy-period and initial busy-period processes of two related models, namely, the restoration time model and the balking and reneging model. The latter models illustrate the methodology adopted and are useful in the study of priority processes.

2-1. Busy–Period Process of the $M/G/1/N$ Model

We study the busy-period process starting at $t = 0$ with i $(0 < i \leqslant N)$ units and define, as in Section I, 2, the following probabilities:

(i) $p^i(m, x, t)\,dx = \Pr[m(t) = m,\ x < z < x + dx,\ m(t_1) > 0$
for all $t_1\ (0 < t_1 < t) \mid m(0) = i]$
$(1 \leqslant m \leqslant N)$

(ii) $b^i(t)\,dt = \Pr[t < b^i < t + dt \mid m(0) = i]$

Using arguments similar to those in Section I, 2, and noting that if there are m units waiting or being serviced, the probability of an arrival in the interval $(t, t + \Delta)$ is $\lambda(N - m)\Delta + o(\Delta)$, we get

$$\frac{\partial}{\partial t} p^i(m, x, t) + \frac{\partial}{\partial x} p^i(m, x, t) + \{(N - m)\lambda + \eta(x)\} p^i(m, x, t)$$
$$= (1 - \delta_{m,1})(N - m + 1)\lambda p^i(m - 1, x, t) \qquad (1 \leqslant m \leqslant N,\ x > 0) \tag{2.1}$$

The boundary conditions are:

$$p^i(m, 0, t) = \int_0^\infty p^i(m + 1, x, t)\eta(x)\,dx \tag{2.2}$$

$$p^i(N, 0, t) = 0 \tag{2.3}$$

and

$$b^i(t) = \int_0^\infty p^i(1, x, t)\eta(x)\,dx \tag{2.4}$$

where $\eta(x)\Delta$ is the conditional probability that a unit will complete service in the interval $(x, x + \Delta)$ if it has been in service for a time x. Equation (2.3) states the fact that a unit after completing service cannot immediately fail, so that the event "N units in the system and one entering service" is not possible.

Equations (2.1)–(2.4) are to be solved subject to the initial condition

$$p^i(m, x, 0) = \delta_{m,i}\delta(x) \tag{2.5}$$

where $\delta(x)$ is the Dirac delta function.

Solution through Discrete Transforms

The generating-function approach, which we generally use for the infinite-source models, cannot be easily applied to this model because of the presence of the variable coefficients such as $(N - m)\lambda$ in (2.1). To solve these equations we define relations called "discrete transforms" (see Appendix I and II) which convert this set of equations into a simpler set of equations. Let

$$u^i(m, x, t) = \sum_{j=m}^{N-1} \binom{j}{m} p^i(N-j, x, t) \qquad (0 \leqslant m \leqslant N-1) \qquad (2.6)$$

where $\binom{j}{m}$ stands for the binomial coefficient which is assumed to be zero if $j < m$. It will be observed that (2.6) defines a system of simultaneous equations in N unknowns. Hence, if $u^i(m, x, t)$ $(0 \leqslant m \leqslant N-1)$ are determined, $p^i(m, x, t)$ $(1 \leqslant m \leqslant N)$ can be found from the inverse relation

$$p^i(m, x, t) = \sum_{e=0}^{m-1} (-1)^e \binom{N-m+e}{e} u^i(N-m+e, x, t) \quad (1 \leqslant m \leqslant N) \qquad (2.7)$$

Changing m to $N-j$ in (2.1), multiplying by $\binom{j}{m}$, and using (2.6), we obtain

$$\frac{\partial}{\partial t} u^i(m, x, t) + \frac{\partial}{\partial x} u^i(m, x, t) + [m\lambda + \eta(x)]u^i(m, x, t) = 0 \qquad (0 \leqslant m \leqslant N-1) \qquad (2.8)$$

Similarly, from (2.2) and (2.3), we get

$$u^i(m, 0, t) = \int_0^\infty u^i(m, x, t)\eta(x)\, dx + \int_0^\infty u^i(m-1, x, t)\eta(x)\, dx - \binom{N}{m} \int_0^\infty p^i(1, x, t)\eta(x)\, dx \qquad (0 \leqslant m \leqslant N-1) \qquad (2.9)$$

The solution of (2.8) is given by

$$u^i(m, x, t) = a^i(m, t-x) \exp[-m\lambda x - \int_0^x \eta(u)\, du] \qquad (0 \leqslant m \leqslant N-1) \qquad (2.10)$$

where $a^i(m, t)$ is an unknown function and is determined by using the boundary condition at $x = 0$ and the initial condition (2.5). Hence,

$$\begin{aligned} a^i(m, t) &= u^i(m, 0, t) \qquad \text{if} \quad t > 0 \\ &= \delta(-t) \binom{N-i}{m} \exp[-m\lambda t] \exp\left[\int_0^{-t} \eta(u)\, du\right] \qquad \text{if} \quad t \leqslant 0 \end{aligned} \qquad (2.11)$$

Substituting (2.10) in (2.9) and using the Laplace transform, we have

$$\bar{u}^i(m, 0, s) = \bar{a}^i(m, s)\bar{S}(m\lambda + s) + \bar{a}^i(m-1, s)\bar{S}[(m-1)\lambda + s]$$
$$- \binom{N}{m} \int_0^\infty \bar{p}^i(1, x, s)\eta(x)\, dx \qquad (0 < m \leqslant N-1) \tag{2.12}$$

and

$$\bar{u}^i(0, 0, s) = \bar{a}^i(0, s)\bar{S}(s) - \int_0^\infty \bar{p}^i(1, x, s)\eta(x)\, dx \tag{2.13}$$

where

$$\bar{a}^i(m, s) = \bar{u}^i(m, 0, s) + \binom{N-i}{m} \tag{2.14}$$

Rewriting (2.12) and (2.13) with the help of (2.4) and (2.14), we get

$$\bar{a}^i(m, s) = \frac{\bar{S}[(m-1)\lambda + s]}{1 - \bar{S}(m\lambda + s)} \bar{a}^i(m-1, s) + \frac{\binom{N-i}{m} - \binom{N}{m}\bar{b}^i(s)}{1 - \bar{S}(m\lambda + s)}$$
$$(0 < m \leqslant N-1) \tag{2.15}$$

$$\bar{a}^i(0, s) = \frac{1 - \bar{b}^i(s)}{1 - \bar{S}(s)} \tag{2.16}$$

Also,

$$\bar{b}^i(s) = \int_0^\infty \bar{p}^i(1, x, s)\eta(x)\, dx = \int_0^\infty \bar{u}^i(N-1, x, s)\eta(x)\, dx$$
$$= \bar{a}^i(N-1, s)\bar{S}[(N-1)\lambda + s]$$

so that

$$\bar{a}^i(N-1, s) = \frac{\bar{b}^i(s)}{\bar{S}[(N-1)\lambda + s]} \tag{2.17}$$

To solve (2.15), which can be regarded as a linear difference equation, we define the function

$$\bar{k}(m, s) = \prod_{e=1}^{m} \frac{\bar{S}[(e-1)\lambda + s]}{1 - \bar{S}(e\lambda + s)} \qquad \text{if} \quad m \neq 0$$
$$= 1 \qquad \text{if} \quad m = 0 \qquad (2.18$$

Dividing (2.15) and (2.16) by $\bar{k}(m, s)$, we get

$$\frac{\bar{a}^i(m, s)}{\bar{k}(m, s)} = \frac{\bar{a}^i(m-1, s)}{\bar{k}(m-1, s)} + \frac{\binom{N-i}{m} - \binom{N}{m}\bar{b}^i(s)}{[1 - \bar{S}(m\lambda + s)]\bar{k}(m, s)}$$
$$(0 < m \leqslant N - 1) \qquad (2.19)$$

$$\frac{\bar{a}^i(0, s)}{\bar{k}(0, s)} = \frac{1 - \bar{b}^i(s)}{1 - \bar{S}(s)} \qquad (2.20)$$

Adding (2.19) for $m = 1, 2, \ldots, m$ and (2.20) we get,

$$\frac{\bar{a}^i(m, s)}{\bar{k}(m, s)} = \Big[\sum_{e=0}^{m} \binom{N-i}{e} \frac{1}{[1 - \bar{S}(e\lambda + s)]\bar{k}(e, s)}$$
$$- \bar{b}^i(s) \sum_{e=0}^{m} \binom{N}{e} \frac{1}{[1 - \bar{S}(e\lambda + s)]\bar{k}(e, s)}\Big]$$
$$(0 \leqslant m \leqslant N - 1) \qquad (2.21)$$

In order to write (2.21) in a neat form, we define another function

$$\bar{v}(m, s) = \prod_{e=0}^{m} \frac{\bar{S}(e\lambda + s)}{1 - \bar{S}(e\lambda + s)} \qquad \text{if} \quad m \neq -1$$
$$= 1 \qquad \text{if} \quad m = -1 \qquad (2.22)$$

The functions $\bar{v}(m, s)$ and $\bar{k}(m, s)$ are related in the following way:

$$\frac{\bar{k}(m, s)}{1 - \bar{S}(s)} = \frac{\bar{v}(m-1, s)}{1 - \bar{S}(m\lambda + s)} = \frac{\bar{v}(m, s)}{\bar{S}(m\lambda + s)} \qquad (2.23)$$

Using (2.23), (2.21) can be written as

$$\frac{\bar{a}^i(m, s)}{\bar{k}(m, s)} = \frac{1}{1 - \bar{S}(s)} \Big[\sum_{e=0}^{m} \binom{N-i}{e} \frac{1}{\bar{v}(e-1, s)} - \bar{b}^i(s) \sum_{e=0}^{m} \binom{N}{e} \frac{1}{\bar{v}(e-1, s)}\Big]$$
$$(0 \leqslant m \leqslant N - 1) \quad (2.24)$$

To evaluate $\bar{b}^i(s)$, we set $m = N - 1$ in (2.24) and use (2.17), so that

$$\bar{b}^i(s) = \Big[\sum_{e=0}^{N} \binom{N}{e} \frac{1}{\bar{v}(e-1, s)}\Big]^{-1} \sum_{e=0}^{N-i} \binom{N-i}{e} \frac{1}{\bar{v}(e-1, s)} \qquad (2.25)$$

and from (2.7) and (2.24), we get

$$\bar{p}^i(m, x, s) = \sum_{e=0}^{m-1} (-1)^e \binom{N-m+e}{e} \bar{a}^i(N-m+e, s) \times \exp\left[-\{(N-m+e)\lambda + s\}x - \int_0^x \eta(u)\,du\right] \quad (1 \leqslant m \leqslant N) \quad (2.26)$$

where

$$\bar{a}^i(m, s) = \frac{\bar{v}(m-1, s)}{1-\bar{S}(m\lambda+s)} \left[\sum_{e=0}^{m} \binom{N-i}{e} \frac{1}{\bar{v}(e-1, s)} - \bar{b}^i(s) \sum_{e=0}^{m} \binom{N}{e} \frac{1}{\bar{v}(e-1, s)}\right] \quad (0 \leqslant m \leqslant N-1) \quad (2.27)$$

and $\bar{b}^i(s)$ is given in (2.25).

Hence, the generating function $\bar{\Pi}^i(\alpha, x, s)$ of $\bar{p}^i(m, x, s)$ is given (see Appendix I, Lemma 2) by

$$\bar{\Pi}^i(\alpha, x, s) = \sum_{m=1}^{N} \alpha^m \bar{p}^i(m, x, s) = \sum_{j=0}^{N-1} \alpha^{N-j}(1-\alpha)^j \bar{a}^i(j, s) \exp\left[-\{j\lambda + s\}x - \int_0^x \eta(u)\,du\right] \quad (2.28)$$

Now, if $\bar{p}_e{}^i(m, s)$ represents the Laplace transform of the probability that at time t a unit enters service during the busy period initiated at $t = 0$ with $i > 0$ units and leaves behind a queue of $m - 1$ units, we have for its generating function

$$\bar{\Pi}_e{}^i(\alpha, s) = \sum_{j=0}^{N-1} \alpha^{N-j}(1-\alpha)^j \bar{a}^i(j, s) \quad (2.29)$$

Also, if $p^i(m, t)$ $(1 \leqslant m \leqslant N)$ represents the joint probability that at time t the busy period is continuing and there are m units irrespective of the elapsed service time, we have

$$\bar{\Pi}^i(\alpha, s) = \sum_{m=1}^{N} \alpha^m \bar{p}^i(m, s) = \sum_{j=0}^{N-1} \alpha^{N-j}(1-\alpha)^j \bar{a}^i(j, s) \frac{1-\bar{S}(j\lambda+s)}{j\lambda+s} \quad (2.30)$$

Finally, the moments of the busy period can be obtained from (2.25) by differentiating with respect to s and setting $s = 0$. For the particular case when the busy period is initiated by the arrival of a unit, putting $i = 1$ and representing $\bar{b}^1(s)$ by $\bar{b}(s)$, we can write (2.25) as

$$\left[\bar{S}(s) + \{1 - \bar{S}(s)\} \sum_{e=1}^{N-1} \binom{N-1}{e} \frac{1}{\bar{\phi}(e-1, s)}\right] \bar{b}(s)$$

$$= \bar{S}(s) + \{1 - \bar{S}(s)\} \sum_{e=1}^{N-1} \binom{N}{e} \frac{1}{\bar{\phi}(e-1, s)} \tag{2.31}$$

where

$$\bar{\phi}(m, s) = \prod_{e=1}^{m} \frac{\bar{S}(e\lambda + s)}{1 - \bar{S}(e\lambda + s)} \quad \text{if} \quad m \neq 0$$

$$= 1 \quad \text{if} \quad m = 0$$

Differentiating (2.31), we obtain

$$E(b) = \nu \sum_{e=0}^{N-1} \binom{N-1}{e} \frac{1}{\phi(e)} \quad \text{if} \quad \nu < \infty$$

$$= \infty \quad \text{if} \quad \nu = \infty \tag{2.32}$$

where

$$\phi(m) = \prod_{e=1}^{m} \frac{\bar{S}(e\lambda)}{1 - \bar{S}(e\lambda)} \quad \text{if} \quad m \neq 0$$

$$= 1 \quad \text{if} \quad m = 0 \tag{2.33}$$

Similarly, other moments can be evaluated. It can be shown that if $N \to \infty$, $\lambda \to 0$ such that $N\lambda \to \lambda'$, (2.32) becomes

$$E(b) = \frac{\nu}{1 - \lambda'\nu} \quad \text{if} \quad \lambda'\nu < 1$$

$$= \infty \quad \text{if} \quad \lambda'\nu \geqslant 1 \tag{2.34}$$

which is the mean busy period for the $M/G/1$ process studied in the previous chapter.

2-2. Initial Busy-Period Process of the $M/G/1/N$ Model

Let the initial busy-period process of the finite-source model be initiated at time $t = 0$ with an initial occupation-time density $\Omega(y)$. Let the process be described by densities $b^{\Omega}(t)$, $p^{\Omega}(m, x, t)$ $(1 \leqslant m \leqslant N)$, and $q^{\Omega}(m, t)$ $(0 \leqslant m \leqslant N)$, which are defined as in Section I, 2. Observing that the initial busy period comprises an initial occupation time and a busy period which is initiated by the number of units that arrive during the initial occupation time, we obtain

$$b^{\Omega}(t) = \sum_{i=0}^{N} \left[\Omega(t) \binom{N}{i} \{1 - \exp(-\lambda t)\}^i \exp\{-(N-i)\lambda t\}\right] * b^i(t) \tag{2.35}$$

$$q^{\Omega}(m, t) = \binom{N}{m} [1 - \exp(-\lambda t)]^m [\exp\{-(N-m)\lambda t\}] \int_t^{\infty} \Omega(t)\, dt \qquad (0 \leqslant m \leqslant N) \tag{2.36}$$

and

$$p^{\Omega}(m, x, t) = \sum_{i=0}^{N} \left[\Omega(t) \binom{N}{i} \{1 - \exp(-\lambda t)\}^i \exp\{-(N-i)\lambda t\}\right] * p^i(m, x, t) \qquad (1 \leqslant m \leqslant N) \tag{2.37}$$

Let us consider (2.35). Expanding $[1 - \exp(-\lambda t)]^i$ by the binomial theorem and taking the Laplace transform, we get

$$\bar{b}^{\Omega}(s) = \sum_{i=0}^{N} \binom{N}{i} \bar{b}^i(s) \sum_{j=0}^{i} (-1)^j \binom{i}{j} \bar{\Omega}[(N - i + j)\lambda + s] \tag{2.38}$$

Using (2.25) in (2.38) and putting $N - i + j = k$ in the last summation, we get

$$\bar{b}^{\Omega}(s) = \left[\sum_{e=0}^{N} \binom{N}{e} \frac{1}{\bar{v}(e-1, s)}\right]^{-1} \left[\sum_{i=0}^{N} \binom{N}{i} \sum_{e=0}^{N-i} \binom{N-i}{e} \frac{1}{\bar{v}(e-1, s)} \times \sum_{k=N-i}^{N} (-1)^{k+i-N} \binom{i}{k+i-N} \bar{\Omega}(k\lambda + s)\right] \tag{2.39}$$

Changing the order of summation, we get

$$\bar{b}^{\Omega}(s) = \left[\sum_{e=0}^{N} \binom{N}{e} \frac{1}{\bar{v}(e-1, s)}\right]^{-1} \left[\sum_{k=0}^{N} \bar{\Omega}(k\lambda + s) \sum_{i=N-k}^{N} (-1)^{k+i-N} \times \binom{i}{k+i-N} \binom{N}{i} \sum_{e=0}^{N-i} \binom{N-i}{e} \frac{1}{\bar{v}(e-1, s)}\right] \tag{2.40}$$

which, on simplification and change of the order of summation, becomes

$$\bar{b}^{\Omega}(s) = \Big[\sum_{e=0}^{N} \binom{N}{e} \frac{1}{\bar{v}(e-1, s)}\Big]^{-1} \Big[\sum_{k=0}^{N} \bar{\Omega}(k\lambda + s) \binom{N}{k}$$

$$\times \sum_{e=0}^{k} \binom{k}{e} \frac{1}{\bar{v}(e-1, s)} \sum_{j=0}^{k-e} (-1)^j \binom{k-e}{j}\Big] \tag{2.41}$$

so that, using the relation

$$\sum_{k=0}^{m} (-1)^k \binom{m}{k} = 1 \quad \text{if} \quad m = 0$$
$$= 0 \quad \text{otherwise}$$

we get

$$\bar{b}^{\Omega}(s) = \frac{\sum_{e=0}^{N} \binom{N}{e} \dfrac{\bar{\Omega}(e\lambda + s)}{\bar{v}(e-1, s)}}{\sum_{e=0}^{N} \binom{N}{e} \dfrac{1}{\bar{v}(e-1, s)}} \tag{2.42}$$

Similarly, taking the Laplace transform of (2.36) and (2.37) and simplifying as above, we get

$$\bar{q}^{\Omega}(m, s) = \binom{N}{m} \sum_{i=0}^{m} \binom{m}{i} \frac{1 - \bar{\Omega}[(N-m+i)\lambda + s]}{(N-m+i)\lambda + s} \tag{2.43}$$

$$\bar{p}^{\Omega}(m, x, s) = \sum_{e=0}^{m-1} (-1)^e \binom{N-m+e}{e} \bar{a}^{\Omega}(N-m+e, s)$$

$$\times \exp\Big[-\{(N-m+e)\lambda + s\}x - \int_0^x \eta(u)\, du\Big] \tag{2.44}$$

where

$$\bar{a}^{\Omega}(m, s) = \frac{\bar{v}(m-1, s)}{1 - \bar{S}(m\lambda + s)} \Big[\sum_{e=0}^{m} \binom{N}{e} \frac{\bar{\Omega}(e\lambda + s)}{\bar{v}(e-1, s)} - \bar{b}^{\Omega}(s) \sum_{e=0}^{m} \binom{N}{e} \frac{1}{\bar{v}(e-1, s)}\Big] \tag{2.45}$$

and $\bar{b}^{\Omega}(s)$ is defined in (2.42).

Finally, differentiating (2.42) as in (2.32), the expected length of the initial busy period is given by

$$E(b^{\Omega}) = E(\Omega) + \nu \sum_{e=1}^{N} \binom{N}{e} \frac{1 - \bar{\Omega}(e\lambda)}{\phi(e-1)} \qquad \text{if} \quad E(\Omega) < \infty, \ \nu < \infty$$

$$= \infty \qquad \text{otherwise} \qquad (2.46)$$

Similarly, other moments can be evaluated.

2-3. Busy-Period Process of the Restoration-Time Model

In the finite-source model, let us assume that after completing the service of a unit, the server spends a random time r on restoring the facility before taking up the next unit. We call r the restoration time and assume that it depends on the service time of the outgoing unit. Let $r(y \mid S)$ denote the probability density of the restoration time conditioned on S, the service time of the outgoing unit. We call this model the "restoration-time model" and study its busy-period process.

Let the busy-period process of the restoration-time model initiated by $i > 0$ units be described by the following joint probabilities:

(i) $p^i(m, x, t, Z)\, dx\, dZ = \Pr[m(t) = m, \quad x < z < x + dx,$
$Z < S < Z + dZ \mid m(0) = i]$
$(x < Z, \quad 1 \leqslant m \leqslant N)$

(ii) $q^i(m, y, t, Z)\, dy\, dZ = \Pr[m(t) = m, \quad y < r < y + dy,$
$Z < S < Z + dZ \mid m(0) = i]$
$(0 \leqslant m \leqslant N)$

(iii) $b^i(t)\, dt = \Pr[t < b^i < t + dt \mid m(0) = i]$

Notice that the random variable z represents the elapsed service time of the unit under service and is different from S. The random variable S in (i) represents the total service time of the unit which is being serviced, and in (ii) it represents the service time of the unit which was last serviced and which has left the system.

The equations connecting these probabilities are

$$\left[\frac{\partial}{\partial t} + \frac{\partial}{\partial x} + (N - m)\lambda\right] p^i(m, x, t, Z)$$

$$= (N - m + 1)\lambda p^i(m - 1, x, t, Z)(1 - \delta_{m,1}) \qquad (1 \leqslant m \leqslant N, x < Z) \qquad (2.47)$$

$$\left[\frac{\partial}{\partial t}+\frac{\partial}{\partial y}+(N-m)\lambda+\eta(y\mid Z)\right]q^i(m,y,t,Z)$$
$$=(N-m+1)\lambda q^i(m-1,y,t,Z)(1-\delta_{m,0})\qquad(0\leqslant m\leqslant N)\qquad(2.48)$$

where $\eta(y \mid Z)\,dy$ is the conditional probability that the restoration time of the server after servicing a unit with service time Z is completed in the interval $(y, y+dy)$ if it has not been completed by time y, so that

$$r(y\mid Z)=\eta(y\mid Z)\exp\left[-\int_0^y\eta(u\mid Z)\,du\right]\qquad(2.49)$$

Equations (2.47) and (2.48) are to be solved subject to the following boundary conditions:

$$p^i(m,0,t,Z)=S(Z)\int_0^\infty\int_0^\infty q^i(m,y,t,Z)\eta(y\mid Z)\,dy\,dZ\qquad(2.50)$$

$$b^i(t)=\int_0^\infty\int_0^\infty q^i(0,y,t,Z)\eta(y\mid Z)\,dy\,dZ\qquad(2.51)$$

$$q^i(m,0,t,Z)=p^i(m+1,Z,t,Z)\qquad(0\leqslant m<N)\qquad(2.52)$$

$$q^i(N,0,t,Z)=0\qquad(2.53)$$

It should be noted that (2.51) indicates that the busy period for this model terminates only if no unit is present at the end of the restoration time. Also, in Eq. (2.50), $S(Z)$ occurs on the right-hand side because the next unit has the service time Z with probability $S(Z)$. The above equations are to be solved subject to the following initial condition

$$p^i(m,x,0,Z)=\delta_{m,i}\delta(x)S(Z)\qquad(2.54)$$

We take the Laplace transform and define the following discrete transforms corresponding to (2.6):

$$\bar{u}_1{}^i(m,x,s,Z)=\sum_{j=m}^{N-1}\binom{j}{m}\bar{p}^i(N-j,x,s,Z)\qquad(0\leqslant m\leqslant N-1)\quad(2.55)$$

$$\bar{u}_2{}^i(m,y,s,Z)=\sum_{j=m}^{N}\binom{j}{m}\bar{q}^i(N-j,y,s,Z)\qquad(0\leqslant m\leqslant N)\qquad(2.56)$$

Using (2.55), and solving (2.47) with the initial condition (2.54), we get

$$\bar{u}_1^i(m, x, s, Z) = \left[\bar{u}_1^i(m, 0, s, Z) + \binom{N-i}{m} S(Z)\right] \exp[-(m\lambda + s)x]$$

$$(x < Z, \quad 0 \leqslant m \leqslant N-1) \quad (2.57)$$

Similarly, using (2.56) and solving (2.48), we get

$$\bar{u}_2^i(m, y, s, Z) = \bar{u}_2^i(m, 0, s, Z) \exp[-(m\lambda + s)y] \exp\left[-\int_0^y \eta(u \mid Z)\, du\right]$$

$$(0 \leqslant m \leqslant N) \quad (2.58)$$

Now, the boundary conditions (2.50)–(2.52) can be written as

$$\bar{u}_1^i(m, 0, s, Z) = S(Z) \int_0^\infty \int_0^\infty \bar{u}_2^i(m, y, s, Z)\eta(y \mid Z)\, dy\, dZ - \binom{N}{m} S(Z)\bar{b}^i(s) \quad (2.59)$$

and

$$\bar{u}_2^i(m, 0, s, Z) = \bar{u}_1^i(m, Z, s, Z) + \bar{u}_1^i(m-1, Z, s, Z) \quad (2.60)$$

Using (2.57) and (2.58) in (2.59) and (2.60), we obtain, after using (2.49),

$$\begin{aligned}\bar{u}_1^i(m, 0, s, Z) = S(Z) \int_0^\infty & \Big[\bar{u}_1^i(m, 0, s, Z) \\ & + \binom{N-i}{m} S(Z)\Big] \exp[-(m\lambda + s)Z]\bar{r}(m\lambda + s \mid Z)\, dZ \\ & + S(Z) \int_0^\infty \Big[\bar{u}_1^i(m-1, 0, s, Z) \\ & + \binom{N-i}{m-1} S(Z)\Big] \exp[-\{(m-1)\lambda + s\}Z] \\ & \times \bar{r}(m\lambda + s \mid Z)\, dZ - \binom{N}{m} S(Z)\bar{b}^i(s)\end{aligned} \quad (2.61)$$

Hence, we can write

$$\bar{u}_1^i(m, 0, s, Z) = \bar{u}_1^i(m, 0, s)S(Z) \quad (2.62)$$

so that (2.57), (2.60), and (2.61) can be written as

$$\bar{u}_1{}^i(m, x, s, Z) = \bar{a}^i(m, s)S(Z) \exp[-(m\lambda + s)x] \qquad (0 \leqslant m \leqslant N - 1) \tag{2.63}$$

$$\bar{u}_2{}^i(m, y, s, Z) = [\bar{a}^i(m, s) + \bar{a}^i(m - 1, s)e^{\lambda Z}]S(Z) \exp[-(m\lambda + s)(y + Z)] \times \exp\left[-\int_0^y \eta(u \mid Z)\, du\right] \qquad (0 \leqslant m \leqslant N) \tag{2.64}$$

The equation corresponding to (2.14) then becomes

$$\bar{a}^i(m, s)[1 - \bar{c}(m\lambda + s)] = \bar{a}^i(m - 1, s)\bar{h}(m\lambda + s) + \binom{N - i}{m} - \binom{N}{m} \bar{b}^i(s) \qquad (0 < m < N - 1) \tag{2.65}$$

where

$$\bar{a}^i(m, s) = \bar{u}_1{}^i(m, 0, s) + \binom{N - i}{m} \tag{2.66}$$

$$\bar{c}(s) = \int_0^\infty S(\tau)e^{-s\tau}\, \bar{r}(s \mid \tau)\, d\tau \tag{2.67}$$

$$\bar{h}(s) = \int_0^\infty S(\tau)e^{-s\tau}e^{\lambda\tau}\, \bar{r}(s \mid \tau)\, d\tau \tag{2.68}$$

and for $m = 0$ and $m = N$, we have, similar to (2.16) and (2.17),

$$\bar{a}^i(0, s)[1 - \bar{c}(s)] = 1 - \bar{b}^i(s) \tag{2.69}$$

$$\bar{a}^i(N - 1, s)\bar{h}(N\lambda + s) = \bar{b}^i(s) \tag{2.70}$$

Equations (2.65), (2.69), and (2.70) are similar to Eqs. (2.15)–(2.17). Hence, following the same method and defining

$$\bar{\omega}(m, s) = \prod_{e=0}^{m} \frac{\bar{h}(e\lambda + s)}{1 - \bar{c}(e\lambda + s)} \quad \text{if} \quad m \neq -1$$
$$= 1 \quad \text{if} \quad m = -1 \tag{2.71}$$

we obtain the following results

$$\bar{b}^i(s) = \frac{\displaystyle\sum_{e=0}^{N-i} \binom{N - i}{e} \frac{1}{\bar{h}(e\lambda + s)\bar{\omega}(e - 1, s)}}{\displaystyle\sum_{e=0}^{N} \binom{N}{e} \frac{1}{\bar{h}(e\lambda + s)\bar{\omega}(e - 1, s)}} \tag{2.72}$$

and

$$\bar{a}^i(m, s) = \bar{\omega}(m, s) \left[\sum_{e=0}^{m} \binom{N-i}{e} \frac{1}{\bar{h}(e\lambda + s)\bar{\omega}(e-1, s)} - \bar{b}^i(s) \sum_{e=0}^{m} \binom{N}{e} \frac{1}{\bar{h}(e\lambda + s)\bar{\omega}(e-1, s)} \right] \tag{2.73}$$

where $\bar{\omega}(m, s)$ is defined in (2.71).

Using the inverse relations of (2.55) and (2.56), the Laplace transforms of the probabilities $p(m, x, t, Z)$ and $q(m, y, t, Z)$, are obtained as

$$\bar{p}(m, x, s, Z) = \sum_{e=0}^{m-1} (-1)^e \binom{N-m+e}{e} \bar{a}^i(N-m+e, s) \times \exp[-\{(N-m+e)\lambda + s\}x] S(Z) \quad (1 \leqslant m \leqslant N) \tag{2.74}$$

and

$$\bar{q}(m, y, s, Z) = \sum_{e=0}^{m} (-1)^e \binom{N-m+e}{e} \times [\bar{a}^i(N-m+e, s) + \bar{a}^i(N-m+e-1, s) \exp(\lambda Z)] \times S(Z) \exp\left[-\{(N-m+e)\lambda + s\}(y+Z) - \int_0^y \eta(u/Z)\, du \right] \quad (0 \leqslant m \leqslant N) \tag{2.75}$$

If $p_e^i(m, t)$ denotes the probability that at time t a unit enters service leaving behind $(m - 1)$ units in the queue, we have

$$\bar{p}_e^i(m, s) = \sum_{e=0}^{m-1} (-1)^e \binom{N-m+e}{e} \bar{a}^i(N-m+e, s) \tag{2.76}$$

Similarly, if $q_e^i(m, t, Z)\, dZ$ denotes the probability that at time t the restoration period is initiated with m units waiting in the queue and the service time of the outgoing unit is between Z and $Z + dZ$, we have

$$\bar{q}_e^i(m, s, Z) = \sum_{e=0}^{m} (-1)^e \binom{N-m+e}{e} [\bar{a}^i(N-m+e, s) \times \exp\{-[(N-m+e)\lambda + s]Z\} + \bar{a}^i(N-m+e-1, s) \times \exp\{-[(N-m+e-1)\lambda + s]Z\}] S(Z) \tag{2.77}$$

where $\bar{a}^i(e, s)$ is defined by (2.73).

Finally, the expected length of the busy period initiated by one unit is given by

$$E(b) = E(c) \sum_{e=0}^{N-1} \binom{N-1}{e} \frac{1}{\psi(e)\bar{h}(e\lambda)} \tag{2.78}$$

where

$$\begin{aligned} \psi(m) &= \prod_{e=1}^{m} \frac{\bar{h}(e\lambda)}{1-\bar{c}(e\lambda)} \qquad \text{if} \quad m \neq 0 \\ &= 1 \qquad\qquad\qquad\quad \text{if} \quad m = 0 \end{aligned} \tag{2.79}$$

and $E(c)$ can be obtained from (2.67) by differentiation at $s = 0$.

2-4. Initial Busy-Period Process of the Restoration-Time Model

The results of the initial busy-period process of the restoration-time model can be obtained from those of the busy-period process obtained above. Since the derivation is similar to the initial busy-period process of the finite-source model, we give only the results.

The initial busy period density $b^{\Omega}(t)$ is given by

$$\bar{b}^{\Omega}(s) = \frac{\displaystyle\sum_{e=0}^{N} \binom{N}{e} \frac{\bar{\Omega}(e\lambda+s)}{\bar{h}(e\lambda+s)\bar{\omega}(e-1,s)}}{\displaystyle\sum_{e=0}^{N} \binom{N}{e} \frac{1}{\bar{h}(e\lambda+s)\bar{\omega}(e-1,s)}} \tag{2.80}$$

and if $p_e^{\Omega}(m, t)$ denotes the probability that at time t a unit enters service leaving $(m-1)$ units in the queue, we have

$$\bar{p}_e^{\Omega}(m, s) = \sum_{e=0}^{m-1} (-1)^e \binom{N-m+e}{e} \bar{a}^{\Omega}(N-m+e, s) \tag{2.81}$$

where $\bar{a}^{\Omega}(m, s)$ is defined below.

Also, if $q_e^{\Omega}(m, t, Z)\, dZ$ denotes the probability that at time t the restoration period is initiated with m units waiting in the queue and with the service time for the outgoing unit between Z and $Z + dZ$, we have

$$\begin{aligned} \bar{q}_e^{\Omega}(m, s, Z) = \sum_{e=0}^{m} (-1)^e \binom{N-m+e}{e} \Big[& \bar{a}^{\Omega}(N-m+e, s) \\ & \times \exp\{-[(N-m+e)\lambda + s]Z\} + \bar{a}^{\Omega}(N-m+e-1, s) \\ & \times \exp[-\{(N-m+e-1)\lambda + s\}Z] \Big] S(Z) \end{aligned} \tag{2.82}$$

where

$$\bar{a}^{\Omega}(m, s) = \bar{v}(m, s) \Big[\sum_{e=0}^{m} \binom{N}{e} \frac{\bar{\Omega}(e\lambda + s)}{\bar{h}(e\lambda + s)\bar{\omega}(e-1, s)}$$

$$- \bar{b}^{\Omega}(s) \sum_{e=0}^{m} \binom{N}{e} \frac{1}{\bar{h}(e\lambda + s)\bar{\omega}(e-1, s)} \Big] \tag{2.83}$$

where $\bar{b}^{\Omega}(s)$ is given by (2.80). Finally, the expected length of the initial busy period is given by

$$E(b^{\Omega}) = E(\Omega) + E(c) \sum_{e=1}^{N} \binom{N}{e} \frac{1 - \bar{\Omega}(e)}{\bar{h}(e\lambda)\psi(e-1)} \tag{2.84}$$

where $\psi(e)$ is defined by (2.79).

2-5. Busy-Period Process of the Balking and Reneging Model

Next, we discuss the busy-period process of the basic infinite-source model with balking and reneging. The reason we study the infinite-source model at this point in this chapter, which is otherwise concerned with finite-source models, is that the infinite-source model under certain assumptions regarding the balking behavior further illustrates the methodology of using discrete transforms, and also because the results of the basic finite-source model can be obtained from it as a particular case. A unit is said to balk if on arrival it does not join the queue, and is said to renege if, after joining the queue, it gets impatient and leaves the queue without getting service. The following assumptions are made to describe the balking and reneging behavior:

(a) If a unit on arrival finds n units in the system, it joins the queue with probability $a_n = 1 - n/N$ $(n = 0, 1,..., N)$, and balks with probability $1 - a_n$.

(b) A unit reneges if its waiting time in the queue exceeds a random time t distributed exponentially with parameter β.

Let $p^i(m, x, t)$ and $b^i(t)$ be defined as in the beginning of this section. Then under the assumptions regarding the balking and reneging behavior made above, we have

$$\Big[\frac{\partial}{\partial t} + \frac{\partial}{\partial x} + \{\lambda(1 - m/N) + (m-1)\beta + \eta(x)\}\Big] p^i(m, x, t)$$

$$= \lambda(1 - \delta_{m,1}) \left(1 - \frac{m-1}{N}\right) p^i(m-1, x, t) + m\beta p^i(m+1, x, t)$$

$$(x > 0, \quad 1 \leqslant m \leqslant N) \tag{2.85}$$

The boundary conditions are

$$p^i(m, 0, t) = \int_0^\infty p^i(m + 1, x, t)\, dx \tag{2.86}$$

$$p^i(N, 0, t) = 0 \tag{2.87}$$

$$b^i(t) = \int_0^\infty p^i(1, x, t)\, dx \tag{2.88}$$

These equations are to be solved subject to the initial condition

$$p^i(m, x, 0) = \delta_{m,i}\delta(x) \tag{2.89}$$

The appropriate "discrete transform" to solve (2.85) is (see Appendix I, Lemma 4):

$$u^i(m, x, t) = \sum_{j=N-m}^{N} (-a)^{j+m-N} \binom{j-1}{j+m-N} \sum_{k=N-j}^{N-1} \binom{k}{N-j} p^i(N-k, x, t) \tag{2.90}$$

where

$$a = N\beta/(N\beta + \lambda)$$

which has the inverse

$$p^i(m, x, t) = \sum_{j=N-m}^{N-1} (-1)^{j+m-N} \binom{j}{j+m-N} \sum_{k=0}^{j} a^{j-k} \binom{N-1-k}{j-k} u^i(k, x, t) \tag{2.91}$$

Using the transform (2.90) and the above procedure, we get the following results:

$$\bar{b}^i(s) = \frac{\displaystyle\sum_{k=0}^{N-1} \frac{\delta^i(k, a)}{\bar{v}(k-1, \beta, s)} - a \sum_{k=1}^{N} \frac{\delta^i(k-1, a)}{\bar{v}(k-1, \beta, s)}}{\displaystyle\sum_{k=0}^{N} \binom{N}{k} \frac{(1-a)^k}{\bar{v}(k-1, \beta, s)}} \tag{2.92}$$

and

$$\bar{p}^i(m, x, s) = \sum_{j=N-m}^{N-1} (-1)^{j+m-N} \binom{j}{j+m-N} \sum_{k=0}^{j} a^{j-k} \binom{N-1-k}{j-k} \bar{a}^i(k, \beta, s)$$
$$\times \exp\left[-k\left(\frac{\lambda}{N} + \beta\right)x - sx - \int_0^x \eta(u)\, du\right] \tag{2.93}$$

where

$$\bar{a}^i(m, \beta, s) = \frac{\bar{v}(m, \beta, s)}{1 - \bar{S}\left[s + m\left(\frac{\lambda}{N} + \beta\right)\right]} \left[\left\{\sum_{k=0}^{m-1} \frac{\delta^i(k, a)}{\bar{v}(k-1, \beta, s)} - a \sum_{k=0}^{m} \frac{\delta^i(k, a)}{\bar{v}(k, \beta, s)}\right\} - \bar{b}^i(s) \sum_{k=0}^{m-1} \binom{N}{k} \frac{(1-a)^k}{\bar{v}(k-1, \beta, s)}\right] \tag{2.94}$$

$$\delta^i(k, a) = \sum_{j=N-k}^{N} (-a)^{j+k-N} \binom{j-1}{j+k-N} \binom{N-i}{N-j} \qquad (0 \leqslant k \leqslant N-1) \tag{2.95}$$

and

$$\begin{aligned} \bar{v}(m, \beta, s) &= \prod_{e=0}^{m} \frac{a + (1-a)\bar{S}\left[e\left(\frac{\lambda}{N} + \beta\right) + s\right]}{1 - \bar{S}\left[e\left(\frac{\lambda}{N} + \beta\right) + s\right]} && \text{if} \quad m \neq -1 \\ &= 1 && \text{if} \quad m = -1 \end{aligned} \tag{2.96}$$

Observe that $\delta^1(k, a) = \delta(k, a) = \binom{N-1}{k}(1-a)^k$, so that the results for the busy-period process initiated by one unit become simplified. The mean busy period for this case is given by

$$\begin{aligned} E(b) &= \nu \sum_{k=0}^{N-1} \binom{N-1}{k} \frac{(1-a)^k}{\phi(k, \beta)} && \text{if} \quad \nu < \infty \\ &= \infty && \text{if} \quad \nu = \infty \end{aligned} \tag{2.97}$$

where

$$\begin{aligned} \phi(m, \beta) &= \prod_{e=1}^{m} \frac{a + (1-a)\bar{S}\left[e\left(\frac{\lambda}{N} + \beta\right)\right]}{1 - \bar{S}\left[e\left(\frac{\lambda}{N} + \beta\right)\right]} && \text{if} \quad m \neq 0 \\ &= 1 && \text{if} \quad m = 0 \end{aligned} \tag{2.98}$$

The above results are due to Subba Rao [80]. Note that if $\beta \to 0$, $a \to 0$, and the results obtained above reduce to the finite-source results with arrival rate λ/N in place of λ. This equivalence is obvious since the probability of an arrival in $(t, t + \Delta)$ is $(N - n)\lambda\Delta + o(\Delta)$ for the finite-source model and is $[1 - (n/N)]\lambda\Delta + o(\Delta)$ for the infinite-source model with balking specified by $a_n = [1 - (n/N)]$, all other assumptions remaining the same.

2-6. Initial Busy-Period Process of the Balking and Reneging Model

To derive the initial busy-period distribution, we require the probability of having $i\,(0 \leqslant i \leqslant N)$ units at the end of the initial occupation time when units are allowed to balk and renege. A brief examination reveals that this probability is the same as the probability of having i units in the generalized birth and death process in which the birth and death coefficients are specified by $\lambda_n = \lambda[1 - (n/N)]$ for $0 \leqslant n \leqslant N$, and $\lambda_n = 0$ otherwise; $\mu_n = n\mu$ with the initial condition $X(0) = 0$, where $X(t)$ denotes the state of the system at time t. It can be easily shown [74, p. 147] that

$$\Pr[X(t) = i] = \binom{N}{i} p^i q^{N-i} \tag{2.99}$$

where

$$p = \lambda/(\lambda + N\beta)\left[1 - \exp\left\{-\left(\frac{\lambda}{N} + \beta\right)t\right\}\right]$$

and

$$q = 1 - p$$

Now,

$$b^{\Omega}(t) = \sum_{i=0}^{N} \int_{y=0}^{t} \Pr[X(y) = i]\Omega(y) b^i(t-y)\, dy \tag{2.100}$$

where $b^i(t)$ is the busy-period density of the balking and reneging model initiated by i units and is given by (2.92). Note that $b^0(t) = \delta(t)$. Therefore

$$\bar{b}^{\Omega}(s) = \sum_{i=0}^{N} \binom{N}{i} \bar{b}^i(s) \sum_{e=0}^{N-i} (-1)^e \binom{N-i}{e} (1-a)^{i+e}$$
$$\times \sum_{r=0}^{i+e} (-1)^r \binom{i+e}{r} \bar{\Omega}\left[r\left(\frac{\lambda}{N} + \beta\right) + s\right] \tag{2.101}$$

The above expression can be shown to be equal to

$$\bar{b}^{\Omega}(s) = \sum_{r=0}^{N} (-1)^r \binom{N}{r} \bar{\Omega}\left[r\left(\frac{\lambda}{N} + \beta\right) + s\right] \sum_{e=0}^{N-r} (-1)^{N-e} \binom{N-r}{e} (1-a)^{N-e}$$
$$\times \sum_{j=0}^{N-e} (-1)^j \binom{N-e}{j} \bar{b}^j(s) \tag{2.102}$$

Substituting the value of $\bar{b}^i(s)$ from (2.92) and noting that

$$\delta^i(k, a) - a\delta^i(k-1, a) = \sum_{j=N-k}^{N} (-a)^{j+k-N} \binom{N-i}{N-j}\binom{j}{j+k-N} \qquad (0 \leqslant k \leqslant N-i)$$

$$= \sum_{j=i}^{N} (-a)^{j+k-N} \binom{N-i}{N-j}\binom{j}{j+k-N} \qquad (k > N-i)$$

we get, after simplification,

$$\bar{b}^{\Omega}(s) = \frac{\sum_{k=0}^{N} \binom{N}{k} (1-a)^k \bar{\Omega}\left[k\left(\frac{\lambda}{N}+\beta\right)+s\right] / \bar{v}(k-1, \beta, s)}{\sum_{k=0}^{N} \binom{N}{k} (1-a)^k / \bar{v}(k-1, \beta, s)} \tag{2.103}$$

The mean duration of the initial busy period is given by

$$\begin{aligned} E(b^{\Omega}) &= E(\Omega) + \nu \sum_{k=0}^{N-1} \binom{N-1}{k} \frac{(1-a)^k}{\phi(k, \beta)} \left[1 - \bar{\Omega}\left\{k\left(\frac{\lambda}{N}+\beta\right)\right\}\right] \\ &\qquad \text{if } \nu < \infty, \quad E(\Omega) < \infty \\ &= \infty \qquad \text{otherwise} \end{aligned} \tag{2.104}$$

where $\phi(k, \beta)$ is defined by (2.98). Similarly, $\bar{p}^{\Omega}(m, x, s)$ and $\bar{q}^{\Omega}(m, s)$ can be obtained.

3. Stochastic Behavior of the Process $\{\hat{m}(t)\}$

In this section, we investigate the stochastic behavior of the process $\{\hat{m}(t)\}$. The reader will recall that this process is termed the general process, and that the probabilities associated with it are obtained from the busy-period probabilities by using renewal-theoretic arguments. Since we used this method in detail in Section I, 3 to discuss the general process for the infinite-source model, we will not reproduce the arguments, but only present the final results.

Let us define the following probabilities:

(i) $\hat{p}^i(m, x, t)\, dx = \Pr\{\hat{m}(t) = m,\ x < z < x + dx \mid \hat{m}(0) = i\} \qquad (1 \leqslant m \leqslant N)$

(ii) $\hat{e}^i(t) = \Pr\{\hat{m}(t) = 0 \mid \hat{m}(0) = i\}$

Then

$$\bar{\bar{\Pi}}^i(\alpha, s) = \sum_{m=1}^{N} \alpha^m \int_0^\infty \bar{\bar{p}}^i(m, x, s)\, dx = \bar{\bar{e}}^i(s)[1 + N\lambda\bar{\bar{\Pi}}(\alpha, s)] + \bar{\Pi}^i(\alpha, s) \quad (3.1)$$

where $\bar{\Pi}^i(\alpha, s)$ is given by (2.30), $\bar{\Pi}^1(\alpha, s) = \bar{\Pi}(\alpha, s)$, $\bar{\Pi}^0(\alpha, s) = 0$, and

$$\bar{\bar{e}}^i(s) = \frac{\bar{b}^i(s)}{N\lambda + s - N\lambda\bar{b}(s)} \quad (3.2)$$

where $\bar{b}^i(s)$ is defined in (2.25), $\bar{b}^1(s) = \bar{b}(s)$, and $\bar{b}^0(s) = 1$.

Inversion of these results is even more complicated than for the results of the infinite-source model. Therefore, we do not attempt to invert the results, but discuss, in the next section, the limiting behavior of the process $\{\hat{m}(t)\}$.

4. Limiting Behavior of the Process $\{\hat{m}(t)\}$

Following arguments analogous to those given in Section I, 4, it follows that the steady state exists if $\nu < \infty$, and we get

$$\hat{p}(m) = N\lambda\hat{e} \int_0^\infty p(m, x)\, dx = N\lambda\hat{e} \sum_{e=0}^{m-1} (-1)^e \binom{N - m + e}{e} l(N - m + e) \quad (4.1)$$

where

$$l(m) = \frac{\phi(m-1)}{m\lambda} \sum_{e=m}^{N-1} \binom{N-1}{e} \frac{1}{\phi(e)} \quad (4.2)$$

$$l(0) = \nu \sum_{e=0}^{N-1} \binom{N-1}{e} \frac{1}{\phi(e)} \quad (4.3)$$

and

$$\hat{e} = \left[1 + N\lambda\nu \sum_{e=0}^{N-1} \binom{N-1}{e} \frac{1}{\phi(e)}\right]^{-1} \quad (4.4)$$

where $\phi(e)$ is defined by (2.33).

The result of the above limiting process obtained as $t \to \infty$ does not correspond to the limit obtained through regeneration points in the Markov chain analysis [86]. Lastly, the mean number of units in the system can be obtained from (4.1) as follows:

Because of the transform relationship given by (2.6) and (2.7), (4.1) can be written as

$$N\lambda\hat{e}\, l(m) = \sum_{e=m}^{N-1} \binom{e}{m} \hat{p}(N-e) = \sum_{e=1}^{N-m} \binom{N-e}{m} \hat{p}(e) \tag{4.5}$$

If we put $m = 0$ in (4.5), we get $N\lambda\hat{e}l(0) = 1 - \hat{e}$, which is true from (4.3) and (4.4), while if we put $m = 1$ in (4.5), we obtain

$$E(\hat{m}) = N(1-\hat{e}) - N\lambda\hat{e}l(1) = N\left[1 - \hat{e}\sum_{e=0}^{N-1}\binom{N-1}{e}\frac{1}{\phi(e)}\right] \tag{4.6}$$

Using (4.4), (4.6) can be written as

$$E(\hat{m}) = N - \frac{1}{\lambda\nu}(1-\hat{e}) \tag{4.7}$$

Similarly, other moments can be easily evaluated.

4-1. Operational Characteristics and Numerical Results

It is observed that the value of the mean queue length depends only upon $\hat{e}$, the proportion of time the server is idle. We can write (4.7) as

$$\frac{N - E(\hat{m})}{N} = \frac{1}{N\lambda\nu}(1-\hat{e}) \tag{4.8}$$

The left-hand side of (4.8) has been called "machine availability" in the literature on machine interference [11] as it represents the expected proportion of time a machine remains in the working condition. It should be noted that if the unit of production is defined as the amount that would be produced by one machine if it runs for a unit time, the machine availability is the rate of production per machine. Since $(1 - \hat{e})$ is the proportion of time the server is busy, it is called the "server's utilization" or "operative efficiency" and the relation (4.8) can then be written as

$$\text{Machine availability} = \text{Server's utilization}/N\lambda\nu \tag{4.9}$$

Relation (4.9) can be obtained by the following simple reasoning (cf. Benson and Cox [11]). Let us consider a long interval of time T and let T' be the total time for which all the machines remain in working order. The total number of times the machines call for service during the time T' is $\lambda T'$. Since each repair takes a time ν on the average, the server will be busy for time $T_0 = \lambda T'\nu$. Hence,

$$\text{Server's utilization} = \frac{T_0}{T} = \lambda\nu\frac{T'}{T} = N\lambda\nu\frac{T'}{NT}$$
$$= N\lambda\nu \times \text{Machine availability} \tag{4.10}$$

Unlike the infinite-source model, the value of $\hat{e}$ depends upon the service-time distribution. Similarly, $E(\hat{m})$ also depends upon the service-time distribution, while for $M/G/1$ it depends upon the first two moments.

In Fig. II.1 and II.2, the values of $\hat{e}$, the proportion of time the server is idle, and $E(\hat{m})$, the mean number of units in the system, respectively, are plotted against N for $\rho^* = N\lambda\nu =$ constant, assuming the service time to be (i) exponentially distributed (unbroken lines) and (ii) constant (broken lines). The results indicate that if $\rho^* \ll 1$, the variability of the service time has insignificant effects on the results. Comparison with the results of the infinite-source model for $\rho = \rho^*$, which are shown on the extreme right in these figures,

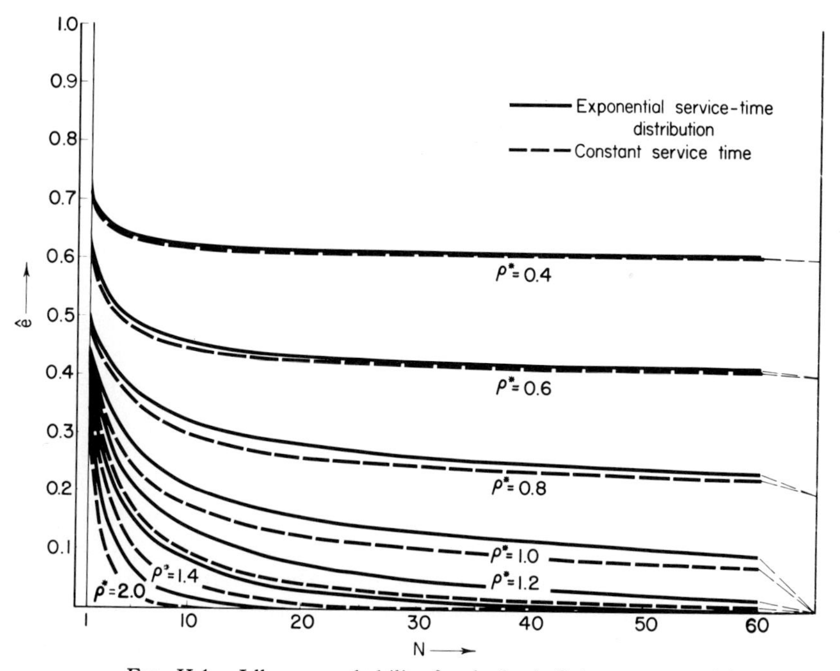

FIG. II.1. Idleness probability for the basic finite-source model.

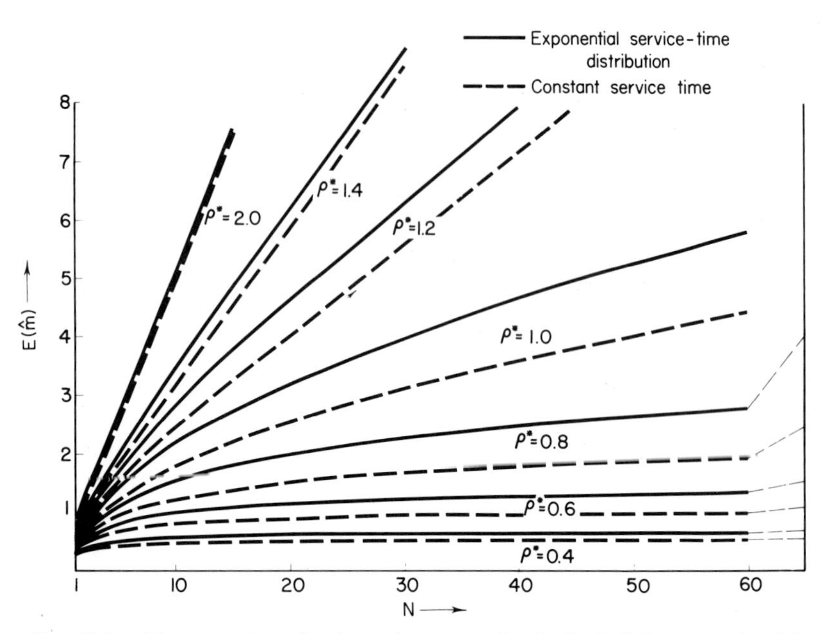

FIG. II.2. Mean number of units in the system for the basic finite-source model.

indicates that in this region one can use the relatively simple results of the infinite-source model without significant error.

The effect of the variability of the service time is predominant when ρ^* is near one. In this region, the use of the infinite-source model is bound to be erroneous if N is not sufficiently large. It should be noted that the conclusions about the variability for $\rho^* \leqslant 1$ are similar to the conclusions for the infinite-source model. However, when $\rho^* \gg 1$, the effect of the variability again decreases. The infinite-source model in this region has no steady-state behavior, and therefore the question of comparing these results with the results of the infinite-source model does not arise. It will be observed from Fig. II.1 that for $\rho^* \gg 1$, $\hat{e}$ becomes zero for large N, so that (4.7) becomes $E(\hat{m}) \approx N(1 - 1/\rho^*)$. Thus, whatever the service-time distribution may be, the curve for $E(\hat{m})$ approaches asymptotically to the line which passes through the point $(1, 1 - 1/\rho^*)$ and is inclined at an angle $\tan^{-1}(1 - 1/\rho^*)$. If $\rho^* \to \infty$, the asymptote becomes $E(\hat{m}) = N$, which is obviously true, since, if $\rho^* \to \infty$, all the units tend to stay away from the source.

From the above discussion, we conclude that if $\rho^* \gg 1$ and N is large, the results can be obtained to a reasonable accuracy by drawing the line through the origin inclined at an angle $\tan^{-1}(1 - 1/\rho^*)$. Also, in this region, the effect of the service time variability is negligible and tends to zero as ρ^* increases.

5. Occupation Time of the Server

We define the occupation time for this model as we did in Section I, 6. If $\xi^i(t)$ denotes the occupation time of the server at time t of the busy period initiated at $t = 0$ with $i > 0$ units, and if

$$w^i(\tau, t)\, d\tau = \Pr[\tau < \xi^i(t) < \tau + d\tau \mid m(0) = i]$$

we have, as in Section I, 6

$$\bar{w}^i(\theta, s) = \int_0^\infty \int_0^\infty e^{-st} e^{-\theta\tau} w^i(t, \tau)\, dt\, d\tau$$

$$= \frac{1}{\bar{S}(\theta)} \int_0^\infty \sum_{m=1}^{N} \bar{p}^i(m, x, s)[\bar{S}(\theta)]^m\, dx \int_0^\infty \frac{S(x+y)}{1 - \int_0^x S(u)\, du} e^{-\theta y}\, dy \quad (5.1)$$

Using (2.28), we get

$$\bar{w}^i(\theta, s) = \frac{1}{\bar{S}(\theta)} \sum_{j=0}^{N-1} [\bar{S}(\theta)]^{N-j}[1 - \bar{S}(\theta)]^j \bar{a}^i(j, s) \frac{\bar{S}(j\lambda + s) - \bar{S}(\theta)}{\theta - j\lambda - s} \quad (5.2)$$

where $\bar{a}^i(j, s)$ is defined by (2.27).

Now, for the general process, if $\hat{w}^i(\tau, t)\, d\tau = \Pr[\tau < \hat{\xi}^i(t) < \tau + d\tau]$, where $\hat{\xi}^i(t)$ is the random variable denoting the occupation time of the server at time t of the general process starting with $i \geqslant 0$ units, we get, proceeding as in Section I, 6,

$$\bar{\hat{w}}^i(\theta, s) = \int_0^\infty \int_0^\infty \hat{w}^i(\tau, t) \exp[-(st + \theta\tau)]\, dt\, d\tau$$

$$= \bar{\hat{e}}^i(s) + \sum_{j=0}^{N-1} [\bar{S}(\theta)]^{N-1-j}[1 - \bar{S}(\theta)]^j \frac{\bar{S}(j\lambda + s) - \bar{S}(\theta)}{\theta - j\lambda - s}$$

$$\times [\bar{a}^i(j, s) + N\lambda \bar{\hat{e}}^i(s) \bar{a}(j, s)] \quad (5.3)$$

where $\bar{a}^0(j, s) = 0$.

As in Section I, 6, it follows that if $\nu < \infty$, $\lim_{t\to\infty} \hat{w}^i(\tau, t) = \hat{w}(\tau)$ irrespective of the initial condition and is given by

$$\hat{w}(\theta) = \int_0^\infty \hat{w}(\tau)e^{-\theta\tau}\, d\tau$$

$$= \hat{e}\left[1 + N\lambda \sum_{j=0}^{N-1} [\bar{S}(\theta)]^{N-1-j}[1 - \bar{S}(\theta)]^j l(j) \frac{j\lambda}{1 - \bar{S}(j\lambda)} \frac{\bar{S}(\theta) - \bar{S}(j\lambda)}{j\lambda - \theta}\right] \tag{5.4}$$

where $l(j)$ and $\hat{e}$ are given by (4.2)–(4.4).

The mean occupation time or the mean virtual waiting time in the queue is obtained as

$$E(\hat{w}) = \frac{N\lambda\nu}{N\lambda\nu + \delta}\left[(N-1)\nu - \frac{1-\delta}{\lambda} + \frac{1}{2}\frac{E(S^2)}{\nu}\right] \tag{5.5}$$

where

$$\frac{1}{\delta} = \sum_{e=0}^{N-1} \binom{N-1}{e} \frac{1}{\phi(e)}$$

Equation (5.5) can be written in terms of $\hat{e}$ as follows

$$\frac{E(\hat{w})}{\nu} = N - \frac{f}{\nu}(1 - \hat{e}) \tag{5.6}$$

where

$$f = \nu + \frac{1}{\lambda} - \frac{1}{2}\frac{E(S^2)}{\nu}$$

For the exponential service-time distribution, $f = 1/\lambda$ and $E(\hat{w}) = \nu E(\hat{m})$.

It must be noted that under steady state, the mean virtual waiting time and the mean waiting time of a unit in queue are different for the finite-source model. However, these are the same for the infinite-source model, since the probability that a unit arrives is independent of the number of units present in the system; this is not the case for the finite-source model. In Fig. II.3, the ratio of the mean virtual waiting time to the mean service time is plotted against N for $\rho^* = N\lambda\nu =$ constant, assuming service time to be (i) exponentially distributed (unbroken line) and (ii) constant (broken line). The results indicate the same behavior as for the queue length, i.e., for small values of ρ^*, the effect of variability is small and the results of the infinite-source model with the same ρ^* can be used with sufficient accuracy.

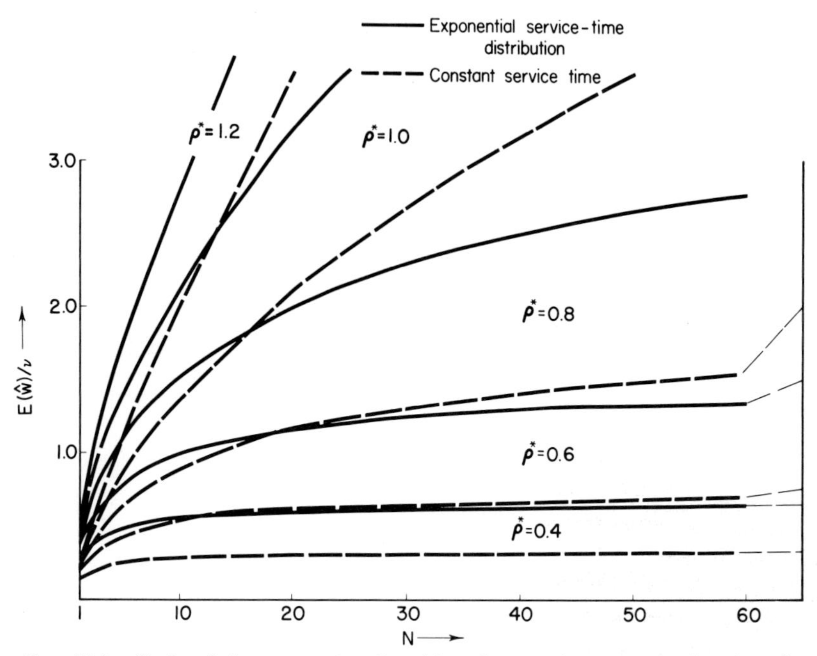

FIG. II.3. Ratio of the mean virtual waiting time to the mean service time for the basic finite-source model.

When $\rho^* = 1$, the effect of variability is predominant, and convergence to the infinite-source results is slow; therefore if N is not large and ρ^* is near one, the approximation to the infinite-source results is not good. For $\rho^* \gg 1$ and large N, following similar arguments as for $E(\hat{m})$, we can write

$$\frac{E(\hat{w})}{\nu} \approx N\left(1 - \frac{1}{\rho^*}\right) - 1 + \frac{1}{2}\frac{E(S^2)}{\nu^2} \tag{5.7}$$

so that the curve for $E(\hat{w})/\nu$ tends asymptotically toward a line which depends upon the second moment of the service-time distribution. Hence, for different distributions, the asymptotes, unlike $E(\hat{m})$, are parallel lines, e.g., the asymptotes for exponentially-distributed and constant service-time cases are parallel and are separated by a distance $\frac{1}{2}$. Thus, we can obtain the results for $\rho^* \gg 1$ by drawing the line which passes through the point $\{1, [E(S^2)/2\nu^2] - 1/\rho^*\}$ and is inclined at an angle $\tan^{-1}(1 - 1/\rho^*)$.

Chapter III

PRIORITY QUEUING MODELS

1. Introduction

In the last two chapters, we considered queuing processes in which only one class of units arrive at the service facility. Each unit in the class is assumed to be identical in all respects except service-time requirement. However, situations commonly occur when a given service facility is made use of by $k\,(>1)$ classes of units which may be distinguished according to some "measure of importance." In order to indicate the relative "measure of importance," we may associate with each class a priority index i $(1 \leqslant i \leqslant k)$, where 1 denotes the class with highest "measure of importance" and k the lowest. The discipline according to which the server selects the next unit and serves it is termed a "priority discipline." Any priority discipline must, therefore, specify the rules for making the following two decisions:

(i) Which unit to select for service once the server is free to take up the next unit.

(ii) Whether to continue or discontinue the service of the unit being serviced.

The decision of selecting the next unit for service may be made exogenously, i.e., it may depend only upon the knowledge of the priority class to which a unit belongs. On the other hand, it may be made endogenously, i.e., the decision may be based solely or partially on other considerations relating to the existing state of the system, e.g., the type of unit last serviced or the waiting time of the units present. The former disciplines are called exogenous priority disciplines, while the latter are called endogenous priority disciplines. It may be noted that in both exogenous and endogenous priority disciplines the decision to continue the service of the unit currently in service may or may not depend on the state of the system. Since not much is known about endogenous priority disciplines, we will defer their consideration to Chapter VII, and devote this chapter and the next few to the study of exogenous priority disciplines.

Since with exogenous priority disciplines the decision to select the next unit for service depends only upon the priority class, a unit of the ith class if present is always taken for service prior to the unit of the jth class ($i < j$). However, if a unit of the jth class is in service and a unit of the ith class ($i < j$) arrives, different alternatives may be followed leading to the following disciplines:

(i) Preemptive: the service of the jth-class unit is immediately interrupted and the server starts serving the ith-class unit.

(ii) Head-of-the-line: the service of the jth-class unit is continued to completion. This is also called nonpreemptive or postponable.

(iii) Discretionary: the server may use his discretion to follow (i) or (ii) depending upon the elapsed service time of the jth-class unit.

The preemptive discipline can be further broken down into the following categories, depending upon the manner in which the jth-class unit is serviced on its reentry:

(i) Preemptive resume: the preempted unit resumes service from the point where it was interrupted.

(ii) Preemptive repeat-identical: the preempted unit on its reentry requires the same amount of service as it required on its earlier entry.

(iii) Preemptive repeat-different: the preempted unit on its reentry requires a random service time independent of past preemptions and wasted service time.

We introduce another important classification for priority queues which depends upon the size of the sources from which the units emanate. If all sources are infinite, we refer to the model as an "infinite-source" priority model, while if one or more sources are finite, we refer to it as a "finite-source" priority model. The latter models can be classified further into two categories: (a) multiple finite-source priority models, in which each class of units emanates from a different finite source, and (b) single finite-source priority models, in which two or more types of units emanate from the same finite source. It must be noted that in the single finite-source priority model, the arrival of a unit of a particular class may effect the arrivals of other classes of units, while in the multiple finite-source priority models, this is not so. Consequently, the latter are easier to handle than the former. We will discuss the single finite-source priority models in Chapter VIII only; in work prior to that chapter, a finite-source priority model will be taken to mean a multiple finite-source priority model.

2. General Model and the Notion of Completion Time

The description of a general model is as follows: $k \geqslant 2$ types of units emanating from independent infinite or finite sources arrive at a single server. Units from the ith source ($1 \leqslant i \leqslant k$) are called the ith-class units and arrive in a Poisson stream with mean rate λ_i if the ith source is infinite. In case the ith source is finite with N_i units, each unit from this source is assumed to call for service after being in the source for a random time distributed exponentially with mean $1/\lambda_i$. The service times of the ith-class ($1 \leqslant i \leqslant k$) units are identically and independently distributed random variables with density $S_i(x)$. The assumption of the service time density can be relaxed, as pointed out in Chapter I. We do not assume here any specific priority discipline, except that if the service mechanism is to select a unit for service, a unit of the ith class is selected prior to the unit of the jth class if $i < j$ even if the jth-class unit arrived before the ith-class unit—a condition true for all exogenous priority disciplines. Within each class, the service discipline is "first come, first served."

We may, extending Kendall's notation [50], represent this model by $M_1, M_2, \ldots, M_k/G_1, G_2, \ldots, G_k/1/N_1, \ldots, N_k$. However, since we consider priority processes with Poisson inputs, general service-time distributions, and a single server (except in Sections VII, 6 and VIII, 2), we prefer to simplify this notation and refer to the process by $(N_1, \ldots, N_k)$ alone.

The priority process $(N_1, \ldots, N_k)$, if the service-time distributions of one or more classes are nonexponential, is non-Markovian, and may be studied either by the imbedded Markov chain analysis, e.g.,

Miller [62], Gaver [29], and Welch [96], or by using the supplementary variable technique, e.g., Jaiswal [44, 45], and Keilson [49]. However, the analysis for priority processes is obviously more difficult, since here the state description has to incorporate information about each class, and is, therefore, multidimensional. The earlier work on the subject was therefore restricted mostly to two priority classes. Another aspect of the previous work which deserves special mention is that the analysis was made with respect to a specific discipline, such as preemptive resume or head-of-the-line.

A significant contribution in this direction which led to an unified discussion of the exogenous priority disciplines is the notion of completion time. This notion appears to have occurred to a number of workers at about the same time, e.g., Keilson [49], Gaver [29], and Avi-Itzhak and Naor [6]. The completion time of a unit is defined as the duration of a period that begins from the instant the service of a unit starts and ends at the instant the server becomes free to take the next unit of that class. If no units of higher priority arrive during the service time, the completion time obviously equals the service time. The completion time was called the basic server sojourn time by Keilson [49] and the residence time by Avi-Itzhak and Naor [6]. The nomenclature "completion time" appears to have been originated by Gaver [29] and will be used here.

The method of solution that we adopt here is to investigate the busy-period probabilities and obtain the general process probabilities using renewal theory, as in the previous two chapters. The busy-period probabilities would have been difficult to investigate because of the multidimensional character of the process. However, because of the exogenous priority discipline, the points at which a completion time is initiated become renewal points, and the stochastic behavior at such points can be obtained from the basic models. Thus, the investigation of the priority process reduces to the investigation of the completion-time process, which is essentially a process with one class less than the priority process. Consequently, a k-class priority process can be reduced to a $(k-1)$-class process, and, proceeding recursively, can be related to the basic infinite or finite-source process. We should remark that the method of studying the completion-time process, generating the busy-period probabilities, and finding the general-process probabilities is essentially one of decomposing the more complex priority process into simple basic processes and may be of value in studying other related stochastic processes.

It will be easier for the sake of understanding to first study the model $(N_1, N_2, \ldots, N_k)$ for the case $k = 2$ and point out generalizations later. Consequently, in Sections III, 3–III, 7, we study the two-class priority model in detail, and point out generalizations in Section III, 8. For the two-class priority processes, it may be more conventional to refer to the first-class units as priority units and to the second-class units as ordinary units; otherwise, the terminology and notations used can be carried over for $k\,(>2)$ priority classes.

3. Completion-Time Process

For the two-class priority model, the completion-time process begins at time $t = 0$ with an ordinary unit entering service and ends when the server is free to accept the next ordinary unit. It should be made clear that during the completion-time process, we consider the service of only one ordinary unit, and that therefore the number of ordinary units is either one or zero. The completion-time cycle can be divided into two parts—the first part, denoted by I_2, when the ordinary unit is present, and the second part, denoted by L_2, when the ordinary unit has left after completion of service and the priority units are being serviced. In Fig. III.1, we present the completion-time cycles for some priority disciplines. At point B, the ordinary unit completes its service, and at point B', the completion-time cycle ends. The dotted lines denote that the priority unit is in service. Note that $L_2 = 0$ in (a) as well as in (c).

Let c_2 be the completion time of an ordinary unit. We denote the

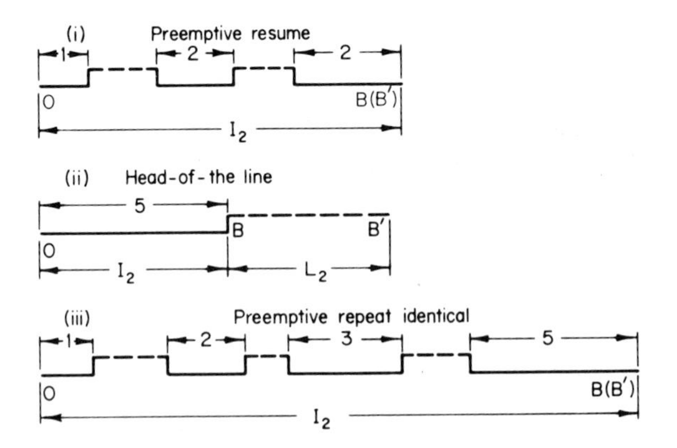

FIG. III.1. Completion time cycles.

random variables during the completion time c_2 or its components I_2 and L_2 by the same symbols as for the basic processes but with c, I and L as superscripts (for the sake of simplicity, we drop the subscript 2), writing, for example, m^c, m^I, and m^L. In addition, we introduce $\tilde{z}$, the service time of the preempted unit. Since we will be concerned both with priority and ordinary units during the completion-time process, we subscript the random variables defined above with 1 or 2 depending upon whether the unit under consideration is a priority or an ordinary unit. For example, m_1^I will denote the priority queue length during I_2, and $\tilde{z}_2^L$ the preempted service time of an ordinary unit during L_2. We may then define the probability densities associated with the state of the completion-time process at time t as follows:

(i) $f^I(m_1, x_2, t)\, dx_2 = \Pr[m_1^I(t) = m_1, x_2 < z_2^I < x_2 + dx_2]$

(ii) $g^I(m_1, x_1, x_2, t)\, dx_1\, dx_2 = \Pr[m_1^I(t) = m_1,$
$x_1 < z_1^I < x_1 + dx_1,$
$x_2 < \tilde{z}_2^I < x_2 + dx_2]$

(iii) $g^L(m_1, x_1, t)\, dx_1 = \Pr[m_1^L(t) = m_1, x_1 < z_1^L < x_1 + dx_1]$

(iv) $c_2(t)\, dt = \Pr[t < c_2 < t + dt]$

Here, f denotes that the ordinary unit is in service and g denotes that the priority unit is in service. Note that these probabilities are joint probabilities, e.g., $f^I(m_1, x_2, t)\, dx_2$ denotes the probability that at time t the state of the system is (m_1, x_2) and the ordinary unit is present.

These probabilities depend, however, on the priority discipline, e.g., for preemptive resume, $m_1 = 0$ in (i) above, and (iii) is not defined. These modifications will be discussed in subsequent chapters.

We finally define

$$p^I(m_1, t) = \Pr[m_1^I(t) = m_1] = \int_0^\infty f^I(m_1, x_2, t)\, dx_2 + \int_0^\infty \int_0^\infty g^I(m_1, x_1, x_2, t)\, dx_1\, dx_2 \qquad (3.1)$$

$$p^L(m_1, t) = \Pr[m_1^L(t) = m_1] = \int_0^\infty g^L(m_1, x_1, t)\, dx_1 \qquad (3.2)$$

and obtain

$$p^c(m_1, m_2, t) = \Pr[m_1^c(t) = m_1, m_2^c(t) = m_2] = \delta_{m_2,1}\, p^I(m_1, t) + \delta_{m_2,0}\, p^L(m_1, t) \qquad (3.3)$$

Hence, if $\bar{\Pi}^c(\alpha_1, \alpha_2, s)$ represents the Laplace transform of the generating function of the probabilities $p^c(m_1, m_2, t)$, we have

$$\bar{\Pi}^c(\alpha_1, \alpha_2, s) = \sum \sum \alpha_1^{m_1} \alpha_2^{m_2} \bar{p}^c(m_1, m_2, s) = \alpha_2 \bar{\Pi}^I(\alpha_1, s) + \bar{\Pi}^L(\alpha_1, s) \quad (3.4)$$

where $\bar{\Pi}^I(\alpha_1, s)$ and $\bar{\Pi}^L(\alpha_1, s)$ are the Laplace transforms of the generating functions of the probabilities defined in (3.1) and (3.2) respectively, i.e.,

$$\bar{\Pi}^I(\alpha_1, s) = \sum_{m_1=0} \alpha_1^{m_1} \bar{p}^I(m_1, s)$$

and

$$\bar{\Pi}^L(\alpha_1, s) = \sum_{m_1=1} \alpha_1^{m_1} \bar{p}^L(m_1, s)$$

the upper limit of summation being either N_1 or ∞ depending upon the priority source size.

We close this section by repeating that the completion-time process is virtually a single-class process with either one ordinary unit or none, and can therefore be studied from the results of the basic processes discussed in Chapters I and II.

4. Busy-Period Process

Let us consider the points at which an ordinary unit enters service during the busy period. The time interval between any two such consecutive points during the busy period is equal to the completion time which was discussed in the previous section. The queue length of the ordinary units at such a point decreases at most by one from the previous point and increases by the number of ordinary units that arrive during the completion time. In addition, there is no priority unit at such points. It becomes apparent that a similarity exists between the stochastic behavior of the ordinary units at service entry points in this process and the basic processes studied in the previous two chapters. We will exploit this similarity in obtaining the busy-period probabilities from the known results of the basic models.

Let us assume that the following condition is satisfied: Either the ordinary unit stays with the server throughout the completion time (i.e., $L_2 = 0$) or, if it goes out (i.e., $L_2 > 0$), it does not effect the arrival rate of ordinary units. We will call this the equivalence condition.

Now, the busy period may be initiated either by the arrival of an ordinary unit or by the arrival of a priority unit. Let us first consider the busy period initiated by an ordinary unit and compare this with the busy period of the ordinary queue in isolation (with no priority units) but with the service time replaced by the completion time. If the equivalence condition is satisfied, the behavior of these two processes at service entry points is obviously identical. Hence, the probability that at time t an ordinary unit enters service for the two-class priority process with a queue of $m_2 - 1$ ordinary units (and no priority units) is obtained from (I, 2.18) replacing (λ, S) by (λ_2, c_2), if the ordinary source is infinite, or from (II, 2.29), replacing (N, λ, S) by (N_2, λ_2, c_2), if the ordinary source is finite.

Before proceeding further, we discuss the conventions that we adopt in regard to the notation. We will need the busy-period densities, occupation-time densities, queue-length probabilities, and certain complicated expressions that arose in Chapters I and II for (i) the priority queue in isolation, (ii) the ordinary queue in isolation, and (iii) the ordinary queue in isolation but with the service time replaced by the completion time. For the cases (i) and (ii), we represent the various expressions used in previous chapters by subscripting them with 1 or 2, depending on whether we are considering the priority queue or the ordinary queue in isolation. An exception, however, is made for the queue-length probabilities, in which case the queue-length variable m in the parenthesis will be subscripted. For example, $b_1(t)$ and $b_2(t)$ represent the busy-period densities for the priority queue and the ordinary queue in isolation respectively, while $p_e(m_2, t)$ represents the probability of finding m_2 ordinary units in the system at service entry points for the ordinary queue in isolation. For the case (iii), the relevant expressions will be denoted by the corresponding capital letters; for example, $B_2(t)$, $P_e(m_2, t)$ represent, respectively, the busy-period density and the queue-length probability at service entry points for the ordinary queue in isolation but with the service time replaced by the completion time.

Thus, in terms of the notation mentioned above, the probability that an ordinary unit enters service at time t leaving a queue of $m_2 - 1$ ordinary units during the busy period initiated by an ordinary unit is $P_e(m_2, t)$. Next, if the busy period is initiated by a priority unit, the server remains occupied with the priority units for a time equal to the busy period of the priority queue in isolation which has the density $b_1(t)$, and if the priority source is infinite, is given by (I, 2.15) with parameters (λ_1, S_1), or, if the priority source is finite, by (II, 2.25) with parameters (N_1, λ_1, S_1). During this time, the ordinary units may arrive but cannot be serviced. After all the priority units have been serviced, an ordinary unit if present enters service. Let us compare this process with the initial busy-period process of the ordinary queue in isolation in which the service time is replaced by the completion time and the initial occupation time is the busy period of the priority queue in isolation. A moment's reflection will reveal that if the equivalence condition is satisfied, the two processes will have the same stochastic behavior at those points at which an ordinary unit enters service.

Hence, the probability that an ordinary unit enters service with a queue of $m_2 - 1$ ordinary units during the busy period of the priority process initiated by the arrival of a priority unit is identical to the probability density that at time t a unit enters service during the initial busy-period process of the ordinary queue in isolation, with the service time replaced by the completion time and the initial occupation time equal to $b_1(t)$. This we represent by $P_e^{b_1}(m_2, t)$, and obtain from the results of the initial busy period process of Section I, 2 or of Section II, 2, depending upon the ordinary source size.

We define $\lambda_1^* = \lambda_1$ if the priority source is infinite and $\lambda_1^* = N_1\lambda_1$ if the priority source is finite. Similarly, $\lambda_2^* = \lambda_2$ if the ordinary source is infinite and $\lambda_2^* = N_2\lambda_2$ if the ordinary source is finite. Apparently, the first type of busy period occurs with probability

$$\frac{\lambda_2^*}{\lambda_1^* + \lambda_2^*}$$

and the second type of busy period occurs with probability

$$\frac{\lambda_1^*}{\lambda_1^* + \lambda_2^*}$$

Hence, if $\mathscr{H}(m_2, t)$ denotes the probability that at time t an ordinary unit enters service with $m_2 - 1$ ordinary units in the queue for the two-class priority process, we have

$$\mathscr{H}(m_2, t) = \frac{\lambda_2^*}{\lambda_1^* + \lambda_2^*} P_e(m_2, t) + \frac{\lambda_1^*}{\lambda_1^* + \lambda_2^*} P_e^{b_1}(m_2, t) \tag{4.1}$$

and if $\gamma_2(t)$ denotes the busy-period density of the two-class priority process, we have

$$\gamma_2(t) = \frac{\lambda_2^*}{\lambda_2^* + \lambda_1^*} B_2(t) + \frac{\lambda_1^*}{\lambda_1^* + \lambda_2^*} B_2^{b_1}(t) \tag{4.2}$$

where $B_2(t)$ and $B_2^{b_1}(t)$ represent, respectively, the busy-period and initial busy-period densities of the ordinary queue in isolation but with the service time replaced by completion time.

Let $\mathscr{M}_1(t)$, $\mathscr{M}_2(t)$ denote, respectively, the queue lengths of the priority and ordinary units at time t of the busy period of the two-class priority process, and let z_1, z_2, and $\tilde{z}_2$ be the elapsed service time of the priority unit, the elapsed service time of the ordinary unit, and the preempted time of the ordinary unit, respectively. As the nature of the results depends upon the size of the ordinary source, we will discuss the busy-period process separately for the cases where ordinary source is infinite and where it is finite. Before doing so, we define the following probabilities associated with the busy period (the ranges of m_1 and m_2 in these definitions depend upon the sizes of the priority and ordinary sources, and will be specified later):

(i) $p(m_1, m_2, x_1, x_2, t)\, dx_1\, dx_2$

$$= \Pr[\mathscr{M}_1(t) = m_1, \mathscr{M}_2(t) = m_2, x_1 < z_1 < x_1 + dx_1, x_2 < \tilde{z}_2 < x_2 + dx_2 \mid \mathscr{M}_1(t_1) + \mathscr{M}_2(t_1) > 0 \text{ for all } t_1, 0 < t_1 < t] \qquad (x_1 > 0, x_2 \geqslant 0)$$

(ii) $q(m_1, m_2, x_2, t)\, dx_2$

$$= \Pr[\mathscr{M}_1(t) = m_1, \mathscr{M}_2(t) = m_2, x_2 < z_2 < x_2 + dx_2 \mid \mathscr{M}_1(t_1) + \mathscr{M}_2(t_1) > 0 \text{ for all } t_1, 0 < t_1 < t] \qquad (x_2 > 0)$$

In other words, $p(m_1, m_2, x_1, x_2, t)\, dx_1\, dx_2$ denotes the probability that there are m_1 priority and m_2 ordinary units; the priority unit is in service with the elapsed service time lying between x_1 and $x_1 + dx_1$, the ordinary unit has preempted time between x_2 and $x_2 + dx_2$, and, up to time t, the busy period which was initiated at $t = 0$ has not terminated. A similar explanation holds for $q(m_1, m_2, x_2, t)$.

It must be noted that (i) denotes the event that a priority unit is in service and (ii) that the ordinary unit is in service.

4-1. Ordinary Source Infinite—The (∞, ∞) and (N_1, ∞) Models

a. *Joint Queue-Length Probabilities during the Busy Period*

For these models, m_2 varies from 0 to ∞ in $p(m_1, m_2, x_1, x_2, t)$ and from 1 to ∞ in $q(m_1, m_2, x_2, t)$. To obtain the first probability, we observe that at time t the preempted time of the ordinary unit x_2 is either greater than zero or is zero. In the former case, an ordinary unit must have entered service at some time $\tau < t$ with a queue of, say, $m_2 - n - 1$ ordinary units and initiated a completion-time cycle. In time $t - \tau$, the completion-time cycle reaches the I_2 phase with m_1 priority units, one of which is in service with elapsed service time lying between x_1 and $x_1 + dx_1$, while the ordinary unit has the preempted time lying between x_2 and $x_2 + dx_2$. In addition, in order that at time t there be m_2 ordinary units, n units must arrive in time $t - \tau$. In the later case, in which $x_2 = 0$, there are two cases to be considered: (i) An ordinary unit initiates the completion-time cycle at $\tau < t$ and the cycle reaches the L_2 phase in time $t - \tau$; and (ii) at $t = 0$, the arrival of a priority unit initiates a busy period which has not ended up to time t. Hence,

$$\begin{aligned}
p(m_1&, m_2, x_1, x_2, t)\\
&= \sum_{n=0}^{m_2-1} \int_0^t \mathscr{H}(m_2 - n, \tau) \frac{[\lambda_2(t-\tau)]^n}{n!} \exp[-\lambda_2(t-\tau)]\\
&\quad \times g^I(m_1, x_1, x_2, t-\tau)\, d\tau\\
&\quad + \delta(x_2) \sum_{n=0}^{m_2} \int_0^t \mathscr{H}(m_2 + 1 - n, \tau) \frac{[\lambda_2(t-\tau)]^n}{n!} \exp[-\lambda_2(t-\tau)]\\
&\quad \times g^L(m_1, x_1, t-\tau)\, d\tau\\
&\quad + \delta(x_2) \frac{\lambda_1^*}{\lambda_1^* + \lambda_2} \cdot \left[\frac{(\lambda_2 t)^{m_2}}{m_2!} \exp(-\lambda_2 t) p(m_1, x_1, t)\right] \qquad (m_1 > 0)
\end{aligned} \tag{4.3}$$

Similarly,

$$\begin{aligned}
q(m_1&, m_2, x_2, t)\\
&= \sum_{n=0}^{m_2-1} \int_0^t \mathscr{H}(m_2 - n, \tau) \frac{[\lambda_2(t-\tau)]^n}{n!} \exp[-\lambda_2(t-\tau)]\\
&\quad \times f^I(m_1, x_2, t-\tau)\, d\tau \qquad (m_2 > 0)
\end{aligned} \tag{4.4}$$

where $\mathscr{H}(m_2, \tau)$ is the probability that at time τ, an ordinary unit enters service leaving behind a queue of $m_2 - 1$ ordinary units during the busy-period process and is given by (4.1).

Hence, if $\Pi(\alpha_1, \alpha_2, t)$ denotes the generating function of the joint queue-length probabilities for the busy-period process, we have

$$\bar{\Pi}(\alpha_1, \alpha_2, t) = \sum_{m_1} \sum_{m_2=0}^{\infty} \alpha_1^{m_1}\alpha_2^{m_2} \int_0^\infty \int_0^\infty p(m_1, m_2, x_1, x_2, t)\, dx_1\, dx_2$$

$$+ \sum_{m_1} \sum_{m_2=1}^{\infty} \alpha_1^{m_1}\alpha_2^{m_2} \int_0^\infty q(m_1, m_2, x_2, t)\, dx_2 \tag{4.5}$$

where the summation on m_1 will depend upon the priority source size.

Taking, the Laplace transform and using (3.4), we get

$$\bar{\Pi}(\alpha_1, \alpha_2, s) = \frac{1}{\alpha_2} \bar{\mathscr{G}}(\alpha_2, s)\bar{\Pi}^c[\alpha_1, \alpha_2, s + \lambda_2(1 - \alpha_2)] + \frac{\lambda_1^*}{\lambda_1^* + \lambda_2}$$

$$\times \bar{\Pi}[\alpha_1, s + \lambda_2(1 - \alpha_2)] \tag{4.6}$$

where

$$\bar{\mathscr{G}}(\alpha_2, s) = \sum \alpha_2^{m_2}\bar{\mathscr{H}}(m_2, s)$$

and $\bar{\Pi}(\alpha_1, s)$ is the Laplace transform of the queue length probability generating function during the busy period of the priority qeuue in isolation and is obtained from (I, 2.19) if the priority source is infinite and by (II, 2.30) if the priority source is finite; $\bar{\Pi}^c(\alpha_1, \alpha_2, s)$ is defined by (3.4) and $\bar{\mathscr{G}}(\alpha_2, s)$ can be obtained from (4.1).

Using the results of Section I, 2 in (4.1), $\bar{\mathscr{G}}(\alpha_2, s)$ is obtained as

$$\frac{1}{\alpha_2} \bar{\mathscr{G}}(\alpha_2, s)$$

$$= \frac{\lambda_2[\alpha_2 - \bar{B}_2(s)] + \lambda_1^*[\bar{b}_1\{\lambda_2(1 - \alpha_2) + s\} - \bar{b}_1\{\lambda_2[1 - \bar{B}_2(s)] + s\}]}{(\lambda_2 + \lambda_1^*)[\alpha_2 - \bar{c}_2\{\lambda_2(1 - \alpha_2) + s\}]} \tag{4.7}$$

where $\bar{B}_2(s)$ is the smallest root of the equation

$$\alpha_2 - \bar{c}_2\{\lambda_2(1 - \alpha_2) + s\} = 0 \tag{4.8}$$

If the intermediate probabilities $p(m_1, m_2, x_1, x_2, t)$ and $q(m_1, m_2, x_2, t)$ are not required, the result (4.6) can be obtained more directly, as follows:

(i) At time $t = 0$ the busy period of the priority queue in isolation is initiated with probability $\lambda_1^*/(\lambda_1^* + \lambda_2)$.

(ii) At any time $t \geqslant 0$, an ordinary unit enters service and initiates a completion time with $m_2 - 1$ ordinary units in the queue.

Hence,

$$p(m_1, m_2, t) = \frac{\lambda_1^*}{\lambda_1^* + \lambda_2} \delta(t) * \left[p(m_1, t) \frac{(\lambda_2 t)^{m_2}}{m_2!} e^{-\lambda_2 t}\right]$$

$$+ \sum_{n=0}^{m_2} \mathscr{H}(m_2 - n, t) * \left[\frac{(\lambda_2 t)^n}{n!} e^{-\lambda_2 t} p^I(m_1, t)\right]$$

$$+ \sum_{n=0}^{m_2+1} \mathscr{H}(m_2 - n + 1, t) * \left[\frac{(\lambda_2 t)^n}{n!} e^{-\lambda_2 t} p^L(m_1, t)\right] \tag{4.9}$$

so that, using (3.4), we obtain

$$\bar{\Pi}(\alpha_1, \alpha_2, s) = \frac{1}{\alpha_2} \bar{\mathscr{G}}(\alpha_2, s) \bar{\Pi}^c[\alpha_1, \alpha_2, s + \lambda_2(1 - \alpha_2)] + \frac{\lambda_1^*}{\lambda_1^* + \lambda_2}$$
$$\times \bar{\Pi}[\alpha_1, s + \lambda_2(1 - \alpha_2)] \tag{4.10}$$

which is the same as (4.6).

b. *Busy Period*

Following the same arguments as above, the busy-period distribution for the two class priority process is given by

$$\Pr(\gamma_2 > t) = \frac{\lambda_1^*}{\lambda_1^* + \lambda_2} \Pr(b_1 > t) + \mathscr{G}(1, t) * \Pr(c_2 > t)$$

Taking Laplace transform, we get for the Laplace transform of the busy period density

$$\frac{1 - \bar{\gamma}_2(s)}{s} = \frac{\lambda_1^*}{\lambda_1^* + \lambda_2} \frac{1 - \bar{b}_1(s)}{s} + \bar{\mathscr{G}}(1, s) \frac{1 - \bar{c}_2(s)}{s}$$

On substituting $\mathscr{G}(1, s)$ from (4.7) and simplifying we get

$$\bar{\gamma}_2(s) = \frac{\lambda_2}{\lambda_1^* + \lambda_2} \bar{B}_2(s) + \frac{\lambda_1^*}{\lambda_1^* + \lambda_2} \bar{b}_1[\lambda_2\{1 - \bar{c}_2(s)\} + s] \tag{4.11}$$

Equation (4.11) can be obtained directly from (4.2) by appropriate substitutions.

At this point we shall summarize the two approaches adopted above in deriving the busy-period densities. In deriving the busy period density through (4.2), we considered that the busy period could be initiated at $t = 0$ either by the arrival of an ordinary unit or by a priority unit which in turn is equivalent to the busy period or the initial busy period of the ordinary queue with the service time replaced by completion time. While deriving (4.11) the busy period was considered as comprising of a busy period of the priority queue in isolation at $t = 0$ and at any time $t \geqslant 0$ a completion time cycle is initiated; the process continuing till there is no ordinary unit to initiate the completion time. These two approaches are identical although they may appear to be different. We may use either of the two approaches depending upon the algebraic simplicity, for example, see Section III, 7.

Finally, if $E(\gamma_2)$ denotes the mean length of the busy period for the (∞, ∞) and (N_1, ∞) models, we have

$$\begin{aligned} E(\gamma_2) &= \frac{\lambda_2}{\lambda_2 + \lambda_1^*} \frac{E(c_2)}{1 - \lambda_2 E(c_2)} + \frac{\lambda_1^*}{\lambda_2 + \lambda_1^*} \frac{E(b_1)}{1 - \lambda_2 E(c_2)} \\ &\qquad \text{if} \quad \lambda_2 E(c_2) < 1 \quad \text{and} \quad E(b_1) < \infty \\ &= \infty \qquad \text{otherwise} \end{aligned} \tag{4.12}$$

4-2. Ordinary Source Finite—The (∞, N_2) and (N_1, N_2) Models

a. *Joint Queue Length Probabilities during the Busy Period*

When the ordinary source is finite, the equivalence condition holds good only for preemptive disciplines. For the head-of-the-line or discretionary priority processes, the ordinary unit completes service and leaves the system before the completion time ends, increasing the arrival rate of the ordinary units by λ_2. Consequently,the equivalence condition does not hold good. The results given below are true for preemptive disciplines only. The modifications needed to study head-of-the-line priority discipline with the ordinary source finite will be discussed in Chapter V.

For preemptive disciplines, g^L is not defined, and, therefore, following the same arguments as above, we get

$$p(m_1, m_2, x_1, x_2, t)$$
$$= \sum_{n=0}^{m_2-1} \int_0^t \Big\{ \mathscr{H}(m_2 - n, \tau) \binom{N_2 - m_2 + n}{n} \{1 - \exp[-\lambda_2(t-\tau)]\}^n$$
$$\times \exp[-\lambda_2(N_2 - m_2)(t-\tau)]\, g^I[m_1, x_1, x_2, t-\tau]\, d\tau \Big\}$$
$$+ \delta(x_2)\delta(t) * \frac{\lambda_1^*}{\lambda_1^* + N_2\lambda_2} \binom{N_2}{m_2} \exp[-(N_2 - m_2)\lambda_2 t]$$
$$\times [1 - \exp(-\lambda_2 t)]^{m_2} p[m_1, x_1, t] \qquad (m_1 > 0) \tag{4.13}$$

and

$$q(0, m_2, x_2, t)$$
$$= \sum_{n=0}^{m_2-1} \int_{\tau=0}^t \Big\{ \mathscr{H}(m_2 - n, \tau) \binom{N_2 - m_2 + n}{n} (1 - \exp[-\lambda_2(t-\tau)])^n$$
$$\times \exp[-\lambda_2(N_2 - m_2)(t-\tau)] f^I[0, x_2, t-\tau]\, d\tau \Big\} \qquad (m_2 > 0) \tag{4.14}$$

Observe that if k units are present with the server, the probability that n units arrive in time t from the finite source of size N is

$$\binom{N-k}{n} (1 - \exp[-\lambda_2 t])^n \exp[-(N - k - n)\lambda_2 t]$$

and $m_1 = 0$ because of preemptive discipline.

Using the Laplace transform in (4.13) and (4.14), we get

$$\bar{p}(m_1, m_2, x_1, x_2, s)$$
$$= \sum_{n=0}^{m_2-1} \bar{\mathscr{H}}(m_2 - n, s) \binom{N_2 - m_2 + n}{n} \sum_{e=0}^{n} (-1)^e \binom{n}{e}$$
$$\times \bar{g}^I[m_1, x_1, x_2, (N_2 - m_2 + e)\lambda_2 + s]$$
$$+ \delta(x_2) \frac{\lambda_1^*}{\lambda_1^* + N_2\lambda_2} \binom{N_2}{m_2} \sum_{e=0}^{m_2} (-1)^e \binom{m_2}{e}$$
$$\times \bar{p}[m_1, x_1, (N_2 - m_2 + e)\lambda_2 + s] \tag{4.15}$$

and

$$\bar{q}(0, m_2, x_2, s) = \sum_{n=0}^{m_2-1} \bar{\mathscr{H}}(m_2 - n, s) \binom{N_2 - m_2 + n}{n} \sum_{e=0}^{n} (-1)^e \binom{n}{e}$$

$$\times \bar{f}^I[0, x_2, (N_2 - m_2 + e)\lambda_2 + s] \qquad (4.16)$$

Changing the order of summation in (4.15) and (4.16), we get after some simplification

$$\bar{p}(m_1, m_2, x_1, x_2, s)$$

$$= \sum_{e=N_2-m_2}^{N_2-1} (-1)^{N_2-m_2-e} \binom{e}{e + m_2 - N_2} \bar{g}^I(m_1, x_1, x_2, e\lambda_2 + s)$$

$$\times \sum_{j=e}^{N_2-1} \binom{j}{e} \bar{\mathscr{H}}(N_2 - j, s)$$

$$+ \delta(x_2) \frac{\lambda_1^*}{\lambda_1^* + N_2\lambda_2} \binom{N_2}{m_2} \sum_{e=N_2-m_2}^{N_2} (-1)^{N_2-m_2-e}$$

$$\times \binom{m_2}{e + m_2 - N_2} \bar{p}(m_1, x_1, e\lambda_2 + s) \qquad (4.17)$$

$$\bar{q}(0, m_2, x_2, s) = \sum_{e=N_2-m_2}^{N_2-1} (-1)^{N_2-m_2-e} \binom{e}{e + m_2 - N_2} \bar{f}^I(0, x_2, e\lambda_2 + s)$$

$$\times \sum_{j=e}^{N_2-1} \binom{j}{e} \bar{\mathscr{H}}(N_2 - j, s) \qquad (4.18)$$

Now, from (4.1), substituting the values of $P_e(m_2, t)$ and $P_e^{b_1}(m_2, t)$, which we obtain from Section II, 2 by replacing (N, λ, S) by (N_2, λ_2, c_2), we obtain

$$\bar{\mathscr{H}}(m_2, s) = \sum_{e=0}^{m_2-1} (-1)^e \binom{N_2 - m_2 + e}{e} \Big[\frac{N_2\lambda_2}{N_2\lambda_2 + \lambda_1^*} \bar{A}_2(N_2 - m_2 + e, s)$$

$$+ \frac{\lambda_1^*}{N_2\lambda_2 + \lambda_1^*} \bar{A}_2^{b_1}(N_2 - m_2 + e, s)\Big] \qquad (4.19)$$

where $\bar{A}_2(m, s)$ and $\bar{A}_2^{b_1}(m, s)$ are given by (II, 2.27) and (II, 2.45) after replacing (N, λ, S) by (N_2, λ_2, c_2).

Using the transform relationship given by (II, 2.6) and (II, 2.7), we obtain

$$\sum_{j=e}^{N_2-1} \binom{j}{e} \mathscr{H}(N_2 - j, s) = \frac{N_2\lambda_2}{N_2\lambda_2 + \lambda_1^*} \bar{A}_2(e, s) + \frac{\lambda_1^*}{N_2\lambda_2 + \lambda_1^*} \bar{A}_2^{b_1}(e, s) \qquad (4.20)$$

Using (4.20) in (4.17) and (4.18), we obtain, after simplification, using Appendix I, Lemma 2, Eq. (24) of Lemma 6, and the identity

$$\binom{N_2}{m_2}\binom{m_2}{e + m_2 - N_2} = \binom{N_2}{e}\binom{e}{e + m_2 - N_2}$$

the following results:

$$\sum_{m_2=0}^{N_2} \alpha_2^{m_2} \bar{p}(m_1, m_2, x_1, x_2, s)$$

$$= \sum_{m_2=0}^{N_2-1} \alpha_2^{N_2-m_2}(1 - \alpha_2)^{m_2} \left[\frac{N_2\lambda_2}{N_2\lambda_2 + \lambda_1^*} \bar{A}_2(m_2, s) + \frac{\lambda_1^*}{N_2\lambda_2 + \lambda_1^*} \bar{A}_2^{b_1}(m_2, s)\right]$$

$$\times \bar{g}^I(m_1, x_1, x_2, m_2\lambda_2 + s) + \delta(x_2) \frac{\lambda_1^*}{\lambda_1^* + N_2\lambda_2}$$

$$\times \sum_{m_2=0}^{N_2} \alpha_2^{N_2-m_2}(1 - \alpha_2)^{m_2} \binom{N_2}{m_2} \bar{p}(m_1, x_1, m_2\lambda_2 + s) \qquad (4.21)$$

and

$$\sum_{m_2=1}^{N_2} \alpha_2^{m_2} \bar{q}(0, m_2, x_2, s)$$

$$= \sum_{m_2=0}^{N_2-1} \alpha_2^{N_2-m_2}(1 - \alpha_2)^{m_2}$$

$$\times \left[\frac{N_2\lambda_2}{N_2\lambda_2 + \lambda_1^*} \bar{A}_2(m_2, s) + \frac{\lambda_1^*}{N_2\lambda_2 + \lambda_1^*} \bar{A}_2^{b_1}(m_2, s)\right]$$

$$\times \bar{f}^I(0, x_2, m_2\lambda_2 + s) \qquad (4.22)$$

Finally, defining $\bar{A}_1(m_2, s)$ and $\bar{A}_2^{b_1}(m_2, s)$ to be zero for $m_2 = N_2$, we obtain the generating function of the joint queue-length probabilities as

$$\bar{\Pi}(\alpha_1, \alpha_2, s) = \sum_{m_2=0}^{N_2-1} \alpha_2^{N_2-m_2}(1-\alpha_2)^{m_2}$$
$$\times \left[\frac{N_2\lambda_2}{N_2\lambda_2+\lambda_1^*} \bar{A}_2(m_2, s) + \frac{\lambda_1^*}{N_2\lambda_2+\lambda_1^*} \bar{A}_2^{b_1}(m_2, s)\right]$$
$$\times \bar{\Pi}^I(\alpha_1, m_2\lambda_2+s) + \frac{\lambda_1^*}{\lambda_1^*+N_2\lambda_2}\binom{N_2}{m_2}\bar{\Pi}(\alpha_1, m_2\lambda_2+s) \tag{4.23}$$

where, from (3.1) and (3.4), we have

$$\bar{\Pi}^I(\alpha_1, s) = \frac{1}{\alpha_2}\bar{\Pi}^c(\alpha_1, \alpha_2, s)$$
$$= \sum_{m_1} \alpha_1^{m_1} \int_0^\infty \int_0^\infty \bar{g}^I(m_1, x_1, x_2, s)\, dx_1\, dx_2 + \int_0^\infty \bar{f}^I(0, x_2, s)\, dx_2 \tag{4.24}$$

b. *Busy Period*

From (4.2), $\bar{\gamma}_2(s)$, the Laplace transform of the busy-period density of the (∞, N_2) and (N_1, N_2) models, is given by

$$\bar{\gamma}_2(s) = \frac{N_2\lambda_2}{N_2\lambda_2+\lambda_1^*}\bar{B}_2(s) + \frac{\lambda_1^*}{\lambda_1^*+N_2\lambda_2}\bar{B}_2^{b_1}(s) \tag{4.25}$$

where $\bar{B}_2(s)$ and $\bar{B}_2^{b_1}(s)$ can be obtained from (II, 2.25) and (II, 2.42) by replacing (N, λ, S) by (N_2, λ_2, c_2). If $E(\gamma_2)$ denotes the mean length of the busy period, we have, either by differentiating (4.25) or directly from (II, 2.32) and (II, 2.46) by replacing (N, λ, S, Ω) with $(N_2, \lambda_2, c_2, b_1)$,

$$E(\gamma_2) = \frac{N_2\lambda_2}{N_2\lambda_2+\lambda_1^*}E(c_2)\sum_{e=0}^{N_2-1}\binom{N_2-1}{e}\frac{1}{\Phi_2(e)} + \frac{\lambda_1^*}{\lambda_1^*+N_2\lambda_2}$$
$$\times\left[E(b_1) + E(c_2)\sum_{e=1}^{N_2}\binom{N_2}{e}\frac{1-\bar{b}_1(e\lambda_2)}{\Phi_2(e-1)}\right] \tag{4.26}$$

for $E(c_2) < \infty$ and $E(b_1) < \infty$, and $E(\gamma_2) = \infty$ otherwise. $\Phi_2(e)$ is obtained from (II, 2.33) by replacing λ and S by λ_2 and c_2.

5. General Process

From the busy-period probabilities, the general-process probabilities can be obtained by the same renewal-theoretic approach as was used in Chapters I and II. The initial conditions can be assumed arbitrarily. However, for the sake of simplicity, we assume that the system is initially empty, so that, proceeding in a manner exactly the same as in Sections I, 3 or II, 3, we obtain the following results:

$$\bar{\bar{p}}(m_1, m_2, x_1, x_2, s) = (\lambda_1^* + \lambda_2^*)\bar{\hat{e}}^{(2)}(s)\bar{p}(m_1, m_2, x_1, x_2, s) \tag{5.1}$$

$$\bar{\bar{q}}(0, m_2, x_2, s) = (\lambda_1^* + \lambda_2^*)\bar{\hat{e}}^{(2)}(s)\bar{q}(0, m_2, x_2, s) \tag{5.2}$$

where $\hat{e}^{(2)}(t)$ is the probability that the server is idle and is given by

$$\bar{\hat{e}}^{(2)}(s) = [s + (\lambda_1^* + \lambda_2^*)\{1 - \bar{\gamma}_2(s)\}]^{-1} \tag{5.3}$$

Defining the generating function of the joint queue length probabilities by $\bar{\bar{\Pi}}(\alpha_1, \alpha_2, s)$, we get from (5.1) and (5.2)

$$\bar{\bar{\Pi}}(\alpha_1, \alpha_2, s) = \bar{\hat{e}}^{(2)}(s)[1 + (\lambda_1^* + \lambda_2^*)\bar{\Pi}(\alpha_1, \alpha_2, s)]$$

where $\bar{\Pi}(\alpha_1, \alpha_2, s)$ is given by (4.6) for the (∞, ∞) and (N_1, ∞) models and by (4.23) for the (∞, N_2) and (N_1, N_2) models. Hence, the Laplace transform of the generating function of the time-dependent joint queue-length probabilities for the (∞, ∞) and (N_1, ∞) models is given by

$$\bar{\bar{\Pi}}(\alpha_1, \alpha_2, s) = \bar{\hat{e}}^{(2)}(s)\Big[1 + (\lambda_1^* + \lambda_2)\frac{1}{\alpha_2}\bar{\mathscr{G}}(\alpha_2, s) \times \bar{\bar{\Pi}}^c[\alpha_1, \alpha_2, s + \lambda_2(1 - \alpha_2)] + \lambda_1^*\bar{\bar{\Pi}}[\alpha_1, s + \lambda_2(1 - \alpha_2)]\Big] \tag{5.4}$$

where $\bar{\mathscr{G}}(\alpha_2, s)$ is given by (4.8) and $\bar{\bar{\Pi}}^c(\alpha_1, \alpha_2, s)$ is defined by (3.4).

Similarly, using (4.19), the Laplace transform of the generating function of the time-dependent joint queue-length probabilities for the (∞, N_2) and (N_1, N_2) models under preemptive disciplines is given by

$$\bar{\bar{\Pi}}(\alpha_1, \alpha_2, s) = \bar{\hat{e}}^{(2)}(s)\Big[1 + \sum_{m_2=0}^{N_2} \alpha_2^{N_2-m_2}(1 - \alpha_2)^{m_2}\Big\{[N_2\lambda_2\bar{A}_2(m_2, s) + \lambda_1^*\bar{A}_2^{b_1}(m_2, s)]\bar{\bar{\Pi}}^I[\alpha_1, m_2\lambda_2 + s] + \lambda_1^*\binom{N_2}{m_2}\bar{\Pi}(\alpha_1, m_2\lambda_2 + s)\Big\}\Big] \tag{5.5}$$

where $\bar{\bar{\Pi}}^I(\alpha_1, s)$ is given by (4.24).

6. Limiting Behavior of the Joint Queue-Length Probabilities

The conditions for the existence of a limiting distribution can be obtained as in previous chapters. Assuming λ_1^* and λ_2^* to be nonzero and finite so as to avoid trivial cases, the condition for the existence of the limiting distribution of the queue length is the same as the condition for the existence of the finite mean of the busy period. Also, if $\hat{\Pi}(\alpha_1, \alpha_2) = \lim_{t\to\infty} \hat{\Pi}(\alpha_1, \alpha_2, t)$ is the generating function of the limiting queue-length probabilities, we have, as in Sections I, 4 or II, 4,

$$\hat{\Pi}(\alpha_1, \alpha_2) = (\lambda_1^* + \lambda_2^*)\hat{e}^{(2)} \int_0^\infty \Pi(\alpha_1, \alpha_2, t)\, dt + \hat{e}^{(2)} \tag{6.1}$$

and

$$\hat{e}^{(2)} = [1 + (\lambda_1^* + \lambda_2^*)E(\gamma_2)]^{-1} \tag{6.2}$$

6-1. Ordinary Source Infinite—The (∞, ∞) and (N_1, ∞) Models

The limiting distribution exists if $\lambda_2 E(c_2) < 1$ and $E(b_1) < \infty$, and is given by

$$\hat{\Pi}(\alpha_1, \alpha_2) = \hat{e}^{(2)} \Big[1 + (\lambda_1^* + \lambda_2) \frac{1}{\alpha_2} \mathscr{G}(\alpha_2, 0)\bar{\Pi}^c[\alpha_1, \alpha_2, \lambda_2(1-\alpha_2)] + \lambda_1^* \bar{\Pi}[\alpha_1, \lambda_2(1-\alpha_2)]\Big] \tag{6.3}$$

where

$$\hat{e}^{(2)} = \frac{1 - \lambda_2 E(c_2)}{1 + \lambda_1 E(b_1)} \tag{6.4}$$

If $E(\hat{\mathscr{M}}_1)$ and $E(\hat{\mathscr{M}}_2)$ denote the mean number of priority and ordinary units, respectively, we have

$$\begin{aligned} E(\hat{\mathscr{M}}_1) &= \lambda_2 \frac{\partial}{\partial\alpha_1} \bar{\Pi}^c[\alpha_1, 1, 0]\big|_{\alpha_1=1} + \frac{\hat{e}^{(2)}}{\hat{e}_1} E(\hat{m}_1) \\ &= \lambda_2 E(m_1{}^c)E(c_2) + \frac{\hat{e}^{(2)}}{\hat{e}_1} E(\hat{m}_1) \end{aligned} \tag{6.5}$$

where $E(m_1{}^c)$ denotes the expected number of priority units during the completion-time cycle. The equivalence of

$$\frac{\partial}{\partial\alpha_1} \bar{\Pi}^c[\alpha_1, 1, 0]\Big|_{\alpha_1=1} = \int_0^\infty \sum_{m_1} m_1\{\Pi^I[m_1, t] + \Pi^L[m_1, t]\}\, dt$$

to $E(m_1{}^c)E(c_2)$ can be established more rigorously as in Section I, 4. And

$$E(\hat{\mathscr{M}}_2) = \lambda_2 E(I_2) + \frac{\lambda_1^* \lambda_2}{2} \frac{E(b_1{}^2)}{1 + \lambda_1^* E(b_1)} + \frac{\lambda_2{}^2}{2} \frac{E(c_2{}^2)}{1 - \lambda_2 E(c_2)} \tag{6.6}$$

where $E(I_2)$ is the expected length of the ordinary unit's stay during the completion time.

6-2. Ordinary Source Finite—The (∞, N_2) and (N_1, N_2) Models

The limiting distribution exists if $E(c_2) < \infty$ and $E(b_1) < \infty$, and is given by

$$\hat{\Pi}(\alpha_1, \alpha_2) = \hat{e}^{(2)} \Big[1 + \sum_{m_2=0}^{N_2} \alpha_2^{N_2-m_2}(1-\alpha_2)^{m_2} \Big\{ [N_2\lambda_2 \bar{A}_2(m_2, 0) + \lambda_1^* \bar{A}_2^{b_1}(m_2, 0)] \times \bar{\Pi}^I(\alpha_1, m_2\lambda_2) + \lambda_1^* \binom{N_2}{m_2} \bar{\Pi}(\alpha_1, m_2\lambda_2) \Big\} \Big] \tag{6.7}$$

where

$$\hat{e}^{(2)} = \Big[1 + N_2\lambda_2 E(c_2) \sum_{e=0}^{N_2-1} \binom{N_2-1}{e} \frac{1}{\Phi_2(e)} + \lambda_1^* E(b_1) + \lambda_1^* E(c_2) \sum_{e=1}^{N_2} \binom{N_2}{e} \frac{1 - \bar{b}_1(e\lambda_2)}{\Phi_2(e-1)} \Big]^{-1} \tag{6.8}$$

It may be verified that the mean number of priority units present in the system for the priority model is the same as of the priority queue in isolation. The mean number of ordinary units is given by

$$E(\hat{\mathscr{M}}_2) = N_2 - \frac{1}{\lambda_2 E(c_2)} \Big[1 - \frac{\hat{e}^{(2)}}{\hat{e}_1}\Big] \tag{6.9}$$

using the following results

$$\bar{\Pi}^I(1, \lambda_2) = \int_0^\infty \Pi^c(1, 1, t) e^{-\lambda_2 t}\, dt = \int_0^\infty e^{-\lambda_2 t} \Pr(c_2 > t)\, dt = \frac{1 - \bar{c}_2(\lambda_2)}{\lambda_2} \tag{6.10}$$

and, similarly,

$$\bar{\Pi}(1, \lambda_2) = \frac{1 - \bar{b}_1(\lambda_2)}{\lambda_2} \tag{6.11}$$

$$\bar{\Pi}'(1, 0) = E(c_2) \tag{6.12}$$

$$\bar{\Pi}(1, 0) = E(b_1) \tag{6.13}$$

$$\bar{A}_2(0, 0) = \sum_{e=0}^{N_2-1} \binom{N_2 - 1}{e} \frac{1}{\Phi_2(e)} \tag{6.14}$$

$$\bar{A}_2(1, 0) = \frac{1}{1 - \bar{c}_2(\lambda_1)} \left[\sum_{e=1}^{N_2-1} \binom{N_2 - 1}{e} \frac{1}{\Phi_2(e)} \right] \tag{6.15}$$

$$\bar{A}_2^{b_1}(0, 0) = \sum_{e=1}^{N_2} \binom{N_2}{e} \frac{1 - \bar{b}_1(e\lambda_2)}{\Phi_2(e - 1)} \tag{6.16}$$

$$\bar{A}_2^{b_1}(1, 0) = \frac{1}{1 - \bar{c}_2(\lambda_1)} \left[\sum_{e=1}^{N_2} \binom{N_2}{e} \frac{1 - \bar{b}_1(e\lambda_2)}{\Phi_2(e - 1)} - N_2\{1 - \bar{b}_1(\lambda_2)\} \right] \tag{6.17}$$

where $\Phi_2(e)$ is defined by (II, 2.33) with the parameters (λ, S) replaced by (λ_2, c_2).

7. Occupation Time of the Server

The occupation time of the server at time t with respect to the ith class is defined as the time the server will remain occupied with units of priority index less than or equal to i if the input of the ith class units is stopped at time t. Since this is also the waiting time a unit of class i will have to wait if it arrived at time t, it is the virtual waiting time of the ith-class unit at time t. Our method of approach for studying the occupation-time of the server is the same as in previous chapters, i.e., we investigate the occupation-time density during the busy period and use renewal-theoretic arguments to investigate the occupation-time density for the general process.

7-1. Occupation-Time of the Server with Respect to Priority Units

To obtain the occupation-time density with respect to priority units during the busy period of the two-class priority model, we can, as in Section III, 4, conceive of the busy period as comprising

(i) a busy period of the priority units in isolation being initiated at time $t = 0$ with probability

$$\frac{\lambda_1^*}{\lambda_1^* + \lambda_2^*}$$

(ii) a completion-time cycle initiated at $t \geqslant 0$ with probability

$$\sum \mathscr{H}(m_2, t) = \mathscr{G}(1, t)$$

Let $\chi_1(t)$ be the random variable denoting the occupation time with respect to the priority unit during the busy-period process and let

$$\mathscr{W}_1(\tau, t)\, d\tau = \Pr[\tau < \chi_1(t) < \tau + d\tau]$$

Then,

$$\mathscr{W}_1(\tau, t) = \frac{\lambda_1^*}{\lambda_1^* + \lambda_2^*}\, \delta(t) * w_1(\tau, t) + \mathscr{G}(1, t) * w_1{}^c(\tau, t) \tag{7.1}$$

where $w_1{}^c(\tau, t)\, d\tau$ represents the joint probability that the occupation time with respect to priority units at time t during the completion-time process lies between τ and $\tau + d\tau$ and that the completion time is in progress; $w_1(\tau, t)\, d\tau$ is the joint probability that the occupation time with respect to priority units at time t during the busy period of the priority queue in isolation lies between τ and $\tau + d\tau$ and that the busy period is in progress and is given by (I, 6.3) for an infinite priority source and by (II, 5.2) for a finite priority source; and $\mathscr{G}(1, t)$ can be obtained from (4.7) by putting $\alpha_2 = 1$ for (∞, ∞) and (N_1, ∞) models and from (4.20) by putting $e = 0$ for the (∞, N_2) and (N_1, N_2) models.

We have related the occupation-time density with respect to the priority units during the busy period of the priority process to the occupation-time density with respect to the priority units during the completion-time process. Obviously, the later is easier to analyze. For the completion-time process discussed in Section III, 3, we have

$$\begin{aligned} w_1{}^c(\tau, t) = \sum_{m_1} \int_{x_2=0}^{\infty} f^I(m_1, x_2, t)\, dx_2 \int_{y=0}^{\tau} \frac{S_2(x+y)}{1 - \int_0^{x_2} S_2(u)\, du}\, S_1^{*m_1}(\tau - y)\, dy \\ + \int_{x_1=0}^{\infty} dx_1 \left[\int_{x_2=0}^{\infty} g^I(m_1, x_1, x_2, t)\, dx_2 + g^L(m_1, x_1, t) \right] \\ \times \int_{y=0}^{\tau} \frac{S_1(x_1 + y)}{1 - \int_0^{x_1} S_1(u)\, du}\, S_1^{*m_1 - 1}(\tau - y)\, dy \end{aligned} \tag{7.2}$$

Defining the double Laplace transform as in (I, 6.2), we get

$$\bar{w}_1{}^c(\theta, s) = \sum_{m_1} \int_0^\infty [\bar{S}_1(\theta)]^{m_1} \bar{f}^I(m_1, x_2, s) \int_{y=0}^\infty \frac{S_2(x_2 + y)}{1 - \int_0^{x_2} S_2(u)\, du} e^{-\theta y}\, dy\, dx_2$$

$$+ \frac{1}{\bar{S}_1(\theta)} \sum_{m_1} \int_{x_1=0}^\infty [\bar{S}_1(\theta)]^{m_1} \left[\int_0^\infty \bar{g}^I(m_1, x_1, x_2, s)\, dx_2 + \bar{g}^L(m_1, x_1, s) \right]$$

$$\times \left[\int_0^\infty \frac{S_1(x_1 + y)}{1 - \int_0^{x_1} S_1(u)\, du} e^{-\theta y}\, dy \right] dx_1 \qquad (7.3)$$

Further results will depend upon the completion-time probabilities, and will be obtained in later chapters. Finally, we can write (7.1) as

$$\bar{\mathscr{W}}_1(\theta, s) = \frac{\lambda_1^*}{\lambda_1^* + \lambda_2^*} \bar{w}_1(\theta, s) + \bar{\mathscr{G}}(1, s) \bar{w}_1{}^c(\theta, s) \qquad (7.4)$$

so that for the general process, the occupation-time density of the server with respect to the priority unit (using the renewal-theoretic arguments as before) is obtained as

$$\bar{\hat{\mathscr{W}}}_1(\theta, s) = \bar{\hat{e}}^{(2)}(s)\{[1 + \lambda_1^* \bar{w}_1(\theta, s)] + (\lambda_1^* + \lambda_2^*) \bar{\mathscr{G}}(1, s) \bar{w}_1{}^c(\theta, s)\} \qquad (7.5)$$

(i) *The* (∞, ∞) *and* (N_1, ∞) *Models*

Substituting the value of $\bar{\mathscr{G}}(1, s)$ from (4.7) and simplifying, we get

$$\bar{\hat{\mathscr{W}}}_1(\theta, s) = \frac{\bar{\hat{e}}^{(2)}(s)}{\bar{\hat{e}}_1(s)} \bar{\hat{w}}_1(\theta, s) + \frac{\bar{\hat{e}}_1(s) - \bar{\hat{e}}^{(2)}(s)}{\bar{\hat{e}}_1(s)} \frac{\bar{w}_1{}^c(\theta, s)}{1 - \bar{c}_2(s)} \qquad (7.6)$$

where $\hat{e}_1(t)$ is the probability that the server is idle at time t if he is servicing the priority units only. Steady-state results follow by the usual limiting arguments. In particular, the mean virtual waiting time is given by

$$E(\hat{\mathscr{W}}_1) = \frac{\hat{e}^{(2)}}{\hat{e}_1} E(\hat{w}_1) + \lambda_2 E(w_1{}^c) E(c_2) \qquad (7.7)$$

where $E(w_1{}^c)$ denotes the mean virtual waiting time of a priority unit during the completion-time process, $E(c_2)$ is the mean completion time, and $\hat{e}^{(2)}$ is given by (6.4).

(ii) *The* (∞, N_2) *and* (N_1, N_2) *Models*

It can be easily verified that under preemptive disciplines the occupation-time of the server with respect to the priority units will be the same as for the priority queue in isolation, and can be obtained directly from Sections I, 6 or II, 5.

7-2. Occupation Time of the Server with Respect to Ordinary Units

We first investigate the occupation-time density of the server with respect to ordinary units during the busy period. We observe that if the input process of ordinary units is stopped at any time during the busy-period process, the server will first complete the present completion time and then complete the service of ordinary units, each requiring an amount of time x, and having a density $c_2(x)$. Thus, for the ordinary units, we need not study the occupation-time density during the completion time and can write the results directly as follows:

If the busy period is initiated by the arrival of an ordinary unit, the occupation time of the server with respect to the ordinary units is the same as that during the busy period of the ordinary units in isolation, but with the service time replaced by completion time. Similarly, if the busy period is initiated by the arrival of a priority unit, the occupation time of the server with respect to an ordinary unit is the same as that during the initial busy period of the ordinary units in isolation with initial occupation-time density $b_1(t)$, again with the service time replaced by the completion time.

Hence, if $\chi_2(t)$ is the random variable denoting the occupation time with respect to the ordinary units during a busy period for the two-class priority process, and if $\mathscr{W}_2(\tau, t) = \Pr[\tau < \chi_2(t) < \tau + d\tau]$, we have

$$\mathscr{W}_2(\tau, t) = \frac{\lambda_2^*}{\lambda_1^* + \lambda_2^*} W_2(\tau, t) + \frac{\lambda_1^*}{\lambda_1^* + \lambda_2^*} W_2^{b_1}(\tau, t) \tag{7.8}$$

where $W_2(\tau, t)$ and $W_2^{b_1}(\tau, t)$ denote, respectively, the occupation-time densities during the busy period and the initial busy period of the ordinary queue in isolation, but with the service time replaced by completion time. Next, defining $\hat{\chi}_2(t)$ as the random variable denoting the occupation time with respect to ordinary units for the general priority process and $\hat{\mathscr{W}}_2(\tau, t) = \Pr\{\tau < \hat{\chi}_2(t) < \tau + d\tau\}$, we have, using the usual renewal arguments,

$$\bar{\hat{\mathscr{W}}}_2(\theta, s) = \bar{e}^{(2)}(s)[1 + (\lambda_1^* + \lambda_2^*)\bar{\mathscr{W}}_2(\theta, s)] \tag{7.9}$$

where $\hat{e}^{(2)}(t)$ is the probability that the system is idle at time t. The steady-state discussion is similar to that for the queue length. The results are summarized below:

(i) *Ordinary Source Infinite—The* (∞, ∞) *and* (N_1, ∞) *Models*

For the (∞, ∞) and (N_1, ∞) models, we obtain, using (I, 6.3) and (I, 6.5), the following results:

$$\bar{\mathscr{W}}_2(\theta, s) = \frac{\lambda_2}{\lambda_1^* + \lambda_2} \cdot \frac{\bar{B}_2(s) - \bar{c}_2(\theta)}{\theta - s - \lambda_2[1 - \bar{c}_2(\theta)]}$$

$$+ \frac{\lambda_1^*}{\lambda_1^* + \lambda_2} \cdot \frac{\bar{b}_1[s + \lambda_2\{1 - \bar{B}_2(s)\}] - \bar{b}_1(\theta)}{\theta - s - \lambda_2[1 - \bar{c}_2(\theta)]}$$

$$= \frac{\lambda_2[\bar{B}_2(s) - \bar{c}_2(\theta)] + \lambda_1^*[\bar{b}_1\{s + \lambda_2(1 - \bar{B}_2(s))\} - \bar{b}_1(\theta)]}{(\lambda_1^* + \lambda_2)[\theta - s - \lambda_2\{1 - \bar{c}_2(\theta)\}]} \tag{7.10}$$

so that, using (7.9), we get

$$\bar{\hat{\mathscr{W}}}_2(\theta, s) = \frac{\bar{\hat{e}}^{(2)}(s)[\theta + \lambda_1^*\{1 - \bar{b}_1(\theta)\}] - 1}{\theta - s - \lambda_2 + \lambda_2\bar{c}_2(\theta)} \tag{7.11}$$

where $\bar{\hat{e}}^{(2)}(s)$ is defined by (5.3) with $\bar{\gamma}_2(s)$ given by (4.11).

If $\bar{\hat{\mathscr{W}}}_2(\theta)$ represents the occupation-time density of the server for the ordinary units under steady state, we have

$$\bar{\hat{\mathscr{W}}}_2(\theta) = \frac{\hat{e}^{(2)}[\theta + \lambda_1^*\{1 - \bar{b}_1(\theta)\}]}{\theta - \lambda_2 + \lambda_2\bar{c}_2(\theta)} \tag{7.12}$$

so that the mean waiting time of an ordinary unit is given by

$$E[\hat{\mathscr{W}}_2] = \frac{\lambda_2 E(c_2{}^2)}{2[1 - \lambda_2 E(c_2)]} + \frac{\lambda_1^* E(b_1{}^2)}{2[1 + \lambda_1^* E(b_1)]} \tag{7.13}$$

The mean delay time of an ordinary unit is equal to the sum of the mean waiting time in the queue [as given by (7.13)] and $E(I_2)$, the mean time spent in service. Hence, if $E(\hat{\mathscr{D}}_2)$ represents the mean delay time of an ordinary unit, we have

$$E(\hat{\mathscr{D}}_2) = E(c_2) + \frac{\lambda_2 E(c_2{}^2)}{2[1 - \lambda_2 E(c_2)]} + \frac{\lambda_1^* E(b_1{}^2)}{2[1 + \lambda_1^* E(b_1)]} \tag{7.14}$$

Comparison with (6.6) gives

$$E[\hat{\mathscr{M}}_2] = \lambda_2 E[\hat{\mathscr{D}}_2] \tag{7.15}$$

which is Little's formula [58].

(ii) *Ordinary Source Finite—The* (∞, N_2) *and* (N_1, N_2) *Models*

To obtain $\mathscr{W}_2(\theta, s)$ for the (∞, N_2) and (N_1, N_2) models using (7.10), we need $\overline{W}_2(\theta, s)$ and $\overline{W}_2^{b_1}(\theta, s)$. We obtain $\overline{W}_2(\theta, s)$ from (II, 5.2) by replacing (N, λ, S) with (N_2, λ_2, c_2). To obtain $\overline{W}_2^{b_1}(\theta, s)$ we first obtain the occupation-time density $\overline{W}^{\Omega}(\theta, s)$ for the initial busy period of the finite-source model proceeding as in Section I, 6, and then using (II, 2.43) and (II, 2.44). Then, replacing Ω by b_1 and (N, λ, S) by (N_2, λ_2, c_2), we obtain

$$\overline{W}_2^{b_1}(\theta, s) = \sum_{j-0}^{N_2-1} [\bar{c}_2(\theta)]^{N_2-j-1}[1-\bar{c}_2(\theta)]^j \bar{A}_2^{b_1}(j, s) \left[\frac{\bar{c}_2(j\lambda_2+s)-\bar{c}_2(\theta)}{\theta - j\lambda_2 - s}\right] \tag{7.16}$$

where $\bar{A}_2^{b_1}(j, s)$ is obtained from (II, 2.45) after replacing (N, λ, S, Ω) by $(N_2, \lambda_2, c_2, b_1)$. Substituting these values in (7.8), we obtain

$$\begin{aligned}\bar{\mathscr{W}}_2(\theta, s) = \sum_{j=0}^{N_2-1} [\bar{c}_2(\theta)]^{N_2-j-1}[1-\bar{c}_2(\theta)]^j \Bigg\{ &\frac{N_2\lambda_2}{\lambda_1^* + N_2\lambda_2} \bar{A}_2(j, s) \\ &+ \frac{\lambda_1^*}{\lambda_1^* + N_2\lambda_2} \bar{A}_2^{b_1}(j, s)\Bigg\} \frac{\bar{c}_2(j\lambda_2+s)-\bar{c}_2(\theta)}{\theta - j\lambda_2 - s}\end{aligned} \tag{7.17}$$

We may remind the reader that the derivation of (7.17) assumes that the equivalence condition holds, and that therefore, the results are true only for preemptive disciplines. Finally,

$$\begin{aligned}\bar{\hat{\mathscr{W}}}_2(\theta, s) = \bar{e}^{(2)}(s) \Bigg[1 + \sum_{j=0}^{N_2-1} [\bar{c}_2(\theta)]^{N_2-j-1}[1-\bar{c}_2(\theta)]^j \{&N_2\lambda_2\bar{A}_2(j, s) \\ &+ \lambda_1^*\bar{A}_2^{b_1}(j, s)\} \frac{\bar{c}_2(j\lambda_2+s)-\bar{c}_2(\theta)}{\theta - j\lambda_2 - s}\Bigg]\end{aligned} \tag{7.18}$$

where $\bar{e}^{(2)}(s)$ is given by (5.3) with $\bar{\gamma}_2(s)$ given by (4.25). The mean virtual waiting time for an ordinary unit is given by

$$\begin{aligned}E[\hat{\mathscr{W}}_2] = [1 - \hat{e}^{(2)}] &\left[(N_2 - 1)E(c_2) + \frac{1}{2}\frac{E(c_2^2)}{E(c_2)} - \frac{1}{\lambda_2}\right] \\ &+ N_2E(c_2)\hat{e}^{(2)}\left[1 + \lambda_1^* \frac{1-\bar{b}_1(\lambda_2)}{\lambda_2}\right]\end{aligned} \tag{7.19}$$

where $\hat{e}^{(2)}$ is given by (6.8).

8. Generalization to More Than Two Priority Classes

The stochastic behavior of the various characteristics of the two-class priority process were expressed above in terms of the corresponding characteristics of the completion-time process of the ordinary unit and the busy-period process of the priority queue in isolation. The completion-time process depends upon the specific discipline, but requires only the results of the one-class process studied in Chapters I and II. Thus, from the results of the one-class process, we obtain results for the two-class priority process. These results for two-class priority processes can then be used to obtain the results for three-class priority processes, and so on to the general kth class. However, as k increases, the evaluation of different characteristics becomes more tedious. For example, the evaluation of the joint queue-length distribution in a k-class priority process is particularly difficult for $k > 2$, although it can be obtained in principle (see Sections IV, 7 and V, 6). However, the marginal queue-length distributions of each class, which from the practical point of view are of obvious importance, are not difficult to obtain, and they will be obtained along with other characteristics for different disciplines in subsequent chapters. We close this chapter by making some general comments on the type of questions the study of priority processes can help us to answer.

9. Management Objectives in Priority Assignment

Let us assume that a service facility is servicing k types of units with different parameters which possibly emanate from sources of different sizes. The evaluation of the various characteristics of this process under given priority disciplines has the same objective as the study of the one-class process, e.g., the queue-length distributions may be important from the design point of view, the waiting time from the customer's point of view, and the busy period from the server's point of view.

To be specific, let us consider a service facility servicing units of type A. The management of the facility wants to study the question of whether or not it should take up the service of the units of another type B. The decision may depend upon the answer to the following question: How much deterioration in servicing efficiency measured in terms of some operating characteristics will be produced if a particular priority discipline is followed? On the other hand, it will also be of importance to know how much the type B units will benefit if, instead of using this facility, a separate facility is provided for them. Thus, the decision requires the comparison of the operating characteristics of a particular type of unit when it is being serviced together with other types of units according to some priority discipline with the corresponding characteristics if that type of unit were serviced alone. We define the following measures for the ith class of units in a k-class priority process: The "design measure," $DM_i^{(k)}$, is equal to the mean queue length of the ith class in isolation divided by the mean queue length of the ith class under a given priority discipline, or

$$DM_i^{(k)} = \frac{E(\hat{m}_i)}{E(\hat{\mathscr{M}}_i)}$$

The "waiting measure," $WM_i^{(k)}$, is equal to the mean waiting time of the ith-class units in isolation divided by the mean waiting time of the ith-class units under a given service discipline, or

$$WM_i^{(k)} = \frac{E(\hat{w}_i)}{E(\hat{\mathscr{W}}_i)}$$

Obviously, these measures lie between 0 and 1. The higher the value, the less is the effect of the presence of units of other classes on the units of the ith class. As an example, the design and waiting measures have the value one for priority units under preemptive discipline. This means that if the server serves other types of units but assigns lower priority to them and follow preemptive discipline, the queue size and the waiting time of the priority units are not affected. On the other hand, lower values of the design measures indicate increased queue size and longer waiting time if units of this class are serviced with other class of units than if these are serviced alone. To illustrate further the use of these measures, let us consider that the waiting measure of the ordinary units in a two-class priority process is 0.5. This means that if instead of servicing both priority and ordinary units, only the ordinary units are serviced, the waiting time will decrease by 50%, and hence there is a 50% reduction in waiting cost. The question of whether we would like to reduce the waiting cost of the ordinary units or prefer servicing the priority units will depend upon the relative waiting costs for priority and ordinary units and on the objectives involved. Thus, the evaluation of these measures will enable us to answer the type of question posed above and will throw light on the behavior of the servicing mechanism under a given priority discipline.

We can interpret the measures defined above in another way. Consider, for example, the waiting measure $WM_i^{(k)}$, which we can rewrite as

$$WM_i^{(k)} = \frac{E(\hat{w}_i)}{E(\hat{\mathscr{W}}_i)} = \frac{E(\hat{w}_i)}{\nu_i} \frac{\nu_i}{E(\hat{\mathscr{W}}_i)}$$

Hence,

$$\frac{E(\hat{\mathscr{W}}_i)}{\nu_i} = \frac{E(w_i)/\nu_i}{WM_i^{(k)}}$$

The expression $E(\hat{\mathscr{W}}_i)/\nu_i$ can be considered as a "performance measure" of the system for the ith-class units, larger values indicating the system's inefficiency for handling the ith-class traffic under given inputs and priority discipline. The expression $E(\hat{w}_i)/\nu_i$ on the right-hand side is given by (I, 6.13) if the ith source is infinite and by (II, 5.6) if the ith source is finite. Hence, from the "waiting measure" one can obtain the "performance measure."

It will be seen later that for most of the exogenous disciplines, the measures defined above remain fixed once the input and service processes of the various classes are specified. However, for most endogenous disciplines, a set of parameters are inherent in the system which enable the system designer to have a control over the system behavior. We will elaborate on this aspect in Chapter VII.

We do not propose to study in detail the various measures that could be associated with the priority processes, simply because a measure appropriate for answering one type of question may not necessarily be the best to answer another type of question.

Situations also arise, which call for the optimization of certain objective functions subject to certain restrictions. In general, this function may depend on the waiting time of units of each class, on the queue length of each class, and on the costs associated with each of these. Such a function may look like $F = f[\hat{\mathscr{W}}_i, \hat{\mathscr{M}}_i, K_i(\hat{\mathscr{W}}_i), K_i'(\hat{\mathscr{M}}_i) \cdots]$ $(1 \leqslant i \leqslant k)$ where $K_i(\hat{\mathscr{W}}_i)$, $K_i'(\hat{\mathscr{M}}_i)$ are the costs associated with the waiting time and with the queue length respectively of ith class, e.g., the cost associated with the queue length may be the cost of the waiting space. Assuming f to be additive in i and considering the waiting costs only, we may write

$$F = \sum_{i=1}^{k} \int_0^\infty \hat{\mathscr{W}}_i(t) K_i(t)\, dt \tag{9.1}$$

The functions $K_i(\hat{\mathscr{W}}_i)$ may, for example, have one of the following forms:

(i) Linear cost: $K_i(\hat{\mathscr{W}}_i) = \alpha_i \hat{\mathscr{W}}_i + \beta_i$. In this case, the contribution of the waiting cost in F will be $\alpha_i E(\hat{\mathscr{W}}_i) + \beta_i$. If $\beta_i = 0$, $\alpha_i = \alpha$, i.e., the cost is linear and is same for all classes, minimization of this part of the cost alone will mean minimizing the expected waiting time of all classes.

(ii) Nonlinear cost: In many situations, the waiting cost is not necessarily linear. Discussion of these costs may require the higher moments of the waiting time distribution, e.g., if the cost is $\alpha_i(\hat{\mathscr{W}}_i)^2 + \beta_i \hat{\mathscr{W}}_i + \gamma_i$, minimization of F will involve the function $\alpha_i E(\hat{\mathscr{W}}_i)^2 + \beta_i E(\hat{\mathscr{W}}_i) + \gamma_i$. Since higher moments are more complicated, the discussion of the models under such cost structures does not generally lead to an interesting decision rule, and as such we will be mostly concerned with the first type of costs. Finally, if the cost is not a polynomial, we may obtain F by evaluating the integrals either analytically or numerically.

Thus, we find that if the operating characteristics of a queuing process are known, economic analysis is always possible irrespective of the nature of the cost functions; however, such analysis has not been made in many cases. In most cases, the structure of the objective function F, as happens in almost all operations research studies, depends heavily on the specific situation. The reader may like to choose his own objective function and use the operating characteristics as pointed out above to study a given situation. In subsequent chapters, we will study cost structures which lead to simple decision rules.

The optimization of the objective function may have to be made under certain restrictions, and may require the techniques of mathematical programming. Attempts in this direction have recently been made, e.g., by Oliver and Pestalozzi [68] (see Section V, 8), and it is hoped that more attempts will follow.

Chapter IV

PREEMPTIVE DISCIPLINES

1. Introduction

In Chapter III, the preemptive priority disciplines, in which a unit of a higher priority class has the right to interrupt the service of a lower priority unit, were defined. It was observed that the rules according to which a preempted unit is serviced give rise to preemptive resume, repeat-identical, and repeat-different disciplines. The purpose of this chapter is to study these disciplines in detail.

The first published account of these disciplines is due to White and Christie [98]. Later, Stephan [82], Heathcote [34–36], Miller [62], Jaiswal [44], Welch [97], Takács [87], and Chang [16] studied these disciplines for infinite-source models under different assumptions about the service-time distributions.

The similarity between these models and the "breakdown models" was first observed by White and Christie [98]. In "breakdown models," the service facility becomes inoperative for a random period of time during which it is repaired. Keilson [49], Gaver [29], Avi-Itzhak and Naor [6], and Avi-Itzhak [2] used this similarity to study preemptive priority models from the breakdown models. The finite-source priority models, in which at least one type of unit emanates from a finite-source, have been studied by Avi-Itzhak and Naor [5], Thiruvengadam [91, 94], and Jaiswal and Thiruvengadam [48].

Situations where preemptive-resume discipline is applicable are obviously numerous. The preemptive-repeat discipline is applicable whenever the technical considerations require the service to be repeated again. For example, if a computing machine breaks down, it may be necessary to rerun the program after it has been repaired, leading to the preemptive repeat-identical discipline. However, if the program is rewritten in the interim, the preemptive repeat-different discipline is applicable. The preemptive repeat-different and repeat-identical disciplines may also arise because of different reasons associated with the variability of the service times. This has been noted by Avi-Itzhak [2] and can be explained as follows: (a) If all units belonging to the same class require an equal and fixed amount of service, but the servicing rate of the facility varies randomly, a preempted unit on its reentry stays in the system for a random period of time independent of past preemptions and wasted service, leading to preemptive repeat-different discipline. (b) If the service times of the units vary while the facility maintains a constant service rate and provides a fixed amount of service in a fixed period of time, a preempted unit on its reentry stays in the system for a random time dependent upon the number of past preemptions and wasted service, leading to a preemptive repeat-identical discipline.

In the previous chapter, we expressed the various characteristics of an exogenous priority process in terms of the corresponding characteristics during the completion-time process. We therefore evaluate the completion-time process probabilities for each of these disciplines and use them in the results obtained in Chapter III to evaluate the desired characteristics. We first study models with only two priority classes, i.e., (∞, ∞), (N_1, ∞), (∞, N_2), and (N_1, N_2) models, and then generalize for $k > 2$ priority classes.

2. Completion Time Processes

In Section III, 3, we defined probabilities associated with the completion-time process for an exogenous priority discipline. Since, for any preemptive discipline, the ordinary unit is serviced only when there is no priority unit, the completion-time process terminates only with the service completion of an ordinary unit. Hence, m_1 in $f^I(m_1, x_2, t)$ is zero, and $L_2 = 0$. Let $\lambda_1^* = \lambda_1$ if the priority source is infinite and $\lambda_1^* = N_1\lambda_1$ if it is finite. It must be noted that the completion-time process does not depend upon the size of the ordinary source, since it pertains to the service of only one ordinary unit. The results for different disciplines can be obtained as follows:

2-1. Preemptive Resume Discipline

The process will be completely defined by the probability densities $f^I(0, x_2, t)$ and $g^I(m_1, x_1, x_2, t)$ which are defined in Section III, 3. The value of m_1 will vary from 1 to ∞ or from 1 to N_1 depending upon whether the priority source is infinite or finite.

Equations governing the completion-time process are

$$\frac{\partial}{\partial t} f^I(0, x_2, t) + \frac{\partial}{\partial x_2} f^I(0, x_2, t) + [\lambda_1^* + \eta_2(x_2)] f^I(0, x_2, t) = \lambda_1^* f^I(0, x_2, t) * b_1(t) \tag{2.1}$$

$$g^I(m_1, x_1, x_2, t) = \lambda_1^* f^I(0, x_2, t) * p(m_1, x_1, t) \tag{2.2}$$

$$c_2(t) = \int_0^\infty f^I(0, x_2, t)\, \eta_2(x_2)\, dx_2 \tag{2.3}$$

where $*$ between two functions denotes the convolution operation; $b_1(t)$ and $p(m_1, x_1, t)$ correspond to the probability densities for the priority queue in isolation and can be obtained from (I, 2.15) and (I, 2.16) if the priority source is infinite and from (II, 2.25) and (II, 2.26) if the priority source is finite.

These equations are to be solved subject to the initial condition $f^I(0, x_2, 0) = \delta(x_2)$. The solution, in terms of the Laplace transform, is given by

$$\bar{f}^I(0, x_2, s) = \exp\left[-\{\lambda_1^*[1 - \bar{b}_1(s)] + s\}\, x_2 - \int_0^{x_2} \eta(u)\, du\right] \tag{2.4}$$

$$\bar{g}^I(m_1, x_1, x_2, s) = \lambda_1^* \bar{f}^I(0, x_2, s)\, \bar{p}(m_1, x_1, s) \tag{2.5}$$

$$\bar{c}_2(s) = \bar{S}_2[\lambda_1^*\{1 - \bar{b}_1(s)\} + s] \tag{2.6}$$

Hence

$$E(c_2) = \nu_2[1 + \lambda_1^* E(b_1)] \tag{2.7}$$

$$E(c_2^2) = E(S_2^2)[1 + \lambda_1^* E(b_1)]^2 + \lambda_1^* E(b_1^2)\, E(S_2) \tag{2.8}$$

If only the completion time density is to be evaluated, the results can be obtained more directly, as in the following example:

Example

Let the service time of an ordinary unit be S_2. Let us consider events B which are characterized by the arrival of a priority unit which preempts the ordinary unit from service. The completion time cycle is shown in Fig. IV.1(b). If C_2 denotes the completion time, we have

$$c_2 = \sum_{i=1}^{n} S_{2,i} + \sum_{i=1}^{n} b_{1,i} = S_2 + \sum_{i=1}^{n} b_{1,i} \tag{2.9}$$

where $S_{2,i}$ is the amount of service time received by the ordinary unit between the $(i-1)$th and ith interruption and $b_{1,i}$ is the duration of the ith interruption. Obviously, each $b_{1,i}$ is an identically and independently distributed random variable having density $b_1(t)$. Since the events B occur following a Poisson process with mean rate λ_1^*, the probability of having n events of type B during the total service time S_2 is

$$\exp[-\lambda_1^* S_2] \frac{(\lambda_1^* S_2)^n}{n!} \tag{2.10}$$

Hence

$$\begin{aligned} E[\exp(-sc_2) \mid S_2, n] &= \exp[-sS_2][E\{\exp(-sb_{1,i})\}]^n \\ &= \exp[-sS_2][\bar{b}_1(s)]^n \end{aligned} \tag{2.11}$$

$$\begin{aligned} E[\exp(-sc_2) \mid S_2] &= \sum_{n=0}^{\infty} \exp(-sS_2)[\bar{b}_1(s)]^n \exp[-\lambda_1^* S_2] \frac{(\lambda_1^* S_2)^n}{n!} \\ &= \exp\{-S_2[s + \lambda_1^*\{1 - \bar{b}_1(s)\}]\} \end{aligned} \tag{2.12}$$

$$E[\exp(-sc_2)] = \bar{S}_2[\lambda_1^*\{1 - \bar{b}_1(s)\} + s] \tag{2.13}$$

This method is due to Gaver [29].

Since $L_2 \equiv 0$, Eq. (III, 3.4) becomes

$$\bar{\bar{\Pi}}^c(\alpha_1, \alpha_2, s) = \alpha_2 \bar{\bar{\Pi}}^I(\alpha_1, s) \tag{2.14}$$

Using (2.4) and (2.5) in (III, 3.1), we get $\bar{\bar{\Pi}}^I(\alpha_1, s)$ so that (2.14) becomes

$$\bar{\bar{\Pi}}^c(\alpha_1, \alpha_2, s) = \frac{\alpha_2[1 - \bar{c}_2(s)][1 + \lambda_1^* \bar{\bar{\Pi}}(\alpha_1, s)]}{\lambda_1^*\{1 - \bar{b}_1(s)\} + s} \tag{2.15}$$

which by virtue of (I, 3.15) or (II, 3.2) can be written as

$$\bar{\bar{\Pi}}^c(\alpha_1, \alpha_2, s) = \alpha_2[1 - \bar{c}_2(s)]\, \bar{e}_1(s)[1 + \lambda_1^* \bar{\bar{\Pi}}(\alpha_1, s)] \tag{2.16}$$

and finally, using (I, 3.13) or (II, 3.1), we get

$$\bar{\Pi}^c(\alpha_1, \alpha_2, s) = \alpha_2[1 - \bar{c}_2(s)]\, \bar{\bar{\Pi}}(\alpha_1, s) \tag{2.17}$$

Observe that (2.17) gives the explicit relation which we have been seeking between the completion-time probabilities and the one-class process probabilities studied in Chapters I and II.

An Alternative Approach to the Derivation of $\bar{\Pi}^c(\alpha_1, \alpha_2, s)$

The result in (2.17) can be obtained more easily by comparing the completion-time cycle and the priority queue cycle in isolation, which are represented in Fig. IV.1. Note that by priority queue in isolation,

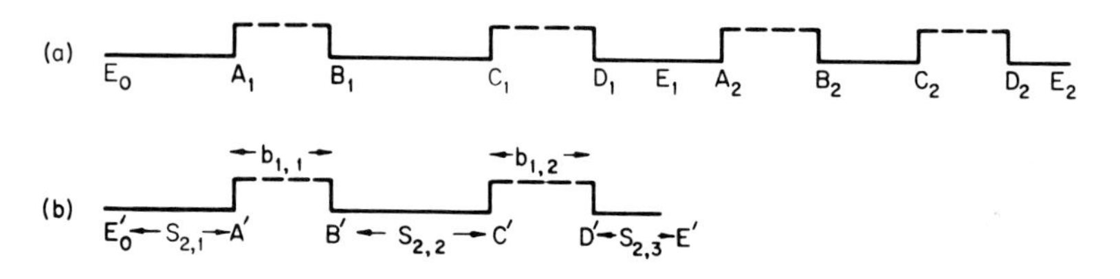

FIG. IV.1. (a) Isolated priority process cycle. (b) Completion time process cycle.

we mean the queuing process generated by the priority units alone, when the ordinary units are considered nonexistent, and as such, it is the basic infinite or finite-source model discussed in Chapter I or Chapter II with the same parameters as those of the priority queue. Henceforth, we will refer to this as the "isolated priority process."

Let Fig. IV.1(a) represent any realization of this process, E_0A_1, B_1C_1, D_1A_2 being the idle periods and A_1B_1, C_1D_1, A_2B_2, C_2D_2, etc., being the busy periods. Also, let S_2^1, S_2^2, $\cdots$ be a sequence of independent realizations of the random variable S_2, the service time of the ordinary unit. Now, let us construct time points E_1, E_2, $\cdots$ such that the total idle time in the isolated priority process between E_{i-1} and E_i is equal to S_2^i. Thus, in Fig. IV.1(a), $E_0A_1 + B_1C_1 + D_1E_1 = S_2^1$, $E_1A_2 + B_2C_2 + D_2E_2 = S_2^2$, etc. Essentially, what we have accomplished now is a breakdown of the isolated priority process into different (non-overlapping) periods such that the total time in each period is identically and independently distributed having density $S_2(t)$. The behavior of the isolated priority process in any one period is stochastically equivalent to the behavior of the priority queue in a completion-time cycle. The reader can immediately note this equivalence by comparing the corresponding parts of any one period, say E_0E_1 of Fig. IV.1(a), with the corresponding part of the completion-time cycle $E_0'E'$ in Fig. IV.1(b). The only difference between the two is that the idle periods in E_0E_1 correspond to the service of the ordinary unit during $E_0'E'$ and, therefore, so far as priority units are concerned, the priority queue length is zero in both. Hence if $\hat{\Pi}(\alpha_1, t)$ is the generating function of the general-process probabilities for the isolated priority process, we have, using renewal arguments,

$$\hat{\Pi}[\alpha_1, t] = \sum_{n=0}^{\infty} [c_2^{n*}(t) * \Pi^I(\alpha_1, t)] \tag{2.18}$$

Taking the Laplace transform and using (2.14), (2.17) is obtained.

2-2. Preemptive Repeat-Identical Discipline

Let us consider the completion time of a particular unit having service time requirement Z. Under this discipline, each time this unit enters service, it will require a service time Z. The completion-time process, therefore, ends only when this unit finds an uninterrupted time duration of length Z. For this particular unit, let $f^I(0, x_2, t \mid Z)$, $g^I(m_1, x_1, t \mid Z)$, and $c_2(t \mid Z)$ denote the densities with the same meaning as above except that these are for a particular unit whose service time is Z. The corresponding equations are

$$\frac{\partial}{\partial t} f^I(0, x_2, t \mid Z) + \frac{\partial}{\partial x_2} f^I(0, x_2, t \mid Z) + \lambda_1^* f^I(0, x_2, t \mid Z) = 0 \quad (x_2 < Z) \tag{2.19}$$

$$f^I(0, 0, t \mid Z) = \left[\lambda_1^* \int_0^Z f^I(0, x_2, t \mid Z)\, dx_2\right] * b_1(t) \tag{2.20}$$

$$g^I(m_1, x_1, t \mid Z) = \left[\lambda_1^* \int_0^Z f^I(0, x_2, t \mid Z)\, dx_2\right] * p(m_1, x_1, t) \tag{2.21}$$

$$c_2(t \mid Z) = f^I(0, Z, t \mid Z) \tag{2.22}$$

These equations are to be solved subject to the initial condition $f^I(0, y, 0 \mid Z) = \delta(y)$.

Since the service time requirements of the ordinary units have density $S_2(Z)$, the densities $f^I(0, x_2, t)$, $g^I(m_1, x_1, t)$, and $c_2(t)$ for the completion time process of an ordinary unit are given by

$$\bar{f}^I(0, x_2, s) = \int_{x_2}^{\infty} \bar{f}^I(0, x_2, s \mid Z)\, S_2(Z)\, dZ$$

$$= \int_{x_2}^{\infty} \frac{\exp[-(\lambda_1^* + s)\, x_2]\, S_2(Z)\, dZ}{1 - \dfrac{\lambda_1^*}{\lambda_1^* + s}\, \bar{b}_1(s)\{1 - \exp[-(\lambda_1^* + s)\, Z]\}} \tag{2.23}$$

and similarly

$$\bar{g}^I(m_1, x_1, s) = \lambda_1^* \bar{p}(m_1, x_1, s) \int_0^{\infty} \frac{[1 - \exp\{-(\lambda_1^* + s)\, Z\}]\, S_2(Z)\, dZ}{\lambda_1^* + s - \lambda_1^* \bar{b}_1(s)\{1 - \exp[-(\lambda_1^* + s)\, Z]\}} \tag{2.24}$$

$$\bar{c}_2(s) = \int_0^{\infty} \frac{\exp[-(\lambda_1^* + s)\, Z]\, S_2(Z)\, dZ}{1 - \dfrac{\lambda_1^*}{\lambda_1^* + s}\, \bar{b}_1(s)(1 - \exp[-(\lambda_1^* + s)\, Z])} \tag{2.25}$$

Hence,

$$E(c_2) = \left[\frac{1}{\lambda_1^*} + E(b_1)\right] [E\{\exp(\lambda_1^* S_2)\} - 1] \tag{2.26}$$

$$E(c_2^2) = 2\left[\frac{1}{\lambda_1^*} + E(b_1)\right]^2 E[\{\exp(\lambda_1^* S_2) - 1\}^2] + \left[E(b_1^2) + \frac{2E(b_1)}{\lambda_1^*} + \frac{2}{\lambda_1^{*2}}\right]$$
$$\times [E\{\exp(\lambda_1^* S_2)\} - 1] - 2\left[E(b_1) + \frac{1}{\lambda_1^*}\right] \int_0^{\infty} x_2 \exp(\lambda_1^* x_2)\, S_2(x_2)\, dx_2 \tag{2.27}$$

2-3. Preemptive Repeat-Different Discipline

Under this discipline, a preempted unit on its reentry stays with the server for a random period of time independent of the previous service times. We define the probability densities $f^I(0, x_2, t)$ and $g^I(m_1, x_1, t)$ and $c_2(t)$ and obtain the following equations:

$$\frac{\partial}{\partial t} f^I(0, x_2, t) + \frac{\partial}{\partial x_2} f^I(0, x_2, t) + [\lambda_1^* + \eta_2(x_2)]\, f^I(0, x_2, t) = 0 \tag{2.28}$$

$$f^I(0, 0, t) = \left[\lambda_1^* \int_0^{\infty} f^I(0, x_2, t)\, dx_2\right] * b_1(t) \tag{2.29}$$

$$g^I(m_1, x_1, t) = \left[\lambda_1^* \int_0^\infty f^I(0, x_2, t)\, dx_2\right] * p(m_1, x_1, t) \tag{2.30}$$

$$c_2(t) = \int_0^\infty f^I(0, x_2, t)\, \eta_2(x_2)\, dx_2 \tag{2.31}$$

The initial condition is specified by $f^I(0, x_2, 0) = \delta(x_2)$. The solution is given by

$$\bar{f}^I(0, x_2, s) = \frac{\exp[-(\lambda_1^* + s)\, x_2 - \int_0^{x_2} \eta_2(u)\, du]}{1 - \dfrac{\lambda_1^*}{\lambda_1^* + s}\, \bar{b}_1(s)[1 - \bar{S}_2(\lambda_1^* + s)]} \tag{2.32}$$

$$\bar{g}^I(m_1, x_1, s) = \lambda_1^* \bar{p}(m_1, x_1, s) \frac{1 - \bar{S}_2(\lambda_1^* + s)}{\lambda_1^* + s - \lambda_1^* \bar{b}_1(s)[1 - \bar{S}_2(\lambda_1^* + s)]} \tag{2.33}$$

and

$$\bar{c}_2(s) = \frac{\bar{S}_2[\lambda_1^* + s]}{1 - \dfrac{\lambda_1^*}{\lambda_1^* + s}\, \bar{b}_1(s)[1 - \bar{S}_2(\lambda_1^* + s)]} \tag{2.34}$$

so that

$$E(c_2) = \left[\frac{1 - \bar{S}_2(\lambda_1^*)}{\bar{S}_2(\lambda_1^*)}\right]\left[E(b_1) + \frac{1}{\lambda_1^*}\right] \tag{2.35}$$

$$E(c_2{}^2) = 2\left[E(b_1) + \frac{1}{\lambda_1^*}\right]^2 \left[\frac{1 - \bar{S}_2(\lambda_1^*)}{\bar{S}_2(\lambda_1^*)}\right]^2 + \left[E(b_1{}^2) + \frac{2}{\lambda_1^*} E(b_1) + \frac{2}{\lambda_1^{*2}}\right]$$
$$\times \left[\frac{1 - \bar{S}_2(\lambda_1^*)}{\bar{S}_2(\lambda_1^*)}\right] - 2\left[E(b_1) + \frac{1}{\lambda_1^*}\right] \frac{\int_0^\infty x_2\, e^{-\lambda_1^* x_2} S_2(x_2)\, dx_2}{[\bar{S}_2(\lambda_1^*)]^2} \tag{2.36}$$

2-4. Comparison of Completion Times

As observed by Thomas [95], some interesting conclusions can be made about the expected duration of the completion times for different disciplines. Since $\exp(-\lambda_1^* S_2)$ and $\exp(\lambda_1^* S_2)$ are negatively correlated, we have

$$E[\exp(-\lambda_1^* S_2)]\, E[\exp(\lambda_1^* S_2)] \geqslant E[\exp(-\lambda_1^* S_2) \exp(\lambda_1^* S_2)] = 1 \tag{2.37}$$

Hence, $E[\exp(\lambda_1^* S_2)] \geqslant 1/\bar{S}_2(\lambda_1)$, and, from (2.26) and (2.35), it follows that for $\rho_1 < 1$, the value of the mean completion time for the preemptive repeat-identical discipline is greater than the value for the preemptive repeat-different discipline. The explanation for this behavior is as follows [29]: For the preemptive repeat-identical discipline, the completion time will be at least as long as the associated service time; however, for the preemptive repeat-different discipline, a new service period is initiated at each service entry of the ordinary unit. Thus, the priority arrivals tend to terminate longer service periods. Hence, on the average, a completion time for the repeat-different discipline is less than that for the repeat-identical discipline.

Also, comparing (2.7) and (2.35), we observe that the expected completion-time duration for the repeat-different discipline is more than that under resume discipline if

$$(1 + \lambda_1 \nu_2)\, \bar{S}_2(\lambda_1) < 1 \tag{2.38}$$

The inequality is obviously satisfied for the case of constant service times, and turns out to be an equality for an exponential service-time distribution; thus, if the service-time distribution of ordinary units is exponentially distributed, we have

$$E(c_2)_{\text{identical}} > E(c_2)_{\text{different}} = E(c_2)_{\text{resume}} \tag{2.39}$$

and if the service times of the ordinary units are constant

$$E(c_2)_{\text{identical}} = E(c_2)_{\text{different}} > E(c_2)_{\text{resume}} \tag{2.40}$$

We make an observation about $E(c_2{}^2)$ for the preemptive repeat-identical discipline which will later be useful in discussing the existence of the mean queue length: In order that $E(c_2{}^2)$ may be finite, the integrals

$$\int_0^\infty [\exp(\lambda_1^* t) - 1]^2\, S_2(t)\, dt$$

and

$$\int_0^\infty t \exp(\lambda_1^* t)\, S_2(t)\, dt$$

must be finite. Since the second integral is finite if the first one is finite, the condition for $E(c_2{}^2)$ under the repeat-identical discipline to be finite is that the

$$\int_0^\infty [\exp(\lambda_1^* t) - 1]^2\, S_2(t)\, dt < A \tag{2.41}$$

where A is finite. Finally, we observe that (2.25) and (2.34) can be obtained as in Gaver [29] by following the method of Example A above, and that for both preemptive repeat-identical and repeat-different disciplines, the relation (2.17) holds good.

The completion-time process probabilities can be used to obtain the results for the priority processes, as explained in Chapter III. The evaluation of the queue characteristics involves appropriate substitutions of the completion-time process results obtained above, and as such we will derive general results for any preemptive discipline and indicate some of the results for different disciplines through examples which the reader can easily verify.

3. Priority and Ordinary Sources Both Infinite—The (∞, ∞) Model

3-1. Busy Period

If $\gamma_2(t)$ denotes the busy-period density for the (∞, ∞) model, its Laplace transform is given by (III, 4.11), so that

$$\bar{\gamma}_2(s) = \frac{\lambda_2}{\lambda_2 + \lambda_1} \bar{B}_2(s) + \frac{\lambda_1}{\lambda_2 + \lambda_1} \bar{b}_1[\lambda_2\{1 - \bar{B}_2(s)\} + s] \tag{3.1}$$

where $\bar{B}_2(s)$ is the root of the equation $\alpha = \bar{c}_2[\lambda_2(1 - \alpha) + s]$ lying inside the unit circle. Substituting appropriate values of $\bar{c}_2(s)$ from Section 2 above, we obtain the results for preemptive resume and repeat-identical and repeat-different disciplines. The mean busy period can be evaluated directly from (III, 4.12) by substituting the appropriate value of $E(c_2)$.

Example A. Busy Period for the Preemptive Resume Discipline

If the service-time distributions for both priority and nonpriority units are exponential with the same mean, we have $\bar{S}_1(s) = \mu/(\mu + s)$, $\bar{S}_2(s) = \mu/(\mu + s)$, where $\mu = 1/\nu$; (3.1) can be inverted (see Example B, below) to give

$$\gamma_2(t) = \left(\frac{\mu}{\lambda_1 + \lambda_2}\right)^{1/2} \frac{\exp[-t(\mu + \lambda_1 + \lambda_2)]}{t} I_1\{2t[\mu(\lambda_1 + \lambda_2)]^{1/2}\} \tag{3.2}$$

where $I_1(t)$ is the modified Bessel function of the first kind.

Observe that if $\lambda_1 = 0$ or $\lambda_2 = 0$, the results reduce to the busy-period density for the $M/M/1$ case [22, p.148].

The mean busy period is obtained as

$$E(\gamma_2) = \frac{\rho_1 + \rho_2}{(1 - \rho_1 - \rho_2)(\lambda_1 + \lambda_2)} \quad \text{if } \rho_1 + \rho_2 < 1$$
$$= \infty \quad \text{otherwise} \tag{3.3}$$

3-2. Joint Queue-Length Probabilities

Substituting (2.16) in (III, 5.4), $\lambda_1^* = \lambda_1$, and simplifying, we obtain the generating function of the Laplace transform of the time-dependent joint queue-length probabilities as

$$\bar{\bar{\Pi}}(\alpha_1, \alpha_2, s) = \bar{\bar{e}}^{(2)}(s)\, \bar{\bar{\Pi}}[\alpha_1, s + \lambda_2(1 - \alpha_2)]\, \bar{K}(\alpha_2, s) \tag{3.4}$$

where $\bar{\bar{\Pi}}[\alpha_1, s]$ is given in (I, 2.19) and

$$\bar{K}(\alpha_2, s) = \lambda_1[1 - \bar{b}_1\{s + \lambda_2(1 - \alpha_2)\}] + \lambda_2(1 - \alpha_2) + s$$
$$+ \frac{1 - \bar{c}_2[\lambda_2(1 - \alpha_2) + s]}{1 - \dfrac{1}{\alpha_2}\bar{c}_2[\lambda_2(1 - \alpha_2) + s]}$$
$$\times [\lambda_2\{\alpha_2 - \bar{B}_2(s)\} + \lambda_1(\bar{b}_1\{\lambda_2(1 - \alpha_2) + s\} - \bar{b}_1\{\lambda_2(1 - \bar{B}_2(s)) + s\})] \tag{3.5}$$

and

$$\bar{\bar{e}}^{(2)}(s) = [s + \lambda_2 + \lambda_1 - \lambda_2\bar{B}_2(s) - \lambda_1\bar{b}_1\{s + \lambda_2(1 - \bar{B}_2(s)\}]^{-1} \tag{3.6}$$

where $\bar{B}_2(s)$ and $\bar{c}_2(s)$ are defined above.

For the preemptive resume discipline, the result (3.4) was obtained by Jaiswal [44] by directly solving the differential difference equation for the general process. The method used in that work is relatively more complex. Keilson [49] modified this approach by using the completion-time arguments and obtained the results by essentially similar arguments as presented above, obtaining (3.4) as well as results for other priority disciplines. Putting $\alpha_2 = 1$, we obtain the marginal queue-length distribution of the priority units:

$$\bar{\bar{\Pi}}[\alpha_1, 1, s] = \bar{\bar{\Pi}}[\alpha_1, s] \tag{3.7}$$

The result (3.7) shows that the priority queue is not affected under the conditions of preemptive discipline, which is obviously true. In addition, putting $\alpha_1 = 1$, we obtain the marginal queue-length distribution of the ordinary class:

$$\bar{\bar{\Pi}}(1, \alpha_2, s) = \frac{\bar{\bar{e}}^{(2)}(s)}{s + \lambda_2(1 - \alpha_2)} \bar{K}[\alpha_2, s] \tag{3.8}$$

Inversion of these results are quite tedious; the following example illustrates the difficulties involved.

Example B

Consider the case in which both service-time distributions are exponential, so that $\bar{S}_1(s) = \mu_1/(\mu_1 + s)$ and $\bar{S}_2(s) = \mu_2/(\mu_2 + s)$, where $\mu_1 = \nu_1^{-1}$ and $\mu_2 = \nu_2^{-1}$. Assuming a preemptive resume discipline, the result (3.4) can be written after simplification as

$$\bar{\Pi}(\alpha_1, \alpha_2, s) = \frac{[\bar{\hat{e}}^{(2)}(s)\, \mu_2(1-\alpha_2) - \alpha_2]}{\left[\mu_2 - \alpha_2 \left\{\dfrac{\mu_1}{\bar{b}_1[s+\lambda_2(1-\alpha_2)]} - \mu_1 + \mu_2\right\}\right]\left[1 - \alpha_1 \dfrac{\lambda_1}{\mu_1}\bar{b}_1\{s+\lambda_2(1-\alpha_2)\}\right]} \tag{3.9}$$

and

$$\bar{\hat{e}}^{(2)}(s) = \frac{\bar{B}_2(s)}{\mu_2[1-\bar{B}_2(s)]} \tag{3.10}$$

where $\bar{b}_1(s)$ is the smaller root of the quadratic equation

$$\lambda_1\alpha_1^2 - \alpha_1[\mu_1 + s + \lambda_1] + \mu_1 = 0 \tag{3.11}$$

and $\bar{B}_2(s)$ is the smallest root of the equation

$$\mu_2 - \alpha_2\left[\frac{\mu_1}{\bar{b}_1\{s+\lambda_2(1-\alpha_2)\}} - \mu_1 + \mu_2\right] = 0 \tag{3.12}$$

Equation (3.12) is a cubic equation. However, when $\mu_1 = \mu_2 = \mu$, the equation reduces to a quadratic, and only in this case does the algebra simplify sufficiently; inverting (3.9) and (3.10), we obtain

$$\begin{aligned}\hat{\Pi}(\alpha_1, \alpha_2, t) = \sum_{k=0}^{\infty}\sum_{j=0}^{k} \alpha_2^{k-j}\alpha_1^j \left(\frac{\lambda_1}{\mu}\right)^{(2j-k)/2} (2j-k) \\ \times \Big\{(1-\alpha_2)\int_0^t \hat{e}^{(2)}(t-\tau)\, \frac{\exp(-\tau[\mu+\lambda_1+\lambda_2-\lambda_2\alpha_2])}{\tau} \\ \times I_{|2j-k|}[2\tau(\lambda_1\mu)^{1/2}]\, d\tau \\ - \alpha_2 \frac{\exp(-t[\mu+\lambda_1+\lambda_2-\lambda_2\alpha_2])}{\mu t} I_{|2j-k|}[2t(\lambda_1\mu)^{1/2}]\Big\}\end{aligned} \tag{3.13}$$

and

$$\hat{e}^{(2)}(t)$$
$$= \frac{\exp[-t(\mu + \lambda_1 + \lambda_2)]}{\mu t} \sum_{j=0}^{\infty} \left(\frac{\mu}{\lambda_1 + \lambda_2}\right)^{(j+1)/2} (j+1)\, I_{j+1}\{2t[\mu(\lambda_1 + \lambda_2)]^{1/2}\} \tag{3.14}$$

where $I_j(t)$ is the modified Bessel function of the first kind. These results are given by Heathcote [34].

a. *Limiting Behavior*

Because of inversion difficulties, we do not proceed further with the transient solution, and turn to a discussion of the limiting behavior. From Section III, 6, we note that if $\rho_1 + \rho_2 < 1$, the limiting distribution exists, and from (III, 6.3) and (III, 6.4) we obtain

$$\hat{\Pi}(\alpha_1, \alpha_2)$$
$$= \hat{e}^{(2)} \left[1 + \frac{\lambda_1\{\alpha_1 - \bar{b}_1[\lambda_2(1-\alpha_2)]\}}{\lambda_1(1-\alpha_1) + \lambda_2(1-\alpha_2)} \frac{1 - \bar{S}_1\{\lambda_1(1-\alpha_1) + \lambda_2(1-\alpha_2)\}}{1 - \dfrac{1}{\alpha_1}\bar{S}_1\{\lambda_1(1-\alpha_1) + \lambda_2(1-\alpha_2)\}}\right]$$
$$\times \frac{(\alpha_2 - 1)\, \bar{c}_2\{\lambda_2(1-\alpha_2)\}}{\alpha_2 - \bar{c}_2\{\lambda_2(1-\alpha_2)\}} \tag{3.15}$$

and

$$\hat{e}^{(2)} = 1 - \rho_1 - \rho_2 \tag{3.16}$$

It is easy to verify that the marginal queue-length distribution of the priority units is the same as the queue-length distribution for the priority queue in isolation, and that the marginal queue-length distribution of ordinary units is given by

$$\hat{\Pi}(1, \alpha_2) = \hat{e}^{(2)} \left[1 + \frac{\lambda_1}{\lambda_2} \frac{1 - \bar{b}_1\{\lambda_2(1-\alpha_2)\}}{1-\alpha_2}\right] \frac{(1-\alpha_2)\, \bar{c}_2\{\lambda_2(1-\alpha_2)\}}{\bar{c}_2\{\lambda_2(1-\alpha_2)\} - \alpha_2} \tag{3.17}$$

From (3.15)–(3.17), the results for different disciplines can be obtained by substituting appropriate value of $\bar{c}_2(s)$. The moments can be obtained by differentiation. The first moment can also be obtained directly from (III, 6.5) and (III, 6.6). The results are listed in the following examples.

Example C. Preemptive Resume Discipline

The mean number of priority and ordinary units are given by

$$E(\hat{\mathscr{M}}_1) = \rho_1 + \frac{1}{2}\frac{\lambda_1{}^2 E(S_1{}^2)}{1-\rho_1} \tag{3.18}$$

$$E(\hat{\mathscr{M}}_2) = \frac{1}{1-\rho_1}\left[\rho_2 + \frac{1}{2}\frac{\lambda_2\lambda_1 E(S_1{}^2) + \lambda_2{}^2 E(S_2{}^2)}{1-\rho_1-\rho_2}\right] \tag{3.19}$$

Observe that $E(\hat{\mathscr{M}}_1)$ is the same as (I, 4.8) with parameter (λ_1, S_1).

Example D. Preemptive Repeat-Identical Discipline

Using $E(c_2)$ from (2.26) in $\lambda_2 E(c_2) < 1$, we observe from Section III, 6 that if

$$\rho_1 + \frac{\lambda_2}{\lambda_1}[E(e^{\lambda_1 S_2}) - 1] < 1 \tag{3.20}$$

the steady state exists. However, this condition is not sufficient. From our earlier discussion about $E(c_2{}^2)$ for this discipline, it follows that apart from the above condition, an additional condition (2.41), namely

$$\int_0^\infty (e^{\lambda t} - 1)^2\, S_2(t)\, dt < \infty$$

is required in order that the expected queue length may be finite. The mean number of priority units is given by (3.18), and the mean number of ordinary units is given by

$$E(\hat{\mathscr{M}}_2) = \lambda_2 E(c_2) + \frac{1}{2}\lambda_1\lambda_2\frac{E(S_1{}^2)}{(1-\rho_1)^2} + \frac{1}{2}\frac{\lambda_2{}^2 E(c_2{}^2)}{1-\lambda_2 E(c_2)} \tag{3.21}$$

where $E(c_2)$ and $E(c_2{}^2)$ are given by (2.26) and (2.27), respectively.

Example E. Preemptive Repeat-Different Discipline

Using $E(c_2)$ from (2.35) in $\lambda_2 E(c_2) < 1$, we observe from Section III, 6 that if

$$\rho_1 + \frac{\lambda_2}{\lambda_1}\frac{1-\bar{S}_2(\lambda_1)}{\bar{S}_2(\lambda_1)} < 1 \tag{3.22}$$

the steady state exists and the mean queue length of the priority and ordinary units are given by (3.18) and (3.21) with $E(c_2)$ and $E(c_2{}^2)$

substituted from (2.35) and (2.36). These results are due to Avi-Itzhak [2].

b. *Design Measures*

In Fig. IV.2, the design measure for the ordinary units, which we defined in Chapter III, has been plotted against λ_2/λ_1 for $\nu_2/\nu_1 = 0.5$,

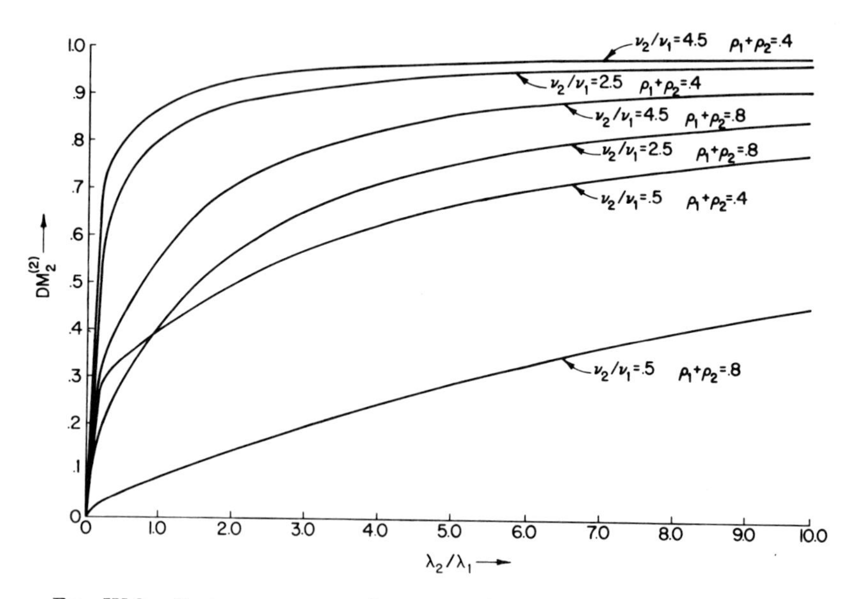

FIG. IV.2. Design measure under preemptive resume discipline—Exponential service time distribution.

2.5, and 4.5, assuming exponential service-time distributions and a preemptive resume discipline. The sum of the traffic intensities of the priority and ordinary units is kept constant at 0.4 and 0.8. Because of the equivalence of the completion-time densities for the preemptive resume and repeat-different disciplines, the same figure represents the design measure for the ordinary units under the preemptive repeat-different discipline. Figure IV.3 represents the design measure for the ordinary units under exponential service-time distributions for the preemptive repeat-identical discipline. Figure IV.4 represents the design measure for the case of constant service times under the preemptive repeat-identical discipline. Again, because the completion-time densities are identical for preemptive repeat-identical and

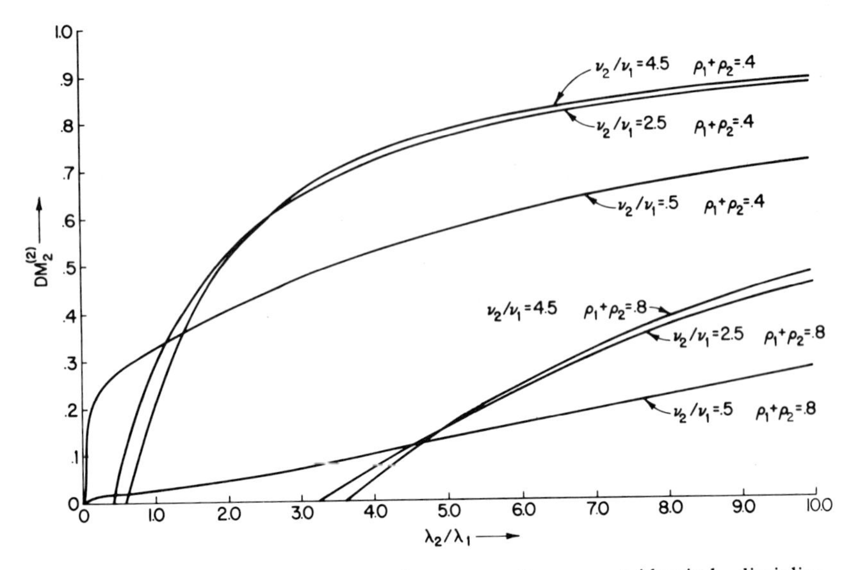

FIG. IV.3. Design measure under preemptive repeat-identical discipline—Exponential service time distribution.

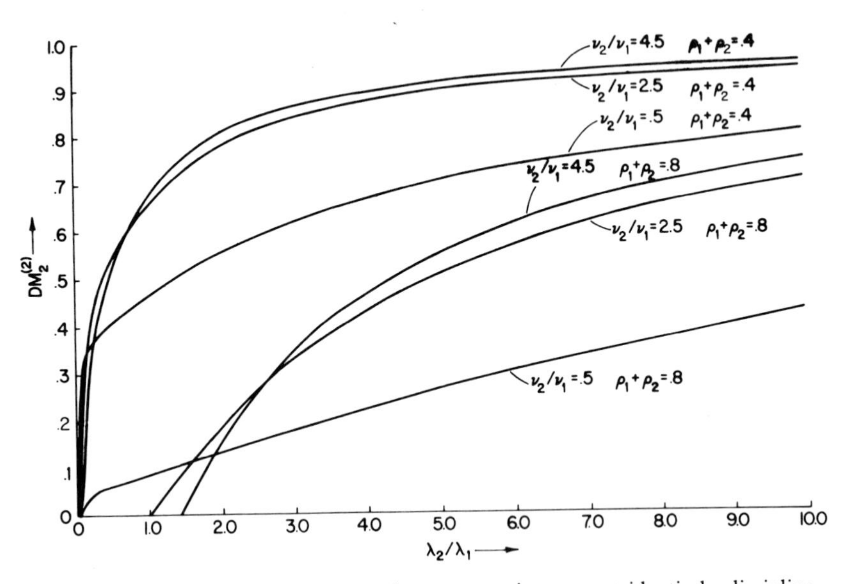

FIG. IV.4. Design measure under preemptive repeat-identical discipline—Constant service time.

preemptive repeat-different disciplines if the service times are constant, Fig. IV.4 represents the design measure under either discipline for the case of constant service times.

As pointed out in Chapter III, the value of the design measure lies between 0 and 1. A higher value indicates a lesser effect of the presence of priority units on the ordinary queue length. From the above figures, we observe that given λ_2/λ_1 and ν_2/ν_1, the design measure increases as $\rho_1 + \rho_2$ decreases. This is so because for given values of λ_2/λ_1 and ν_2/ν_1, the value of ρ_1 will be less for a smaller value of $\rho_1 + \rho_2$, making the effect of priority units less and increasing the design measure. For preemptive resume and repeat-different disciplines, the design measure increases with ν_2/ν_1 for a given value of λ_2/λ_1. This is so because for given λ_2/λ_1, increasing ν_2/ν_1 amounts to decreasing the priority traffic intensity, so that $E(\hat{\mathscr{M}}_2)$ decreases and the design measure increases. However, for the preemptive repeat-identical discipline, such a behavior is not observed for smaller values of λ_2/λ_1.

The explanation of this behavior appears to lie in the fact that for the preemptive repeat-identical discipline, the service-time requirement of a unit remains the same at each entry, so that an ordinary unit with longer service time has to make repeated attempts before completing service. Consequently, the presence of ordinary units with long service times increases $E(\hat{\mathscr{M}}_2)$ and reduces the design measure. For lower values of λ_2/λ_1, this factor appears to dominate, so that increasing ν_2/ν_1 for lower values of λ_2/λ_1 reduces the design measure, while for higher values of λ_2/λ_1, the design measure increases, as it does in the case of other disciplines.

3-3. Occupation Time of the Server

For any of the preemptive disciplines, it is easy to show from (III, 7.3) or directly by comparing the completion-time process with the isolated priority process as for the queue length, that

$$\bar{\varpi}_1{}^c(\theta, s) = \bar{\varpi}_1(\theta, s) \tag{3.23}$$

so that, from (III, 7.5), we get

$$\bar{\mathscr{W}}_1(\theta, s) = \bar{\varpi}_1(\theta, s) \tag{3.24}$$

This result is obviously true, since the priority units are not affected by the presence of ordinary units under preemptive discipline.

The occupation-time density of the server with respect to the ordinary unit is obtained from (III, 7.12) by substituting appropriate values of $\bar{c}_2(s)$.

Example F. Preemptive Resume Discipline

If $\rho_1 + \rho_2 < 1$, the steady-state waiting-time densities exist and are given by

$$\bar{\hat{\mathscr{W}}}_1(\theta) = \bar{\hat{w}}_1(\theta) \tag{3.25}$$

and

$$\bar{\hat{\mathscr{W}}}_2(\theta) = \frac{\hat{e}^{(2)}[\theta + \lambda_1\{1 - \bar{b}_1(\theta)\}]}{\theta - \lambda_2 + \lambda_2 \bar{S}_2[\lambda_1\{1 - \bar{b}_1(\theta)\} + \theta]} \tag{3.26}$$

The first two moments of the waiting-time density for the ordinary units are given by

$$E(\hat{\mathscr{W}}_2) = \frac{\lambda_1 E(S_1^2) + \lambda_2 E(S_2^2)}{2(1 - \rho_1)(1 - \rho_1 - \rho_2)} \tag{3.27}$$

$$E(\hat{\mathscr{W}}_2^2) = \frac{\lambda_1 E(S_1^3) + \lambda_2 E(S_2^3)}{3(1 - \rho_1)^2(1 - \rho_1 - \rho_2)} + \frac{[\lambda_1 E(S_1^2) + \lambda_2 E(S_2^2)]^2}{2(1 - \rho_1)^2(1 - \rho_1 - \rho_2)^2} + \frac{\lambda_1 E(S_1^2)[\lambda_1 E(S_1^2) + \lambda_2 E(S_2^2)]}{2(1 - \rho_1)^3(1 - \rho_1 - \rho_2)} \tag{3.28}$$

These results were first obtained by Miller [62].

Similarly, the results for other disciplines can be obtained. The mean delay time is obtained from (3.27) by adding the mean completion time, so that

$$E[\hat{\mathscr{D}}_2] = \frac{\nu_2}{1 - \rho_1} + \frac{\lambda_1 E(S_1^2) + \lambda_2 E(S_2^2)}{2(1 - \rho_1)(1 - \rho_1 - \rho_2)} \tag{3.29}$$

4. Priority Source Finite and Ordinary Source Infinite The (N_1, ∞) Model

This model, for $N_1 = 1$, is a simple "breakdown model" in which the server is subject to random breakdowns, rendering it inoperative for random periods of time during which it is repaired and restored to its proper activity. One can conceive of various types of such models, depending upon the way the "breakdowns" appear and are repaired. The following two types of breakdowns have been studied in detail:

(i) The breakdowns may occur independent of server's position (i.e., whether the server is busy or not). These are called "independent" breakdowns.

(ii) The breakdowns occur only when the server is servicing the units. These are called "active" breakdowns.

Several other variants of the "breakdown model" have been studied [6]. The independent and active breakdown models have also been considered by Keilson [49] Gaver [29], and Thiruvengadam [88–91].

From the simple breakdown model, we may obtain the results for the (∞, ∞) priority model discussed in Section 3 by observing that the arrival of a priority unit in the latter corresponds to the arrival of a breakdown in the former, and the interval during which the breakdown is repaired is identical to the busy period of the isolated priority process. This argument has been used by Keilson [49], Gaver [29], and Avi-Itzhak and Naor [6] to obtain results for the (∞, ∞) model from the results of simple breakdown model.

The (N_1, ∞) model for $1 < N_1 < \infty$ may be considered as generalizing the breakdown model considered above to the case in which breakdowns occur from N_1 identical sources and can queue up. It may, for example, be regarded as a servicing process of an N_1-component service station, each component having a Poisson failure law with the same mean rate.

The (N_1, ∞) model can also be considered as describing the situation in which the server serves primarily a finite population, e.g., a group of machines, and serves during his idle time another type of units from an infinite population. Various other interpretations of this model are possible.

Let us consider the (N_1, ∞) model under the assumption that if the server is busy, a priority unit, if it is free to arrive, arrives in the interval $(t, t + \Delta)$ with probability $\lambda_1 \Delta + o(\Delta)$, while if the server is idle, it arrives with probability $\tilde{\lambda}_1 \Delta + o(\Delta)$. The assumption of different arrival rates helps us in studying the active and independent breakdowns, because, if $\tilde{\lambda}_1 = \lambda_1$, the above model reduces to the independent breakdown model, and if $\tilde{\lambda}_1 = 0$, it reduces to the active breakdown model.

4-1. Busy Period

Proceeding as in Section III, 4, we obtain the Laplace transform of the busy-period density for this model as

$$\bar{\gamma}_2(s) = \frac{\lambda_2}{\lambda_2 + N_1\tilde{\lambda}_1} \bar{B}_2(s) + \frac{N_1\tilde{\lambda}_1}{\lambda_2 + N_1\tilde{\lambda}_1} \bar{b}_1[s + \lambda_2\{1 - \bar{B}_2(s)\}] \tag{4.1}$$

where $\bar{B}_2(s)$ is the smallest root of the equation $\alpha = \bar{c}_2[\lambda_2(1 - \alpha) + s]$ and $\bar{b}_1(s)$ can be obtained from (II, 2.25).

The moments can be obtained from (4.1) by differentiation; e.g., for the resume discipline, if $\lambda_2 E(c_2) = \lambda_2\nu_2[1 + N_1\lambda_1 E(b_1)] < 1$, the busy period terminates, and its mean duration is given by

$$E(\gamma_2) = \frac{\lambda_2\nu_2[1 + N_1\lambda_1 E(b_1)] + N_1\tilde{\lambda}_1 E(b_1)}{[\lambda_2 + N_1\tilde{\lambda}_1][1 - \lambda_2\nu_2\{1 + N_1\lambda_1 E(b_1)\}]} \tag{4.2}$$

where $E(b_1)$ can be obtained from (II, 2.32).

4-2. Joint Queue-Length Probabilities

Taking into consideration the different arrival rates during the idle and busy periods, it follows from (III, 5.4) that

$$\begin{aligned}\bar{\bar{\Pi}}(\alpha_1, \alpha_2, s) = \bar{e}^{(2)}(s) \Big[1 &+ N_1\tilde{\lambda}_1\bar{\Pi}[\alpha_1, s + \lambda_2(1 - \alpha_2)] \\ &+ \frac{\lambda_2[\alpha_2 - \bar{B}_2(s)] + N_1\tilde{\lambda}_1[\bar{b}_1\{s + \lambda_2(1 - \alpha_2)\} - \bar{b}_1\{s + \lambda_2(1 - \bar{B}_2(s)\}]}{N_1\lambda_1[1 - \bar{b}_1\{s + \lambda_2(1 - \alpha_2)\}] + \lambda_2(1 - \alpha_2) + s} \\ &\times \frac{1 - \bar{c}_2[\lambda_2(1 - \alpha_2) + s]}{1 - \dfrac{1}{\alpha_2}\bar{c}_2[\lambda_2(1 - \alpha_2) + s]} \\ &\times \{1 + N_1\lambda_1\bar{\Pi}[\alpha_1, s + \lambda_2(1 - \alpha_2)]\}\Big]\end{aligned} \tag{4.3}$$

where

$$\bar{e}^{(2)}(s) = [s + N_1\tilde{\lambda}_1 + \lambda_2 - \lambda_2\bar{B}_2(s) - N_1\tilde{\lambda}_1\bar{b}_1\{s + \lambda_2(1 - \bar{B}_2(s)]\}]^{-1} \tag{4.4}$$

This result is obtained by Thiruvengadam [89] for the preemptive resume discipline. The results for the independent and active breakdown models can be obtained by setting $\tilde{\lambda}_1 = \lambda_1$ and $\tilde{\lambda}_1 = 0$, respectively, as in the following examples:

Example A. Independent Breakdown Model

If

$$\lambda_2\nu_2\left[1 + N_1\lambda_1\nu_1 \sum_{e=0}^{N_1-1} \binom{N_1 - 1}{e} \frac{1}{\phi_1(e)}\right] < 1$$

the steady state exists, and

$$\hat{e}^{(2)} = \left[1 + N_1\lambda_1\nu_1 \sum_{e=0}^{N_1-1} \binom{N_1 - 1}{e} \frac{1}{\phi_1(e)}\right]^{-1} - \lambda_2\nu_2 \tag{4.5}$$

$$\hat{\Pi}(1, \alpha_2) = \hat{e}^{(2)}\left[1 + \frac{N_1\lambda_1}{\lambda_2} \frac{1 - \bar{b}_1\{\lambda_2(1 - \alpha_2)\}}{(1 - \alpha_2)}\right] \frac{\bar{c}_2[\lambda_2(1 - \alpha_2)][\alpha_2 - 1]}{\alpha_2 - \bar{c}_2[\lambda_2(1 - \alpha_2)]} \tag{4.6}$$

If $N_1 = 1$, we get the results of the simple independent breakdown model. Observe that $\hat{e}^{(2)}$ does not depend upon $\tilde{\lambda}_1$.

Example B. Active Breakdown Model

The steady state exists under the same condition as in Example A above, and we obtain

$$\hat{e}^{(2)} = 1 - \lambda_2\nu_2\left[1 + N_1\lambda_1\nu_1 \sum_{e=0}^{N_1-1} \binom{N_1 - 1}{e} \frac{1}{\phi_1(e)}\right] \tag{4.7}$$

and

$$\hat{\Pi}(1, \alpha_2) = \frac{\hat{e}^{(2)}[\alpha_2 - 1]}{\dfrac{\alpha_2}{\bar{c}_2[\lambda_2(1 - \alpha_2)]} - 1} \tag{4.8}$$

This result could have been written directly, since, if the breakdowns are active, each busy period starts only with the arrival of an ordinary unit, and therefore the process is identical to an $M/G/1$ process with the service time replaced by completion time.

4-3. Occupation Time of the Server

The results for the occupation-time densities can be obtained as in Section III, 7. The main results are

$$\bar{\bar{\mathscr{W}}}_1(\theta, s) = \bar{\bar{e}}^{(2)}(s)\left[1 + \frac{N_1\tilde{\lambda}_1 + \lambda_2}{N_1\lambda_1 + \lambda_2} N_1\lambda_1\bar{\bar{w}}_1(\theta, s)\right] + [\bar{\bar{e}}_1(s) - \bar{\bar{e}}^{(2)}(s)][1 + N_1\lambda_1\bar{\bar{w}}_1(\theta, s)] \tag{4.9}$$

$$\bar{\bar{\mathscr{W}}}_2(\theta, s) = \frac{\bar{\bar{e}}^{(2)}(s)[\theta + N_1\tilde{\lambda}_1\{1 - \bar{b}_1(\theta)\}] - 1}{\theta - s - \lambda_2[1 - \bar{c}_2(\theta)]} \tag{4.10}$$

from which the steady-state results can be obtained.

5. Priority Source Infinite and Ordinary Source Finite The (∞, N_2) Model

This model is just the opposite of the model in Section 4. Hence, if the priorities are interchanged in the model of Section 4, we get the corresponding model of this type. One obvious reason for studying this model, is to compare the system behavior if priorities are interchanged in situations where the server serves two classes of units—one emanating from an infinite source and the other from a finite source. The results for the busy period, queue length, and occupation time can be obtained as above from the results of Chapter III, and some of these are given in the following example.

Example

If $\nu_2 < \infty$, $\lambda_1\nu_1 < 1$, the busy period for the independent-interruption model terminates, and its expected value is given by

$$E(\gamma_2) = \frac{1}{N_2\lambda_2 + \lambda_1}\frac{1}{1-\rho_1}\left[\rho_1 + N_2\lambda_2\nu_2 \sum_{e=0}^{N_2-1}\binom{N_2-1}{e}\frac{1}{\Phi_2(e)} + \lambda_1\nu_2\sum_{e=1}^{N_2}\binom{N_2}{e}\frac{1-\bar{b}_1(e\lambda_2)}{\Phi_2(e-1)}\right] \tag{5.1}$$

Hence, the proportion of time the server is idle is given by

$$\hat{e}^{(2)} = (1-\rho_1) \times \left[1 + N_2\lambda_2\nu_2\sum_{e=0}^{N_2-1}\binom{N_2-1}{e}\frac{1}{\Phi_2(e)} + \lambda_1\nu_2\sum_{e=1}^{N_2}\binom{N_2}{e}\frac{1-\bar{b}_1(e\lambda_2)}{\Phi_2(e-1)}\right]^{-1} \tag{5.2}$$

Also, the mean number of ordinary units is given by

$$E(\hat{\mathscr{M}}_2) = N_2 - \frac{1}{\lambda_2\nu_2}[1-\rho_1-\hat{e}^{(2)}] \tag{5.3}$$

6. Priority and Ordinary Sources Both Finite—The (N_1, N_2) Model

This model can be interpreted as a machine-interference model in which the operator looks after two independent sets of machines each having different failure and repair rates. This situation is quite common, since new machines are frequently introduced either through expansion or replacement, and, since the complete elimination of old machines takes years, the operator is quite likely to have a heterogeneous mixture of old and new machines. The question of deciding which type of machines should be assigned priority so as to minimize the loss due to interference is of obvious importance.

If $N_1 = 1$, the model may be interpreted as being the machine-interference model with limited server's availability. We explain by noting that the usual assumption in the machine-interference model is that the operator is either busy repairing machines or is idle waiting for a machine to fail. This assumption is called the "complete availability" of the server. However, in practice, the operator also takes up ancillary duties, which may be indirectly or directly related to his main task of repairing machines, e.g., the fetching of raw materials or tools, and these ancillary duties may be attended by the operator on a preemptive basis, leading to this type of model.

The reader can visualize a large number of situations where the server has to decide the allocation of priorities to one of the two types of units which emanate from a finite source. It is easy to see that this question is more difficult to answer than the (∞, ∞) situation because the size of the two sources are additional parameters affecting the priority allocation decision.

The results of this model can be derived for any discipline from the results of Chapter III.

Example

If the operator is responsible for servicing two sets of machines with parameters (N_1, λ_1, S_1) and (N_2, λ_2, S_2), the first type having preemptive priority over the second, it can be shown from Section III, 6 and in particular from (III, 6.9) that, under steady state, the mean number of first- and second-type units present are given by

$$E(\hat{\mathscr{M}}_1) = N_1 - \frac{1}{\lambda_1 \nu_1}(1 - \hat{e}_1) \tag{6.1}$$

$$E(\hat{\mathscr{M}}_2) = N_2 - \frac{1}{\lambda_2 \nu_2}[\hat{e}_1 - \hat{e}^{(2)}] \tag{6.2}$$

respectively, where

$$\hat{e}_1 = \left[1 + N_1 \lambda_1 \nu_1 \sum_{e=0}^{N_1-1} \binom{N_1 - 1}{e} \frac{1}{\phi_1(e)}\right]^{-1} \tag{6.3}$$

and

$$\hat{e}^{(2)} = \hat{e}_1 \left[1 + \nu_2 \left\{N_2 \lambda_2 \sum_{e=0}^{N_2-1} \binom{N_2 - 1}{e} \frac{1}{\Phi_2(e)} + N_1 \lambda_1 \sum_{e=1}^{N_2} \binom{N_2}{e} \frac{1 - \bar{b}_1(e\lambda_2)}{\Phi_2(e-1)}\right\}\right]^{-1} \tag{6.4}$$

Numerical Results

The results for (6.1) and (6.2) are presented in Table IV.1 assuming

TABLE IV.1

N_1		N_2 = 1 P	1 O	2 P	2 O	3 P	3 O	4 P	4 O	5 P	5 O	10 P	10 O
1	A	.02	.09 (.09)	.02	.20 (.19)	.02	.33 (.31)	.02	.48 (.43)	.02	.66 (.58)	.02	2.22 (1.86)
	B	.09	.02 (.02)	.09	.05 (.05)	.09	.08 (.07)	.09	.11 (.10)	.09	.14 (.12)	.09	.30 (.26)
2	A	.04	.10 (.10)	.04	.21 (.20)	.04	.34 (.31)	.04	.49 (.44)	.04	.68 (.59)	.04	2.30 (1.93)
	B	.20	.03 (.03)	.20	.06 (.05)	.20	.10 (.08)	.20	.14 (.11)	.20	.17 (.14)	.20	.40 (.31)
3	A	.06	.10 (.10)	.06	.21 (.20)	.06	.35 (.32)	.06	.51 (.45)	.06	.70 (.61)	.06	2.38 (2.01)
	B	.32	.04 (.03)	.32	.08 (.06)	.32	.13 (.10)	.32	.17 (.13)	.32	.22 (.17)	.32	.51 (.37)
4	A	.08	.10 (.10)	.08	.22 (.21)	.08	.36 (.33)	.08	.53 (.47)	.08	.72 (.63)	.08	2.46 (2.09)
	B	.47	.05 (.04)	.47	.11 (.07)	.47	.16 (.11)	.47	.22 (.15)	.47	.29 (.19)	.47	.66 (.44)
5	A	.11	.10 (.10)	.11	.23 (.21)	.11	.37 (.34)	.11	.54 (.48)	.11	.75 (.64)	.11	2.55 (2.17)
	B	.64	.07 (.04)	.64	.14 (.08)	.64	.21 (.13)	.64	.29 (.18)	.64	.37 (.23)	.64	.87 (.54)
10	A	.24	.12 (.12)	.24	.26 (.24)	.24	.44 (.39)	.24	.64 (.56)	.24	.89 (.75)	.24	3.04 (2.66)
	B	2.15	.24 (.08)	2.15	.50 (.19)	2.15	.78 (.32)	2.15	1.08 (.48)	2.15	1.41 (.68)	2.15	3.47 (2.31)

the premptive resume discipline. In this table, the P and O columns represent the expected queue lengths for priority and ordinary units, respectively. The figures without parentheses represent the values for exponentially distributed service times, while those in the parenthesis represent the values for constant service times. The A rows have parameter values $\lambda_1 = 0.4$, $\lambda_2 = 1.0$, $\nu_1 = 0.05$, and $\nu_2 = 0.1$, while the B rows have the parameter values $\lambda_1 = 1.0$, $\lambda_2 = 0.4$, $\nu_1 = 0.1$, and $\nu_2 = 0.05$, so that consecutive A and B rows represent the effect of interchanging priority.

To illustrate the use of the above results, let us consider the following specific situation: A moving and storage company has two types of vans: Type I—large vans for long-distance moving, and Type II—small vans for short-distance moving. After failure, the vans are sent to a repair shop owned by the company. The important parameters for the two types of vans are specified in Table IV.2.

TABLE IV.2

Type of van	Number of vans	Failure rate	Mean repair time	Space requirement
I	5	0.4	0.05	2
II	10	1.0	0.1	1

The question to be answered is, What type of vans should be assigned priority while repairing, assuming that the preemptive resume discipline is feasible?

From Table IV.1, we observe that assigning priority to type I results in an average space requirement of $0.22 + 2.55 = 2.77$ while assigning priority to type II results in an average space requirement of $0.64 + 1.74 = 2.38$. This shows that if the repair policy is to assign priority to type II vans, the space requirement would be less than that resulting from assigning priority to type I vans. The above conclusion is based upon the fact that the repair times are exponentially distributed. It can be easily verified that the same conclusion results when the repair times are constant.

Table IV.3 represents the results for the preemptive repeat-identical discipline assuming exponentially distributed service times. For the above example, it is easy to verify that assigning priority to type I vans would now be preferable. More numerical work is needed to make specific comments about the effect of different parameters.

TABLE IV.3

		N_2											
		1		2		3		4		5		10	
		P	O	P	O	P	O	P	O	P	O	P	O
N_1 = 1	A	.02	.13	.02	.28	.02	.45	.02	.64	.02	.84	.02	2.48
	B	.09	.07	.09	.25	.09	.52	.09	.88	.09	1.31	.09	4.34
2	A	.04	.17	.04	.35	.04	.56	.04	.78	.04	1.04	.04	2.94
	B	.20	.13	.20	.35	.20	.67	.20	1.05	.20	1.51	.20	4.62
3	A	.06	.21	.06	.43	.06	.66	.06	.91	.06	1.19	.06	3.26
	B	.32	.18	.32	.46	.32	.81	.32	1.23	.32	1.71	.32	4.88
4	A	.08	.25	.08	.50	.08	.76	.08	1.04	.08	1.35	.08	3.58
	B	.47	.24	.47	.56	.47	.95	.47	1.41	.47	1.92	.47	5.14
5	A	.11	.28	.11	.57	.11	.87	.11	1.18	.11	1.51	.11	3.90
	B	.64	.30	.64	.67	.64	1.10	.64	1.59	.64	2.13	.64	5.41
10	A	.24	.47	.24	.93	.24	1.39	.24	1.86	.24	2.35	.24	5.62
	B	2.15	.62	2.15	1.27	2.15	1.95	2.15	2.65	2.15	3.38	2.15	7.28

7. *k*-Class Priority Processes

We indicated in Section III, 8 the method of generalization to processes with more than two priority classes. Consider, for example, a priority queuing process with $k > 2$ classes. We will study for this process the completion time, the busy period, the joint queue length probabilities, and the occupation-time densities by extending essentially the same arguments which we used to study the two-class priority process from the basic processes. We extend, for $(k > 2)$-class processes, the notations that we used for two-class processes, e.g., $\gamma_k(t)$ denotes the busy-period density for a priority queuing process with k classes. We may define $\gamma_j^{(k)}(t)$ which denotes the density of the busy-period duration for units with priority index $\leqslant j$ for the k-class process. Notice that $\gamma_k(t) = \gamma_k^{(k)}(t)$. Also, since for the preemptive discipline the jth-class units are not affected by units of classes $j + 1, j + 2, \ldots, k$, we have $\gamma_j^{(k)}(t) = \gamma_j^{(j)}(t) = \gamma_j(t)$. Hence, in the following we will use $\gamma_j(t)$ in place of $\gamma_j^{(k)}(t)$, $(j \leqslant k)$.

7-1. Completion Time for *j*th-Class Unit

The completion time of a *j*th-class unit in the *k*-class priority process is the time between the entry of a *j*th-class unit into service and the time when the server becomes free to take the next *j*th-class unit. Because of preemptive discipline, one may define the completion time as the duration of the period that elapses between the instant at which the *j*th-class unit enters service and the instant at which it departs. The completion time of the *j*th-class unit is just the service time of the *j*th-class unit if units with priority index less than j do not interrupt its service. Since the units with index less than j initiate a busy period whose duration has density $\gamma_{j-1}(t)$, the completion time density can be obtained as in Section IV, 2 by assuming the rate of interruptions to be

$$\Lambda_{j-1}^* = \sum_{i=1}^{j-1} \lambda_i^*$$

and their duration γ_{j-1} (we will evaluate γ_{j-1} later and assume it to be known here). Hence, the following results can be written immediately:

(a) Preemptive resume

$$\bar{c}_j(s) = \bar{S}_j[s + \Lambda_{j-1}^*\{1 - \bar{\gamma}_{j-1}(s)\}] \tag{7.1}$$

$$E(c_j) = \nu_j[1 + \Lambda_{j-1}^* E(\gamma_{j-1})] \tag{7.2}$$

$$E(c_j^2) = E(S_j^2)[1 + \Lambda_{j-1}^* E(\gamma_{j-1})]^2 + \Lambda_{j-1}^* \nu_j E(\gamma_{j-1}^2) \tag{7.3}$$

(b) Preemptive repeat-identical

$$\bar{c}_j(s) = \int_0^\infty \frac{\exp(-[s + \Lambda_{j-1}^*]x)\, S_j(x)\, dx}{1 - \bar{\gamma}_{j-1}(s) \dfrac{\Lambda_{j-1}^*}{s + \Lambda_{j-1}^*} [1 - \exp(-[\Lambda_{j-1}^* + s]x)]} \tag{7.4}$$

$$E(c_j) = \left[\frac{1}{\Lambda_{j-1}^*} + E(\gamma_{j-1})\right] [E\{\exp(\Lambda_{j-1}^* S_j)\} - 1] \tag{7.5}$$

$$E(c_j^2) = 2\left[\frac{1}{\Lambda_{j-1}^*} + E(\gamma_{j-1})\right]^2 E[\{\exp(\Lambda_{j-1}^* S_j) - 1\}^2]$$

$$+ \left\{[E(\gamma_{j-1})^2] + \frac{2E(\gamma_{j-1})}{\Lambda_{j-1}^*} + \frac{2}{\Lambda_{j-1}^{*2}}\right\} [E\{\exp(\Lambda_{j-1}^* S_j)\} - 1]$$

$$- 2\left[E(\gamma_{j-1}) + \frac{1}{\Lambda_{j-1}^*}\right] E[S_j \exp(\Lambda_{j-1}^* S_j)] \tag{7.6}$$

(c) Preemptive repeat-different

$$\bar{c}_j(s) = \frac{\bar{S}_j[\Lambda_{j-1}^* + s]}{1 - \dfrac{\Lambda_{j-1}^*}{\Lambda_{j-1}^* + s}\bar{\gamma}_{j-1}(s)[1 - \bar{S}_j(\Lambda_{j-1}^* + s)]} \tag{7.7}$$

$$E(c_j) = \left[\frac{1 - \bar{S}_j(\Lambda_{j-1}^*)}{\bar{S}_j(\Lambda_{j-1}^*)}\right]\left[E(\gamma_{j-1}) + \frac{1}{\Lambda_{j-1}^*}\right] \tag{7.8}$$

$$E(c_j^2) = 2\left[E(\gamma_{j-1}) + \frac{1}{\Lambda_{j-1}^*}\right]^2 \left[\frac{1 - \bar{S}_j(\Lambda_{j-1}^*)}{\bar{S}_j(\Lambda_{j-1}^*)}\right]$$

$$+ \left\{E(\gamma_{j-1}^2) + \frac{2}{\Lambda_{j-1}^*} E(\gamma_{j-1}) + \frac{2}{\Lambda_{j-1}^{*2}}\right\}\left[\frac{1 - \bar{S}_j(\Lambda_{j-1}^*)}{\bar{S}_j(\Lambda_{j-1}^*)}\right]$$

$$- 2E(\gamma_{j-1}) + \frac{1}{\Lambda_{j-1}^*} \frac{\int_0^\infty x_j \exp(-\Lambda_{j-1}^* x_j)\, S_j(x_j)\, dx_j}{[\bar{S}_j(\Lambda_{j-1}^*)]^2} \tag{7.9}$$

7-2. Busy Period

Let us consider $\gamma_j^{(k)}(t)$, the busy-period density for units with priority index $\leqslant j$ in the k $(\geqslant j)$-class process. Because of the preemptive discipline, the presence of lower priority units does not influence the busy period of higher priority units, we can consider the busy period as initiated by units with priority index $\leqslant j$ who arrive when the server is either idle or servicing a unit of priority index $> j$. Hence, $\gamma_j^{(k)} = \gamma_j$. Furthermore, the units of priority index $< j$ can be grouped into one class and the process can be considered a two-class process as follows:

(1) Either the busy period is initiated by the arrival of a jth-class unit, in which case its duration will be the same as of the basic infinite or finite source models with the service time of the jth-class replaced by its completion time; or

(2) The busy period is initiated by the arrival of a unit of priority index less than j, in which case its duration is the same as the initial busy-period process of the basic infinite or finite source model with the service time of the jth-class replaced by its completion time and the initial occupation time equal to γ_{j-1}.

Hence,

$$\bar{\gamma}_j(s) = \frac{\lambda_j^*}{\Lambda_j^*} \bar{B}_j(s) + \frac{\Lambda_{j-1}^*}{\Lambda_j^*} \bar{B}_j^{\gamma_{j-1}}(s) \tag{7.10}$$

a. *jth Source Infinite*

If the jth source is infinite, $\bar{B}_j(s)$ is the smallest root of the equation $\alpha_j = \bar{c}_j[\lambda_j(1 - \alpha_j) + s]$ and $\bar{B}_j^{\gamma_{j-1}}(s) = \bar{\gamma}_{j-1}[s + \lambda_j\{1 - \bar{B}_j(s)\}]$. In addition, if $\lambda_j E(c_j) < 1$ and $E(\gamma_{j-1}) < \infty$, the busy period has a finite mean which is given by

$$E(\gamma_j) = \frac{\lambda_j}{\Lambda_j^*} \frac{E(c_j)}{1 - \lambda_j E(c_j)} + \frac{\Lambda_{j-1}^*}{\Lambda_j^*} \frac{E(\gamma_{j-1})}{1 - \lambda_j E(c_j)} \tag{7.11}$$

and the second moment is given by

$$E(\gamma_j^2) = \frac{\lambda_j}{\Lambda_j^*} \frac{E(c_j^2)}{[1 - \lambda_j E(c_j)]^3} + \frac{\Lambda_{j-1}^*}{\Lambda_j^*} \left[\frac{E(\gamma_{j-1})^2}{[1 - \lambda_j E(c_j)]^2} + \frac{\lambda_j E(\gamma_{j-1}) E(c_j^2)}{[1 - \lambda_j E(c_j)]^3} \right] \tag{7.12}$$

The results for the particular disciplines are listed in the following examples.

Example A. Preemptive Resume Discipline

If all the sources are infinite, we get, using (7.2) and (7.3) in (7.11) and (7.12),

$$E(\gamma_j) = \frac{\sum_{i=1}^{j} \rho_i}{\Lambda_j \left[1 - \sum_{i=1}^{j} \rho_i\right]} \tag{7.13}$$

$$E(\gamma_j^2) = \frac{\sum_{i=1}^{j} \lambda_i E(S_i^2)}{\Lambda_j \left[1 - \sum_{i=1}^{j} \rho_i\right]^3} \tag{7.14}$$

where

$$\rho_i = \lambda_i \nu_i$$

These results were first obtained by Miller [62].

Example B. Preemptive Repeat-Identical

If all the sources are infinite, we get from (7.5) and (7.11) after some simplification

$$[1 + \Lambda_{j-1}E(\gamma_{j-1})]^{-1} - [1 + \Lambda_j E(\gamma_j)]^{-1} = \lambda_j \zeta_j \tag{7.15}$$

where

$$\zeta_j = \frac{1}{\Lambda_{j-1}} E(e^{\Lambda_{j-1}S_j} - 1) \tag{7.16}$$

Equation (7.15) is a recurrence relation from which $E(\gamma_j)$ can be evaluated, so that

$$E(\gamma_j) = \frac{\sum_{i=1}^{j} \zeta_i}{\Lambda_j \left[1 - \sum_{i=1}^{j} \zeta_i\right]} \tag{7.17}$$

Finally, using (7.9), together with (7.16) in (7.12), we obtain the second moment of γ_j as

$$E(\gamma_j^2) = \frac{\left\{\sum_{i=1}^{j} \left[\lambda_i l_i \left(1 - \sum_{e=1}^{i-1} \zeta_e\right) + \frac{2\lambda_i}{\Lambda_{i-1}^2} \sum_{e=1}^{i-1} \zeta_e E(e^{\Lambda_{e-1}S_e} - 1)\right]\right\}}{2\left[1 - \sum_{i=1}^{j} \zeta_i\right]^2 \sum_{i=1}^{j} \zeta_i} \tag{7.18}$$

where

$$l_i = \frac{2}{\Lambda_{i-1}^2} E[(e^{\Lambda_{i-1}S_i} - 1)^2] + \frac{2}{\Lambda_{i-1}} [\zeta_i - E(S_i e^{\Lambda_{i-1}S_i})] \tag{7.19}$$

and $\Lambda_0 = 0$.

Example C. Preemptive Repeat-Different

Using (7.8), (7.9), (7.11), and (7.12) we obtain the same expression for $E(\gamma_j)$ as (7.17) with ζ_j given by the following

$$\zeta_j = \frac{\lambda_j}{\Lambda_j} \frac{1 - \bar{S}_j(\Lambda_{j-1})}{\bar{S}_j(\Lambda_{j-1})} \tag{7.20}$$

In addition,

$$E(\gamma_j^2) = \frac{\sum_{i=1}^{j} \left\{ \lambda_i l_i^2 \left(1 - \sum_{e=1}^{i-1} \zeta_i\right) + \frac{2\zeta_i^2}{\lambda_i} \sum_{e=1}^{i-1} \zeta_e \right\}}{\left(1 - \sum_{i=1}^{j} \zeta_i\right)^3 \Lambda_j} \tag{7.21}$$

where

$$l_j = 2\left(\zeta_j + \frac{1}{\Lambda_{j-1}}\right)\left\{\zeta_j - \frac{1}{\bar{S}_j(\Lambda_{j-1})} E(S_j e^{-\Lambda_{j-1} S_j})\right\} \tag{7.22}$$

Results of Examples B and C above are obtained by Avi-Itzhak [2] through direct probability arguments.

b. *jth Source Finite*

If the jth source is finite, we have from (II, 2.25) and (II, 2.42)

$$\bar{B}_j(s) = \left[\sum_{e=0}^{N_j} \binom{N_j}{e} \frac{1}{\bar{V}_j(e-1, s)}\right]^{-1} \left[\sum_{e=0}^{N_j-1} \binom{N_j - 1}{e} \frac{1}{\bar{V}_j(e-1, s)}\right] \tag{7.23}$$

$$\bar{B}_j^{\gamma_{j-1}}(s) = \left[\sum_{e=0}^{N_j} \binom{N_j}{e} \frac{1}{\bar{V}_j(e-1, s)}\right]^{-1} \left[\sum_{e=0}^{N_j-1} \binom{N_j - 1}{e} \frac{\bar{\gamma}_{j-1}(e\lambda_j + s)}{\bar{V}_j(e-1, s)}\right] \tag{7.24}$$

If $\nu_j < \infty$ and $E(\gamma_{j-1}) < \infty$, the mean length of the busy period is given by

$$E(\gamma_j) = \frac{N_j\lambda_j}{\Lambda_j^*} E(c_j) \sum_{e=0}^{N_j-1} \binom{N_j - 1}{e} \frac{1}{\Phi_j(e)}$$
$$+ \frac{\Lambda_{j-1}^*}{\Lambda_j^*} \left[E(\gamma_{j-1}) + E(c_j) \sum_{e=1}^{N_j} \binom{N_j}{e} \frac{1 - \bar{\gamma}_{j-1}(e\lambda_j)}{\Phi_j(e-1)}\right] \tag{7.25}$$

The results for resume and repeat disciplines can be obtained from (7.25) using $E(c_j)$ from (7.2), (7.5), and (7.8), and solving recursively.

7-3. Joint Queue-Length Probabilities

Let us consider the case in which all the sources are infinite; we can extend the arguments which lead to (III, 5.4) to obtain

$$\bar{\Pi}(\alpha_1, \alpha_2, \ldots, \alpha_k, s)$$
$$= \bar{e}^{(k)}(s) \Big[1 + \Lambda_k \frac{1}{\alpha_k} \bar{\mathscr{G}}(\alpha_k, s)\, \bar{\Pi}^c\{\alpha_1, \alpha_2, \ldots, \alpha_k, s + \lambda_k(1 - \alpha_k)\}$$
$$+ \Lambda_{k-1} \bar{\Pi}\{\alpha_1, \alpha_2, \ldots, \alpha_{k-1}, s + \lambda_k(1 - \alpha_k)\}\Big] \tag{7.26}$$

where

$$\frac{1}{\alpha_k}\bar{\mathscr{G}}(\alpha_k, s)$$
$$= \frac{\lambda_k[\alpha_k - \bar{B}_k(s)] + \Lambda_{k-1}[\bar{\gamma}_{k-1}\{\lambda_k(1-\alpha_k)+s\} - \bar{\gamma}_{k-1}\{\lambda_k[1-\bar{B}_k(s)]+s\}]}{\Lambda_k[\alpha_k - \bar{c}_k\{\lambda_k(1-\alpha_k)+s\}]} \tag{7.27}$$

Now, if we compare the completion time process of a k-class unit with that of the $(k-1)$-class priority process, we can show by arguments essentially similar to those which led to (2.18) that

$$\bar{\bar{\Pi}}(\alpha_1, \alpha_2, \ldots, \alpha_{k-1}, s) = \frac{\bar{\Pi}^I(\alpha_1, \alpha_2, \ldots, \alpha_{k-1}, s)}{1 - \bar{c}_k(s)} \tag{7.28}$$

where

$$\bar{\Pi}^c(\alpha_1, \alpha_2, \ldots, \alpha_k, s) = \alpha_k \bar{\Pi}^I(\alpha_1, \alpha_2, \ldots, \alpha_{k-1}, s) \tag{7.29}$$

where $\bar{\Pi}^I(\alpha_1, \alpha_2, \ldots, \alpha_{k-1}, s)$ is the Laplace transform of the generating function of the joint queue length probabilities of $(k-1)$ classes during the completion time $(c_k = I_k)$ cycle of the kth class unit. Hence,

$$\bar{\Pi}^c(\alpha_1, \alpha_2, \ldots, \alpha_k, s) = \alpha_k [1 - \bar{c}_k(s)]\, \bar{\bar{\Pi}}(\alpha_1, \alpha_2, \ldots, \alpha_{k-1}, s) \tag{7.30}$$

Using (7.30) in (7.26), we get

$$\begin{aligned}\bar{\bar{\Pi}}&(\alpha_1, \alpha_2, \ldots, \alpha_k, s)\\ &= \bar{e}^{(k)}(s)\{1 + \Lambda_k \bar{\mathscr{G}}(\alpha_k, s)\{1 - \bar{c}_k[s + \lambda_k(1-\alpha_k)]\}\\ &\qquad \times \bar{\bar{\Pi}}[\alpha_1, \ldots, \alpha_{k-1}, s + \lambda_k(1-\alpha_k)]\\ &\qquad + \Lambda_{k-1}\bar{\Pi}[\alpha_1, \alpha_2, \ldots, \alpha_{k-1}, s + \lambda_k(1-\alpha_k)]\}\end{aligned} \tag{7.31}$$

and since

$$\bar{\bar{\Pi}}(\alpha_1, \alpha_2, \ldots, \alpha_{k-1}, s) = \bar{e}^{(k-1)}(s)[1 + \Lambda_{k-1}^*\bar{\Pi}(\alpha_1, \alpha_2, \ldots, \alpha_{k-1}, s)] \tag{7.32}$$

we get

$$\begin{aligned}\bar{\bar{\Pi}}(\alpha_1, \alpha_2, \ldots, \alpha_k, s) &= \bar{\bar{\Pi}}(\alpha_1, \alpha_2, \ldots, \alpha_{k-1}, s)\frac{\bar{e}^{(k)}(s)}{\bar{e}^{(k-1)}(s)}\\ &\quad \times [1 + \Lambda_k \bar{\mathscr{G}}(\alpha_k, s)\,\bar{e}^{(k-1)}(s)\{1 - \bar{c}_k[s + \lambda_k(1-\alpha_k)]\}]\end{aligned} \tag{7.33}$$

where

$$\bar{e}^{(k)}(s) = [s + \Lambda_k\{1 - \bar{\gamma}_k(s)\}]^{-1} \tag{7.34}$$

Equations (7.33) and (7.34) can be recursively used to obtain the k-dimensional generating function of the joint queue-length probabilities. The result is, however, complicated. Putting $\alpha_k = 1$, we get

$$\bar{\bar{\Pi}}(\alpha_1, \alpha_2, \ldots, \alpha_{k-1}, 1, s) = \bar{\bar{\Pi}}(\alpha_1, \alpha_2, \ldots, \alpha_{k-1}, s) \tag{7.35}$$

so that the marginal joint queue-length distribution of the $(k-1)$th class in a k-class process is the same as the joint queue-length distribution of the $(k-1)$ classes in a $(k-1)$-class process. From (7.35), it follows that

$$\bar{\bar{\Pi}}[1, 1, \ldots, \alpha_j, 1, \ldots, 1, s] = \bar{\bar{\Pi}}[1, 1, \ldots, \alpha_j, s] \tag{7.36}$$

where the generations functions on the left- and right-hand sides are of k and j dimensions, respectively.

Relation (7.36) is obviously true. It means that the marginal queue-length distribution of the jth-class units in a k-class priority process is the same as the marginal queue-length distribution of the jth-class units in the j-class process. Hence, the marginal queue-length distribution of the jth-class units in the k-class priority process can be obtained from the $(1, \infty)$ model by assuming that the breakdown arises exponentially with mean rate Λ_{j-1}^* and has duration γ_{j-1}, or it can be obtained directly from (7.33) using (7.34), (7.36) and the relation $\bar{\bar{\Pi}}(1, 1, \ldots, 1, s) = 1/s$. Thus,

$$\bar{\bar{\Pi}}[1, 1, \ldots, \alpha_j, 1, \ldots, s]$$

$$= \frac{\bar{e}^{(j)}(s)}{s} \Big[s + \Lambda_{j-1}\{1 - \bar{\gamma}_{j-1}(s)\} + \alpha_j\{1 - \bar{c}_j[s + \lambda_j(1 - \alpha_j)]\}$$

$$\times \frac{\lambda_j[\alpha_j - \bar{B}_j(s)] + \Lambda_{j-1}[\bar{\gamma}_{j-1}\{\lambda_j(1 - \alpha_j) + s\} - \bar{\gamma}_{j-1}\{\lambda_j[1 - \bar{B}_j(s)] + s\}}{\alpha_j - \bar{c}_j[s + \lambda_j(1 - \alpha_j)]} \Big] \tag{7.37}$$

where

$$\bar{e}^{(j)}(s) = [s + \Lambda_j\{1 - \bar{\gamma}_j(s)\}]^{-1} \tag{7.38}$$

If $E(\gamma_j) < \infty$ and $\lambda_j E(c_j) < 1$, the limiting distribution exists and is given by

$$\hat{\Pi}(1, 1, \ldots, \alpha_j, 1, \ldots) = \hat{e}^{(j)} \frac{\bar{c}_j[\lambda_j(1 - \alpha_j)][\lambda_j\alpha_j - \Lambda_j + \Lambda_{j-1}\bar{\gamma}_{j-1}\{\lambda_j(1 - \alpha_j)\}]}{\lambda_j[\alpha_j - \bar{c}_j\{\lambda_j(1 - \alpha_j)\}]} \tag{7.39}$$

where

$$\hat{e}^{(j)} = [1 + \Lambda_{j-1}E(\gamma_{j-1})]^{-1}[1 - \lambda_j E(c_j)] \tag{7.40}$$

The expected marginal queue length of the jth class is

$$E(\hat{\mathscr{M}}_j) = \lambda_j E(c_j) + \Lambda_{j-1}\frac{\lambda_j}{2}\frac{E(\gamma_{j-1}^2)}{1 + \Lambda_{j-1}E(\gamma_{j-1})} + \frac{1}{2}\lambda_j^2\frac{E(c_j^2)}{1 - \lambda_j E(c_j)} \tag{7.41}$$

These results were obtained by Chang [16] and, for the preemptive resume discipline, by Welch [97] using Markov chain analysis. The results for the specific disciplines are given in the following examples:

Example D. Preemptive Resume Discipline

If

$$\sum_{i=1}^{j} \rho_i < 1$$

the steady state exists and the expected number of jth-class units is given by

$$E(\hat{\mathscr{M}}_j) = \frac{\rho_j}{1 - \sum_{i=1}^{j-1} \rho_i} + \frac{\lambda_j \sum_{i=1}^{j} \lambda_i E(S_i^2)}{2\left(1 - \sum_{i=1}^{j-1} \rho_i\right)\left(1 - \sum_{i=1}^{j} \rho_i\right)} \tag{7.42}$$

This result was obtained by Avi-Itzhak and Naor [6] through direct probability arguments.

Example E. Preemptive Repeat-Identical Discipline

The mean number of jth-class units is obtained by using the results (7.5), (7.6), (7.17), and (7.18) in (7.41), and is given by

$$E(\hat{\mathscr{M}}_j) = \frac{\zeta_j}{1 - \sum_{i=1}^{j=1} \zeta_i} + \frac{\lambda_j \sum_{i=1}^{j} \left[\lambda_i l_i \left(1 - \sum_{e=1}^{i-1} \zeta_e\right) + \frac{2\lambda_i}{\Lambda_{i-1}^2} \sum_{e=1}^{i-1} \zeta_e E(e^{\Lambda_{e-1}S_e} - 1)^2\right]}{2\left[1 - \sum_{i=1}^{j-1} \zeta_i\right]\left[1 - \sum_{i=1}^{j} \zeta_i\right]} \tag{7.43}$$

where ζ_i and l_i are defined by (7.16) and (7.19).

Example F. Preemptive Repeat-Different Discipline

The mean number of jth-class units is obtained by using (7.8), (7.9), and the results of example C above in (7.41), and is given by

$$E(\hat{\mathscr{M}}_j) = \frac{\zeta_j}{1 - \sum_{i=1}^{j-1} \zeta_i} + \frac{\lambda_j \sum_{i=1}^{j} \left[\lambda_i l_i \left(1 - \sum_{e=1}^{j-1} \zeta_e\right) + \frac{2\zeta_i^2}{\lambda_i} \sum_{e=1}^{i-1} \zeta_e\right]}{2\left[1 - \sum_{i=1}^{j} \zeta_i\right]\left[1 - \sum_{i=1}^{j-1} \zeta_i\right]} \tag{7.44}$$

where ζ_i and l_i are defined by (7.20) and (7.22). This result was obtained by Avi-Itzhak [2] by direct probability arguments.

k Finite-Sources

Let us next discuss the case in which all the sources are finite. Following similar arguments as for the infinite-source case, we can write the marginal queue length distribution of the jth-class units from the results of the $(1, N_2)$ model. From (III, 6.7), we obtain

$$\begin{aligned}\hat{\Pi}(1, 1, \ldots, \alpha_j, 1, \ldots) = \hat{e}^{(j)} \Bigg[1 &+ \sum_{m_j=0}^{N_j-1} \alpha_j^{N_j-m_j}(1 - \alpha_j)^{m_j} \frac{\Phi_j(m_j - 1)}{m_j\lambda_j} \partial_j(m_j) \\ &+ \Lambda_{j-1}^* \sum_{m_j=0}^{N_j} \alpha_j^{N_j-m_j}(1 - \alpha_j)^{m_j} \binom{N_j}{m_j} \frac{1 - \bar{\gamma}_{j-1}(m_j\lambda_j)}{m_j\lambda_j}\Bigg]\end{aligned} \tag{7.45}$$

$$\hat{e}^{(j)} = [1 + \Lambda_{j-1}^* E(\gamma_{j-1})][1 + \partial_j(0)]^{-1} \tag{7.46}$$

where

$$\partial_j(m_j) = \left[N_j\lambda_j \sum_{e=m_j}^{N_j-1} \binom{N_j - 1}{e} \frac{1}{\Phi_j(e)} + \Lambda_{j-1}^* \sum_{e=m_j+1}^{N_j} \binom{N_j}{e} \frac{1 - \bar{\gamma}_{j-1}(e\lambda_j)}{\Phi_j(e)}\right] \tag{7.47}$$

and

$$\left.\frac{\Phi_j(m_j - 1)}{m_j\lambda_j}\right|_{m_j=0} = \nu_j \tag{7.48}$$

Finally, the mean number of jth-class units is given by

$$E(\hat{\mathscr{M}}_j) = N_j - \frac{1}{\lambda_j E(c_j)} \left[1 - \frac{\hat{e}^{(j)}}{\hat{e}^{(j-1)}}\right] \tag{7.49}$$

which can be used in combination with (7.46) and the values of $E(c_j)$, $E(\gamma_j)$ for different disciplines.

7-4. Occupation Time of the Server

Let us consider the occupation time of the server with respect to the jth-class units ($j \leqslant k$) under steady state. Because of the preemptive discipline, units of classes $j + 1, \ldots, k$ do not in any way affect the occupation time of the server with respect to the jth-class units. Further, the j classes can be conceived of as divided into two groups, the first group comprising units belonging to classes 1 to $j - 1$, and the second group comprising the jth-class units. If the server is occupied with a unit belonging to the second group (jth-class unit), and a unit belonging to the first group arrives, it interrupts the service of the second group unit, and this interruption continues until there are no units of the first group left in the system. Obviously, the duration of this interruption is γ_{j-1}, the length of the busy-period duration for the $(j - 1)$-class process. Thus, we can obtain the results from those of the two-class process by replacing (1) the arrival rate λ_1 of the first-class units by $\Lambda_{j-1} = \sum_{i=1}^{j-1} \lambda_i$ and the busy period duration b_1 by γ_{j-1}, and (2) λ_2, S_2, c_2 by λ_j, S_j, c_j, respectively.

The following are then the results for the occupation-time density of the server with respect to the jth-class units.

a. *jth Source Infinite*

If $E(\gamma_{j-1}) < \infty$ and $\lambda_j E(c_j) < 1$, the waiting time density for the jth class exists, and its Laplace transform is given by

$$\bar{\mathscr{W}}_j(\theta) = \frac{\hat{e}^{(j)}[\theta + \Lambda_{j-1}^*\{1 - \bar{\gamma}_{j-1}(\theta)\}]}{\theta - \lambda_j + \lambda_j \bar{c}_j(\theta)} \tag{7.50}$$

where $\hat{e}^{(j)}$ is given by (7.40).

Example. Preemptive Resume Discipline

The expected delay time of the jth unit is given by

$$E(\hat{\mathscr{D}}_j) = \frac{\nu_j}{1 - \sum_{i=1}^{j-1} \rho_i} + \frac{\sum_{i=1}^{j} \lambda_i E(S_i^2)}{2\left(1 - \sum_{i=1}^{j-1} \rho_i\right)\left(1 - \sum_{i=1}^{j} \rho_i\right)} \tag{7.51}$$

Results for other disciplines can be obtained in a similar manner.

b. *jth Source Finite*

If $E(c_j) < \infty$, $E(\gamma_{j-1}) < \infty$, the Laplace transform of the steady state virtual waiting time density is given by

$$\bar{\mathscr{W}}_j(\theta) = \hat{e}^{(j)} \Big[1 + \sum_{m=0}^{N_j-1} \{\bar{c}_j(\theta)\}^{N_j-m-1}\{1 - \bar{c}_j(\theta)\}^m \{N_j\lambda_j \bar{A}_j(m, 0) + \Lambda^*_{j-1}\bar{A}_j^{\gamma_{j-1}}(m, 0)\} \frac{\bar{c}_j(m\lambda_j) - \bar{c}_j(\theta)}{\theta - m\lambda_j}\Big] \tag{7.52}$$

where $\Lambda^*_m = \sum_{i=1}^m N_i\lambda_i$ and $\hat{e}^{(j)}$ is given by (7.46). The mean virtual waiting time is given by (III, 7.19) with appropriate substitutions.

An important observation should be made here regarding the statistical equilibrium conditions. The steady-state occupation-time density for the jth-class units does not impose any restriction on the $j + 1,..., k$ classes. Hence, even if the $j + 1,..., k$ classes experience infinite delays, partial equilibrium up to j classes exists provided $E(\gamma_{j-1}) < \infty$, $\lambda_j E(c_j) < 1$ if the jth source is infinite and $E(\gamma_{j-1}) < \infty$, $E(c_j) < \infty$ if the jth source is finite.

8. Optimal Ordering of k Priority Classes to Minimize Total Delay Cost

In this section, we investigate rules according to which priorities should be assigned to the different classes of arriving units so as to minimize the total delay cost. It is assumed that the delay cost for each class is linear, so that if K_i is the unit delay cost for a type i unit, the delay cost for the ith-class unit is $K_i E(\hat{\mathscr{D}}_i)$, where $E(\hat{\mathscr{D}}_i)$ is the mean delay time of the ith-class unit. We shall consider the case of the preemptive resume discipline with exponential service times. The method that we follow is due to Brosh and Naor [13].

Let the classes of arriving customers be numbered 1, 2,..., m, n,..., k. We start by initially assigning the priority ordering such that the class number is equal to the priority number, and investigate the effect of interchanging the priority of just two classes. The important thing to observe is that interchanging the priority of just two neighboring classes, say m and n, does not change the mean delay times for all other classes.

Let m and n be two neighboring classes with priority index $m < n$, and let l be the preceding class with higher priority. Since λ_i/λ ($\lambda = \sum \lambda_i$) is the probability than an arriving unit is of the ith type, the contribution to the total delay cost by units of type m and n only is obtained from (7.51) as

$$T(m, n) = K_m \frac{\lambda_m}{\lambda} \left[\frac{\nu_m}{1 - \sum_{i=1}^{l} \rho_i} + \frac{\sum_{i=1}^{l} \rho_i \nu_i + \rho_m \nu_m}{\left(1 - \sum_{i=1}^{l} \rho_i\right)\left(1 - \sum_{i=1}^{l} \rho_i - \rho_m\right)} \right]$$

$$+ K_n \frac{\lambda_n}{\lambda} \left[\frac{\nu_m}{1 - \sum_{i=1}^{l} \rho_i - \rho_m} + \frac{\sum_{i=1}^{l} \rho_i \nu_i + \rho_m \nu_m + \rho_n \nu_n}{\left(1 - \sum_{i=1}^{l} \rho_i - \rho_m\right)\left(1 - \sum_{i=1}^{l} \rho_i - \rho_m - \rho_n\right)} \right] \tag{8.1}$$

where

$$\rho_i = \lambda_i \nu_i$$

Now, using the notation

$$\sum_{i=1}^{l} \rho_i = \alpha$$

and

$$\sum_{i=1}^{l} \rho_i \nu_i = \beta$$

we get

$$T(m, n) = K_m \frac{\lambda_m}{\lambda} \left[\frac{\nu_m}{1 - \alpha} + \frac{\beta + \rho_m \nu_m}{(1 - \alpha)(1 - \alpha - \rho_m)} \right]$$

$$+ K_n \frac{\lambda_n}{\lambda} \left[\frac{\nu_n}{1 - \alpha - \rho_m} + \frac{\beta + \rho_m \nu_m + \rho_n \nu_n}{(1 - \alpha - \rho_m)(1 - \alpha - \rho_m - \rho_n)} \right] \tag{8.2}$$

We now interchange the priorities of class m and n while keeping the priorities of all other classes the same. The contribution to the delay cost by units of types m and n is

$$T(n, m) = K_n \frac{\lambda_n}{\lambda} \left[\frac{\nu_n}{1 - \alpha} + \frac{\beta + \rho_n \nu_n}{(1 - \alpha)(1 - \alpha - \rho_n)} \right]$$

$$+ K_m \frac{\lambda_m}{\lambda} \left[\frac{\nu_m}{1 - \alpha - \rho_n} + \frac{\beta + \rho_n \nu_n + \rho_m \nu_m}{(1 - \alpha - \rho_n)(1 - \alpha - \rho_n - \rho_m)} \right] \tag{8.3}$$

If we can show that $T(m, n) - T(n, m) > 0$, then assigning to n a higher priority than m will be helpful in minimizing the total delay cost. Observe that the inequality does not change if we multiply both terms by a positive constant or add any constant to both terms. We may call these "simple operations". Observe further that $T(m, n)$ and $T(n, m)$ are symmetric in m and n, i.e., one can be obtained from the other by interchanging m and n. Thus, if we perform only simple operations which are symmetric in m and n, it is sufficient to consider just one expression, say, $T(m, n)$.

As a first step towards reducing the above inequality to a simple form, we subtract the terms with K_n in $T(m, n)$ and K_m in $T(n, m)$ from $T(m, n)$. This gives

$$T_1(m, n) = K_m \frac{\lambda_m}{\lambda} \Big[\frac{\nu_m}{1-\alpha} + \frac{\beta + \rho_m \nu_m}{(1-\alpha)(1-\alpha-\rho_m)} - \frac{\nu_m}{1-\alpha-\rho_n} - \frac{\beta + \rho_n \nu_n + \rho_m \nu_m}{(1-\alpha-\rho_n)(1-\alpha-\rho_n-\rho_m)}\Big] \tag{8.4}$$

We then multiply by their common denominator, giving

$$\begin{aligned} T_2(m, n) = K_m \frac{\lambda_m}{\lambda} [&\nu_m(1-\alpha-\rho_m)(1-\alpha-\rho_n)(1-\alpha-\rho_m-\rho_n) \\ &+ (\beta + \rho_m\nu_m)(1-\alpha-\rho_n)(1-\alpha-\rho_n-\rho_m) \\ &- \nu_m(1-\alpha)(1-\alpha-\rho_m)(1-\alpha-\rho_m-\rho_n) \\ &- (\beta + \rho_n\nu_n + \rho_m\nu_m)(1-\alpha-\rho_m)(1-\alpha)] \end{aligned} \tag{8.5}$$

where $T_2(m, n)$ is again a symmetric expression. After some simplification, we get

$$\begin{aligned} T_2(m, n) = -K_m\lambda_m\rho_n \Big[&\frac{\beta}{\lambda}\{2(1-\alpha) - \rho_m - \rho_n\} \\ &+ \frac{1-\alpha}{\lambda}\{(1-\alpha-\rho_n)\,\nu_m + \nu_n(1-\alpha-\rho_m)\}\Big] \end{aligned} \tag{8.6}$$

Since the expression in the bracket is positive and symmetric in (m, n), we can divide by it and consider

$$T_3(m, n) = -K_m\lambda_m\rho_n \tag{8.7}$$

Finally, dividing by $\rho_m \rho_n$, we get

$$T_4(m, n) = -K_m \frac{\lambda_m}{\rho_m} = -\frac{K_m}{\nu_m} \tag{8.8}$$

and, by symmetry, $T_4(n, m) = -K_n/\nu_n$.

Therefore, $T(m, n) - T(n, m) > 0$, or class n should be given higher priority than m if

$$\frac{K_n}{\nu_n} > \frac{K_m}{\nu_m} \tag{8.9}$$

The optimal priority assignment is therefore in descending order of K_i/ν_i, with the highest priority for the class with the highest value of K_i/ν_i. To show this, we only need observe that except for equal values, the ordering is unique and any other ordering could be improved by interchanging some neighboring classes. We may remind the reader that simple optimal ordering policy in (8.9) is true only for the preemptive resume discipline with exponential service-time distributions. For the preemptive resume discipline with an arbitrary distribution and also for repeat disciplines, such a simple policy does not exist.

9. Allocation of Priorities on the Basis of Service-Time Requirements

In Section IV, 8, we assumed that the service time of a unit is known only at the completion of service. However, situations exist where the service time of a unit can be known on arrival, and in such cases the effect of dividing the arriving units according to the length of service may be of value in reducing congestion in the system. Let us consider, for example, the case where the arriving units are divided into $k + 1$ classes, the first priority class comprising of units whose service time is less than σ_1, the second priority class comprising of units whose service time lies between σ_1 and σ_2, and so on, the kth priority class comprising units whose service time lies between σ_{k-1} and σ_k, and the $(k + 1)$th priority class, units whose service time is more than σ_k. From the general results obtained above, we can write the total waiting cost for this model. The determination of values $\sigma_1, \sigma_2, \ldots, \sigma_k$ which minimize the waiting cost can then be made. This has been done by Oliver and Pestalozzi [68] for the head-of-the-line case by using dynamic programming methods, and will be discussed in Chapter V.

Let us examine this model for the simplest case of $k = 1$, i.e., we divide the arriving units whose service times vary according to the density $S(x)$ with mean ν into two classes: Units whose service time is less than σ_1 are assigned preemptive resume priority over the units whose service time is more than σ_1. Hence,

$$\lambda_1 = \int_0^{\sigma_1} S(x)\,dx, \qquad S_1(x) = \frac{S(x)}{\int_0^{\sigma_1} S(x)\,dx} \qquad (0 \leqslant x \leqslant \sigma_1)$$

$$\lambda_2 = \int_{\sigma_1}^{\infty} S(x)\,dx, \qquad S_2(x) = \frac{S(x)}{\int_{\sigma_1}^{\infty} S(x)\,dx} \qquad (x > \sigma_1)$$

If the discipline is assumed to be preemptive resume, we have, on substituting these values in (3.18) and (3.19) and dividing by λ_1 and λ_2 so as to obtain the mean delay time the following results:

$$E(\hat{\mathscr{D}}_1) = \frac{\int_0^{\sigma_1} xS(x)\,dx}{\int_0^{\sigma_1} S(x)\,dx} + \frac{1}{2}\,\frac{\lambda \int_0^{\sigma_1} x^2 S(x)\,dx}{\left[1 - \int_0^{\sigma_1} xS(x)\,dx\right]} \tag{9.1}$$

$$E(\hat{\mathscr{D}}_2) = \frac{1}{\left[1 - \lambda \int_0^{\sigma_1} xS(x)\,dx\right]} \left[\frac{\int_{\sigma_1}^{\infty} xS(x)\,dx}{\int_{\sigma_1}^{\infty} S(x)\,dx} + \frac{\lambda E(S^2)}{2[1 - \lambda\nu]}\right] \tag{9.2}$$

where $\lambda = \lambda_1 + \lambda_2$

Since the probability that the arriving unit is of the first type or the second type is λ_1/λ and λ_2/λ respectively, $E(\hat{\mathscr{D}})$, the total expected delay time is given as

$$E(\hat{\mathscr{D}}) = \int_0^{\sigma_1} xS(x)\,dx + \frac{\int_{\sigma_1}^{\infty} xS(x)\,dx}{1 - \lambda \int_0^{\sigma_1} xS(x)\,dx} + \frac{\lambda}{2\left[1 - \lambda \int_0^{\sigma_1} xS(x)\,dx\right]}$$

$$\times \left[\int_0^{\sigma_1} S(x)\,dx \int_0^{\sigma_1} x^2 S(x)\,dx + \frac{E(S^2) \int_{\sigma_1}^{\infty} S(x)\,dx}{1 - \lambda\nu}\right] \tag{9.3}$$

Determination of σ_1 so as to minimize $E(\mathscr{D})$ is a simple problem of differentiation.

Example

If the service-time distribution is exponential with mean ν, we have $S(x) = (1/\nu)\, e^{-x/\nu}$, and the optimal value σ_1 is given by the value of z that satisfies

$$(1 - \rho + \rho e^{-z} + \rho z e^{-z}) \left[1 - 2z + \frac{z^2}{2} - e^{-z} - \frac{1}{1 - \rho} + e^{-z}(z + z^2)\right]$$
$$+ z \left[1 + \rho e^{-z} \left\{z + \frac{1}{1 - \rho} - \frac{z^2}{2} - e^{-z}\left(z + \frac{z^2}{2}\right)\right\}\right] = 0$$

where $z = \sigma_1/\nu$. Then, for optimum σ_1

$$\frac{E(\mathscr{D})}{\nu} = \frac{1 + \rho e^{-z}\left(z + \dfrac{1}{1 - \rho} - \dfrac{z^2}{2}\right) - \rho e^{-2z}\left(z + \dfrac{z^2}{2}\right)}{1 - \rho + \rho e^{-z} + \rho z e^{-z}}$$

The implementation of the priority rule discussed above is easier and is therefore of practical significance, since it requires that the units may fall into only two categories, one having service time less than and one having service time greater than a fixed value. However, this policy need not be optimal, since the high-priority unit on arrival may preempt a lower priority unit whose remaining service-time is less than the service time of the high-priority unit. Two policies based upon the remaining service-time have been defined and studied by Schrage and Miller [77]:

(i) *Semipreemptive Priority.* The units are classified into a finite number of classes depending upon the remaining service-time and the preemptive discipline is followed between the classes. This differs from the preemptive resume discipline because a unit's priority class is improved as its service progresses.

(ii) *Shortest Remaining Processing-Time Discipline.* The unit which has the lowest remaining service-time is selected for service, and an arriving unit will preempt the unit if and only if the service time of the new arrival is less than the remaining service-time of the unit in service.

Obviously, the first rule tends to the second rule if the number of classes are increased indefinitely.

The discussion in this section has been presented under the assumption that after preemption a unit can resume service from the point at which it was interrupted. Obviously, if this is possible, the shortest remaining processing-time discipline will be optimal if the objective is to minimize the mean delay time or the congestion in the system.

Chapter V

HEAD-OF-THE-LINE PRIORITY DISCIPLINE

1. Introduction

In this chapter, we investigate the head-of-the-line priority discipline. Under this discipline, if an ordinary unit enters service, it cannot be preempted by the arrival of a priority unit, so that the priority unit has to wait until the ordinary unit completes its service. This discipline is, therefore, also called "nonpreemptive."

This discipline was introduced by Cobham [18] and has been studied subsequently by Holley [39], Dressin and Reich [24], Kesten and Runnenburg [52], Morse [63], Miller [62], Jaiswal [45], Welch [96], and Takács [87] under different assumptions regarding the service-time distribution and under the assumption that the units emanate from infinite sources.

The process can be considered as a "breakdown model" in which the repair of a breakdown can be postponed until the unit in service completes its service. Situations obviously exist where such a postponement is possible. We may, therefore, call such breakdowns "postponable interruptions," or just interruptions. Viewed as an "interruption model," this has been studied by Keilson [49] and Gaver [29]. The multiple finite-source priority model under this discipline has been studied by Thiruvengadam [91] and Hodgson and Hebble [38]. As in Chapter IV, we use the results of Chapter III to first investigate the two-class process and then generalize to $k > 2$ classes.

2. Completion-Time Process

The process begins at $t = 0$ with the entry of an ordinary unit in service. Because of the nonpreemptive discipline, the priority units, if any, that arrive during the service time of the ordinary unit wait until the ordinary unit completes service. The process ends when all priority units that have accumulated during the service time of the ordinary unit and those which arrived subsequently complete service. From Section III, 3, it follows that the process is specified completely by the densities $f^I(m_1, x_2, t)$ and $g^L(m_1, x_1, t)$. The process can be conceived of as the initial busy-period process of the infinite- or finite-source model (depending upon the size of the priority source) with the initial occupation time equal to the service time of the ordinary unit. The following results follow directly from the results of the initial busy-period processes of Sections I, 2 and II, 2.

a. *Priority Source Infinite*

For the case in which the priority source is infinite, we have:

$$\bar{f}^I(m_1, x_2, s) = \frac{(\lambda_1 x_2)^{m_1}}{m_1!} \exp\left[-(\lambda_1 + s)x_2 - \int_0^{x_2} \eta_2(u)\, du\right] \tag{2.1}$$

$$\bar{g}^L(m_1, x_1, s) = \bar{p}^{S_2}(m_1, x_1, s) \tag{2.2}$$

$$\bar{c}_2(s) = \bar{b}_1^{S_2}(s) = \bar{S}_2[\lambda_1\{1 - \bar{b}_1(s)\} + s] \tag{2.3}$$

so that

$$E(c_2) = \frac{\nu_2}{1 - \rho_1} \tag{2.4}$$

$$E(c_2^2) = \frac{E(S_2^2)}{(1 - \rho_1)^2} + \nu_2 \frac{\lambda_1 E(S_1^2)}{(1 - \rho_1)^3} \tag{2.5}$$

and

$$\bar{\Pi}^c(\alpha_1, \alpha_2, s) = \alpha_2 \frac{1 - \bar{S}_2[s + \lambda_1(1 - \alpha_1)]}{s + \lambda_1(1 - \alpha_1)} + \frac{\bar{S}_2[s + \lambda_1(1 - \alpha_1)] - \bar{S}_2[s + \lambda_1\{1 - \bar{b}_1(s)\}]}{1 - (1/\alpha_1)\, \bar{S}_1[s + \lambda_1(1 - \alpha_1)]} \tag{2.6}$$

Observe that the completion-time density for preemptive resume and head-of-the-line disciplines are the same.

b. *Priority Source Finite*

Using the results of Section II, 2, we obtain

$$\bar{f}^{I}(m_1, x_2, s) = \binom{N_1}{m_1}[1 - \exp(-\lambda_1 x_2)]^{m_1}$$
$$\times \exp\left[-\{(N_1 - m_1)\lambda_1 + s\}x_2 - \int_0^{x_2}\eta_2(x)\,dx\right] \tag{2.7}$$
$$\bar{g}^{L}(m_1, x_1, s) = \bar{p}^{S_2}(m_1, x_1, s) \tag{2.8}$$

where $\bar{p}^{S_2}(m_1, x_2, s)$ is defined by (II, 2.44) with (N, λ, S) replaced by (N_1, λ_1, S_1), and

$$\bar{c}_2(s) = \bar{b}_1^{S_2}(s) = \left[\sum_{e=0}^{N_1}\binom{N_1}{e}\frac{\bar{S}_2(e\lambda_1 + s)}{\bar{v}_1(e-1, s)}\right]\left[\sum_{e=0}^{N_1}\binom{N_1}{e}\frac{1}{\bar{v}_1(e-1, s)}\right]^{-1} \tag{2.9}$$

so that

$$E(c_2) = \nu_2 + \nu_1\sum_{e=1}^{N_1}\binom{N_1}{e}\frac{1 - \bar{S}_2(e\lambda_1)}{\phi_1(e-1)} \tag{2.10}$$

$$E(c_2{}^2) = E(S_2{}^2) + 2\nu_1\nu_2 + 2E(c_2)\,\nu_1\left[1 - \sum_{e=1}^{N_1}\binom{N_1}{e}\frac{1}{\phi_1(e)}\right]$$
$$+ E(S_1{}^2)\sum_{e=1}^{N_1}\binom{N_1}{e}\frac{1 - \bar{S}_2(e\lambda_1)}{\phi_1(e)}$$
$$+ 2\nu_1\sum_{e=1}^{N_1}\binom{N_1}{e}\frac{\bar{S}_2'(e\lambda_1) - [1 + \bar{S}_2(e\lambda_1)]}{\phi_1(e)}\sum_{m=1}^{e}\frac{\bar{S}_1'(m\lambda_1)}{[1 - \bar{S}_1(m\lambda_1)]\,\bar{S}_1(m\lambda_1)} \tag{2.11}$$

and

$$\bar{\Pi}^{c}(\alpha_1, \alpha_2, s) = \alpha_2\sum_{m_1=0}^{N_1}\alpha_1^{m_1}\binom{N_1}{m_1}\sum_{e=0}^{m_1}(-1)^e\binom{m_1}{e}\frac{1 - \bar{S}_2[(N_1 - m_1 + e)\lambda_1 + s]}{(N_1 - m_1 + e)\lambda_1 + s}$$
$$+ \sum_{j=0}^{N_1-1}\alpha_1^{N_1-j}(1 - \alpha_1)^j\,\bar{a}_1^{S_2}(j, s)\frac{1 - \bar{S}_1(j\lambda_1 + s)}{j\lambda_1 + s} \tag{2.12}$$

Observe that if $N_1 = 1$, (2.9) reduces to

$$\bar{c}_2(s) = \bar{S}_2(s)\,\bar{S}_1(s) + \bar{S}_2(\lambda_1 + s)[1 - \bar{S}_1(s)] \tag{2.13}$$

which can be interpreted as follows: the completion time is equal to the service time of an ordinary unit if no priority unit arrives, and is equal to the convolution of the service time of the ordinary unit with the service time of the priority unit if a priority unit arrives.

Observe that if the priority units emanate from a finite source the ratio $E(c_2)/\nu_2$, which gives an idea of average service elongation for an ordinary unit because of the interruptions from priority units, depends upon the service-time distribution of the ordinary unit, while this is not so if the priority units emanate from an infinite source. A more significant observation is that under preemptive discipline, the completion time density for (N_1, ∞) and (N_1, N_2) models could be obtained directly from the completion time density of the $(1, \infty)$ and $(1, N_2)$ models by replacing the breakdown duration by the busy period duration of the basic finite-source model with parameters (N_1, λ_1, S_1). The same is not true for the head-of-the-line discipline. This is because a priority unit on arrival may have to wait for the service completion of the ordinary unit, and if the priority source is finite, this affects the input of the priority units.

We use the results of Chapter III to discuss the stochastic behavior of different characteristics of the (∞, ∞), (N_1, ∞), (∞, N_2), and (N_1, N_2) models.

3. Priority and Ordinary Sources Both Infinite The (∞, ∞) Model

3-1. Busy Period

Since the completion time density under this discipline is the same as under preemptive resume discipline, $\gamma_2(t)$, the density of the busy period duration is the same as under preemptive resume discipline and is given by (IV, 3.1).

3-2. Joint Queue-Length Probabilities

Substituting (2.6) in (III, 5.4), we obtain

$$\bar{\Pi}(\alpha_1, \alpha_2, s) = \bar{e}^{(2)}(s)$$
$$\times \Big[1 + \frac{\lambda_2[\alpha_2 - \bar{B}_2(s)] + \lambda_1[\bar{b}_1\{\lambda_2(1-\alpha_2)+s\} - \bar{b}_1\{\lambda_2(1-\bar{B}_2(s))+s\}]}{\alpha_2 - \bar{c}_2[\lambda_2(1-\alpha_2)+s]}$$
$$\times \Big\{\alpha_2 \frac{1 - \bar{S}_2[\lambda_1(1-\alpha_1)+\lambda_2(1-\alpha_2)+s]}{\lambda_1(1-\alpha_1)+\lambda_2(1-\alpha_2)+s}$$
$$+ \frac{\bar{S}_2[\lambda_1(1-\alpha_1)+\lambda_2(1-\alpha_2)+s] - \bar{c}_2[\lambda_2(1-\alpha_2)+s]}{1-(1/\alpha_1)\,\bar{S}_1[\lambda_1(1-\alpha_1)+\lambda_2(1-\alpha_2)+s]}\, k(\alpha_1, \alpha_2, s)\Big\}$$
$$+ \lambda_1 \frac{\alpha_1 - \bar{b}_1\{s+\lambda_2(1-\alpha_2)\}}{1-(1/\alpha_1)\,\bar{S}_1\{\lambda_1(1-\alpha_1)+\lambda_2(1-\alpha_2)+s\}}\, k(\alpha_1, \alpha_2, s)\Big] \qquad (3.1)$$

where

$$k(\alpha_1, \alpha_2, s) = \frac{1 - \bar{S}_1[\lambda_1(1 - \alpha_1) + \lambda_2(1 - \alpha_2) + s]}{\lambda_1(1 - \alpha_1) + \lambda_2(1 - \alpha_2) + s}$$

This result has been obtained by Jaiswal [45], Gaver [29], and Keilson [49]. Inversion of these results is, in general, difficult as will be seen in the following example.

Example A

In the case of exponential service-time distributions with equal means, ($\nu_1 = 1/\mu$, $\nu_2 = 1/\mu$), inversion can be done as in Section IV, 3. The value of $\hat{e}^{(2)}(t)$ is given by (IV, 3.14), and

$$\Pi(\alpha_1, \alpha_2, t) = e^{-at} + \mu(1 - 1/\alpha_1) \int_0^t \hat{e}^{(2)}(t - \tau)\, e^{-a\tau}\, d\tau + \lambda_2(\alpha_1 - \alpha_2)$$
$$\times \int_0^t \hat{e}^{(2)}(t - \tau)\{e^{-a\tau} - e^{-(a+\mu/\alpha_1)\tau} + X(\alpha_1, \alpha_2, \tau) - Y(\alpha_1, \alpha_2, \tau)\}\, d\tau \tag{3.2}$$

where

$$X(\alpha_1, \alpha_2, t) = \int_0^t \exp[-a(t - \tau)]\, \phi(\alpha_2, \tau)\, d\tau$$

$$Y(\alpha_1, \alpha_2, t) = \int_0^t \exp[-\{a + \mu/\alpha_1\}(t - \tau)]\, \phi(\alpha_2, \tau)\, d\tau$$

$$a = \mu + \lambda_1(1 - \alpha_1) + \lambda_2(1 - \alpha_2) - \mu/\alpha_1$$

and

$$\phi(\alpha, t) = \sum_{n=1}^{\infty} n^2 \left(\frac{\mu}{\lambda_1}\right)^{n/2} \exp[-\{\mu + \lambda_1 + \lambda_2(1 - \alpha)\}\, t]$$
$$\times \int_0^t \frac{\exp(-\lambda_2\alpha\tau)}{\tau(t - \tau)}\, I_n[2(\lambda_1\mu)^{1/2}\,(t - \tau)]\, I_n[2(\lambda_1 + \lambda_2)^{1/2}\, \mu^{1/2}\tau]\, d\tau$$

where I_n is the modified Bessel function of the first kind. These results are given in Jaiswal [45].

a. *Limiting Behavior*

From Section III, 6 with $\rho_1 + \rho_2 < 1$, the limiting distribution exists, and is given by

$$\hat{\Pi}(\alpha_1, \alpha_2) = \hat{e}^{(2)} \Bigg[1 + \frac{\lambda_2(\alpha_2 - 1) + \lambda_1[\bar{b}_1\{\lambda_2(1-\alpha_2)\} - 1]}{\alpha_2 - \bar{c}_2\{\lambda_2(1-\alpha_2)\}}$$
$$\times \Bigg\{\alpha_2 \frac{1 - \bar{S}_2[\lambda_1(1-\alpha_1) + \lambda_2(1-\alpha_2)]}{\lambda_1(1-\alpha_1) + \lambda_2(1-\alpha_2)}$$
$$+ \frac{\bar{S}_2[\lambda_1(1-\alpha_1) + \lambda_2(1-\alpha_2)] - \bar{c}_2[\lambda_2(1-\alpha_2)]}{1 - (1/\alpha_1)\,\bar{S}_1[\lambda_1(1-\alpha_1) + \lambda_2(1-\alpha_2)]} k(\alpha_1, \alpha_2)\Bigg\}$$
$$+ \lambda_1 \frac{\alpha_1 - \bar{b}_1\{\lambda_2(1-\alpha_2)\}}{1 - (1/\alpha_1)\,\bar{S}_1\{\lambda_1(1-\alpha_1) + \lambda_2(1-\alpha_2)\}} k(\alpha_1, \alpha_2)\Bigg] \tag{3.3}$$

where

$$\hat{e}^{(2)} = 1 - \rho_1 - \rho_2 \tag{3.4}$$

and

$$k(\alpha_1, \alpha_2) = \frac{1 - \bar{S}_1[\lambda_1(1-\alpha_1) + \lambda_2(1-\alpha_2)]}{\lambda_1(1-\alpha_1) + \lambda_2(1-\alpha_2)}$$

This problem was studied by Miller [62] through the imbedded Markov chain technique. He considers first the Markov chain at time-points at which either a priority or an ordinary unit leaves the system. The analysis of this chain gives a relationship which contains the ordinary queue length probabilities at those points at which the priority queue is zero. To obtain these probabilities, Miller defines a second Markov chain only at those time points which are the service termination periods leaving no priority units. However, the results so obtained are different from the results obtained above because the supplementary variable technique studies the non-Markovian process in continuous time, while the imbedded Markov chain technique considers the distribution at only those points at which a customer departs. The two limiting probabilities $\lim_{t\to\infty} \hat{p}(m_1, m_2, t)$ and $\lim_{n\to\infty} \hat{p}^{(n)}(m_1, m_2)$, where n denotes the nth departure point, are not the same as for the $M/G/1$ process [see discussion below equation (I, 4.7), and also Fabens [103] for the relationship between these two limiting probabilities]. The moments can be obtained from (3.3) by differentiation and are given in the following example.

Example B

The mean number of priority units present in the system is given by

$$E(\hat{\mathscr{M}}_1) = \rho_1 + \frac{\lambda_1^2 E(S_1^2) + \lambda_1\lambda_2 E(S_2^2)}{2(1-\rho_1)} \tag{3.5}$$

where

$$\rho_1 = \lambda_1 \nu_1$$

The mean number of ordinary units is given by

$$E(\mathscr{M}_2) = \rho_2 + \frac{\lambda_2^2 E(S_2^2) + \lambda_1 \lambda_2 E(S_1^2)}{2(1-\rho_1)(1-\rho_1-\rho_2)} \tag{3.6}$$

where

$$\rho_2 = \lambda_2 \nu_2$$

By similar means, other moments can be evaluated.

Through Markov chain analysis, Miller [62] obtains the following results for mean queue lengths considered at service termination points:

$$E(\hat{\mathscr{M}}_1) = \frac{\lambda_1}{\lambda_1 + \lambda_2}(\rho_1 + \rho_2) + \frac{\lambda_1^2[\lambda_1 E(S_1^2) + \lambda_2 E(S_2^2)]}{2(\lambda_1 + \lambda_2)(1-\rho_1)} \tag{3.7}$$

$$E(\hat{\mathscr{M}}_2) = \frac{\lambda_2}{\lambda_1 + \lambda_2}(\rho_1 + \rho_2) + \frac{1}{2}\lambda_2[\lambda_1 E(S_1^2) + \lambda_2 E(S_2^2)]\left[\frac{\lambda_2(1 + \nu_1/\nu_2) + \rho_1(1-\rho_1-\rho_2)}{(1-\rho_1-\rho_2)(1-\rho_1)}\right] \tag{3.8}$$

These results can also be obtained from the continuous-time results obtained above through the supplementary variable method [45].

b. *Design Measures*

Figure V.1 represents the design measures for priority as well as ordinary units under head-of-the-line priority discipline. The sum of the traffic intensities is constant, so that for a given value of ν_2/ν_1, the value of ρ_2 increases as λ_2/λ_1 increases. The effect on the priority queue is thus least at the origin, and increases as λ_2/λ_1 increases. Consequently, the design measure for the priority units decreases as λ_2/λ_1 increases. In addition, the design measure for the priority units has a higher value for constant service times than for exponentially distributed service times. The behavior of the design measure for the ordinary units is just the opposite, for obvious reasons.

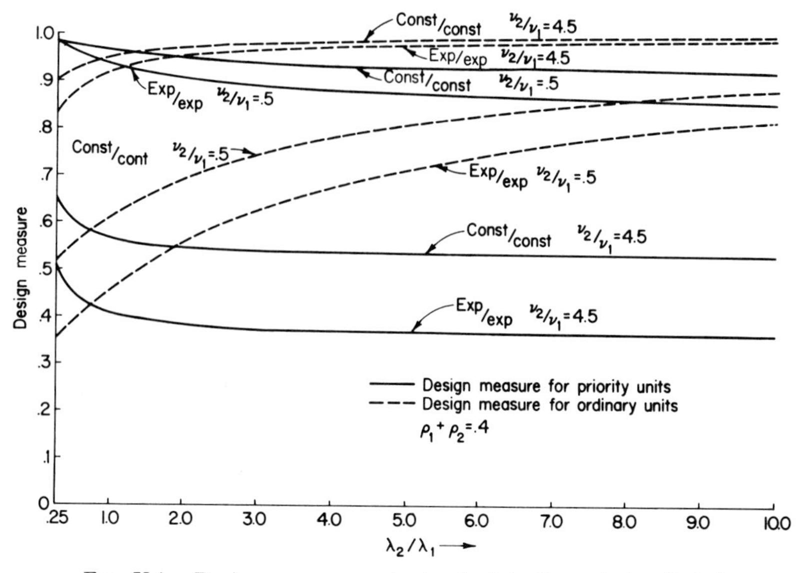

FIG. V.1. Design measures under head-of-the-line priority discipline.

3-3. Occupation Time of the Server

To determine the occupation time of the server with respect to priority units, we derive $\bar{w}_1{}^c(\theta, s)$, the Laplace transform of the occupation-time density with respect to the priority unit during the completion time process. Using (III, 7.2) with (2.1) and (2.2), or noting directly that the required density is equal to the occupation-time density for the initial busy-period process with the initial occupation time equal to the service time of the priority unit, we obtain from (I, 6.5)

$$\bar{w}_1{}^c(\theta, s) = \frac{\bar{S}_2(\theta) - \bar{b}_1(s)}{s - \theta + \lambda_1\{1 - \bar{S}_1(\theta)\}} \tag{3.9}$$

Substituting (3.9) in (III, 7.5), we obtain, using (I, 6.9),

$$\bar{\mathscr{W}}_1(\theta, s) = \frac{\bar{e}^{(2)}(s)}{\bar{e}_1(s)}\left[\frac{\theta\bar{e}_1(s) - 1}{\theta - s - \lambda_1[1 - \bar{S}_1(\theta)]}\right]$$
$$+ \frac{[\bar{e}^{(2)}(s) - \bar{e}_1(s)][\bar{S}_2(\theta) - \bar{b}_1(s)]}{\bar{e}_1(s)[1 - \bar{c}_2(s)](\theta - s - \lambda_1[1 - \bar{S}_1(\theta)])} \tag{3.10}$$

Under steady state, we obtain

$$\bar{\hat{\mathscr{W}}}_1(\theta) = \frac{(1 - \rho_1 - \rho_2)\theta + \lambda_2[1 - \bar{S}_2(\theta)]}{\theta - \lambda_1[1 - \bar{S}_1(\theta)]} \tag{3.11}$$

so that the moments are given by

$$E(\hat{\mathscr{W}}_1) = \frac{\lambda_1 E(S_1^2) + \lambda_2 E(S_2^2)}{2(1 - \rho_1)} \tag{3.12}$$

$$E(\hat{\mathscr{W}}_1^2) = \frac{\lambda_1 E(S_1^3) + \lambda_2 E(S_2^3)}{3(1 - \rho_1)} + \lambda_1 E(S_1^2) \frac{[\lambda_1 E(S_1^2) + \lambda_2 E(S_2^2)]}{2(1 - \rho_1)^2} \tag{3.13}$$

The server's occupation time with respect to the ordinary unit is the same as under the preemptive resume discipline. This is because the completion-time densities are the same for both disciplines. The steady-state distribution is therefore given by (IV, 3.26). However, the delay time of an ordinary unit is different for the head-of-the-line discipline, because here we have only to put the service time of the ordinary unit in place of the completion time; thus, from (IV, 3.27), the mean delay time of an ordinary unit is given by

$$E(\hat{\mathscr{D}}_2) = \nu_2 + \frac{\lambda_1 E(S_1^2) + \lambda_2 E(S_2^2)}{2(1 - \rho_1)(1 - \rho_1 - \rho_2)} \tag{3.14}$$

4. Priority Source Finite and Ordinary Source Infinite The (N_1, ∞) Model

This model for $N_1 = 1$ is a simple postponable interruption model in which the interruption can be postponed until the end of the service of the unit. One can therefore speak of "independent" interruption or "active" interruption models. These have been considered by Gaver [29], Keilson [49], and Thiruvengadam [91]. The (N_1, ∞) model is a generalization to the above stituation. For other interpretations of the model, the reader may conceive of similar situations as mentioned in Section IV.4 with regard to this discipline. Although by assuming different arrival rates during the busy and idle periods, we can derive, as in Section IV.4, both models in which priority units arrive homogenously in time and those in which they arrive only during the busy period of the server (conditions corresponding to independent and active interruption models, respectively), we confine ourselves mainly to the first type of model.

4-1. Busy Period

The Laplace transform of the busy-period density is obtained from (III, 4.11), where $\bar{B}_2(s)$ is now the root of the equation $\alpha - \bar{b}_1^{S_2}[\lambda_2(1-\alpha)+s] = 0$ lying inside the unit circle $|\alpha| = 1$.

Obviously, the busy-period densities for the preemptive resume and head-of-the-line disciplines are different when the priority units emanate from a finite source, while these are same if the priority source is infinite.

4-2. Joint Queue-Length Probabilities

Substituting (2.6) in (III, 5.4), we get, after simplification,

$$\bar{\Pi}(\alpha_1, \alpha_2, s) = \bar{e}^{(2)}(s)\Big[1 + N_1\lambda_1 \sum_{m_1=0}^{N_1-1} \alpha_1^{N_1-m_1}(1-\alpha_1)^{m_1}\, \bar{a}_1[m_1, s+\lambda_2(1-\alpha_2)]$$
$$\times \frac{1-\bar{S}_1[m_1\lambda_1+\lambda_2(1-\alpha_2)+s]}{m_1\lambda_1+\lambda_2(1-\alpha_2)+s}$$
$$+ \frac{1-[N_1\lambda_1\{1-\bar{b}_1[\lambda_2(1-\alpha_2)+s]\}]\,\bar{e}_2(s)}{\alpha_2-\bar{c}_2[\lambda_2(1-\alpha_2)+s]}$$
$$\times \Big\{\alpha_2 \sum_{m_1=0}^{N_1} \alpha_1^{N_1-m_1}(1-\alpha_1)^{m_1}\binom{N_1}{m_1}$$
$$\times \frac{1-\bar{S}_2[m_1\lambda_1+\lambda_2(1-\alpha_2)+s]}{m_1\lambda_1+\lambda_2(1-\alpha_2)+s}$$
$$+ \sum_{m_1=0}^{N_1-1} \alpha_1^{N_1-m_1}(1-\alpha_1)^{m_1}\, \bar{a}_1^{S_2}[m_1, s+\lambda_2(1-\alpha_2)]$$
$$\times \frac{1-\bar{S}_1[m_1\lambda_1+\lambda_2(1-\alpha_2)+s]}{m_1\lambda_1+\lambda_2(1-\alpha_2)+s}\Big\}\Big] \tag{4.1}$$

and, from (III, 4.25) and (III, 5.3),

$$\bar{e}^{(2)}(s) = [s+\lambda_2\{1-\bar{B}_2(s)\}+\lambda_1\{1-\bar{b}_1(s+\lambda_2[1-\bar{B}_2(s)])\}]^{-1} \tag{4.2}$$

where $\bar{a}_1(m_1, s)$ and $\bar{a}_1^{S_2}(m_1, s)$ are defined by (II, 2.27) and (II, 2.45) and $\bar{B}_2(s)$ is defined above. These results are obtained by Thiruvengadam [91].

The above results can be easily modified to incorporate different arrival rates during the idle and busy periods.

Example

If the arrival rate of the interruptions during the idle period is modified so that $\tilde{\lambda}_1$ replaces λ_1, the steady-state probability of finding the server empty is given by

$$\hat{e}_2 = \left\{1 - \lambda_2\nu_2 \left[1 + \frac{\nu_1}{\nu_2} \sum_{e=1}^{N_1} \binom{N_1}{e} \frac{1 - \bar{S}_2(e\lambda_1)}{\phi_1(e-1)}\right]\right\}$$

$$\times \left\{1 + N_1\tilde{\lambda}_1\nu_1 \sum_{e=0}^{N_1-1} \binom{N_1 - 1}{e} \frac{1}{\phi_1(e)}\right\}^{-1} \tag{4.3}$$

and the marginal queue-length distribution of ordinary units is given by

$$\hat{\Pi}(1, \alpha_2) = \hat{e}_2 \frac{(\alpha_2 - 1)\, \bar{S}_2[\lambda_2(1 - \alpha_2)]}{\alpha_2 - \bar{c}_2[\lambda_2(1 - \alpha_2)]} \left[1 + N_1\tilde{\lambda}_1 \frac{1 - \bar{b}_1\{\lambda_2(1 - \alpha_2)\}}{\lambda_2(1 - \alpha_2)}\right] \tag{4.4}$$

5. Ordinary Source Finite—The (∞, N_2) and (N_1, N_2) Models

Our basic method so far has been to equate the ordinary queue-length distribution at epochs at which the ordinary units enter service during a priority process to the queue-length distribution at service entry points of the basic (one-class) process, replacing the service time by the completion time. It was mentioned in Chapter III that this is true only if the equivalence condition is satisfied, i.e., the departure of the ordinary unit during the completion time does not affect the arrival process of the ordinary units during the remaining part L_2 of the completion time. Obviously, this condition is violated for the (∞, N_2) and (N_1, N_2) models, since, as soon as the ordinary unit completes service and returns to the source, the arrival rate increases by λ_2 because of the finite size of the source.

Thus, the study of these models requires a modification of the basic models. Such a modification is not difficult to visualize. Let us consider the following modified finite-source model: After servicing each unit, the server spends a random time called the "restoration time" during which the facility is restored in preparation for taking up the next unit. Let us assume that this restoration time is dependent on the service time of the outgoing unit. It will be recalled that this model is the restoration-time model of Section II, 2

Let us now consider the (∞, N_2) and (N_1, N_2) models. A completion-time cycle is initiated when an ordinary unit enters service. The completion-time cycle, as we discussed earlier, is identical to the initial busy period of the infinite- or finite-source model with the initial occupation time equal to the service time of the ordinary unit. Let us consider, as usual, the completion-time cycle as consisting of two parts, I_2, during which the ordinary unit is present, and L_2, during which the ordinary unit is no longer present. Notice that L_2 depends stochastically on the length I_2. Hence, if the restoration-time density $r(t \mid \tau)$, where τ is the service time of the outgoing unit, is replaced in the restoration-time model by $L_2(t \mid \tau)$, where τ is the service time of the ordinary unit, the stochastic behavior of the queue length in the restoration-time model and of the ordinary queue length in the (∞, N_2) and (N_1, N_2) models are the same. Hence, from Section II, 2, we can obtain the distributions of ordinary units, at service entry and termination points and these will be used to discuss the behavior of these models.

5-1. Busy Period

Let us first evaluate $L_2(t \mid \tau)$ for the (∞, N_2) and (N_1, N_2) models. As discussed above,

$$L_2(t \mid \tau)\, dt = \Pr[t + \tau < b_1^{S_2} < t + \tau + dt \mid S_2 = \tau] \tag{5.1}$$

so that

$$\bar{L}_2(s \mid \tau) = E[\exp(-sL_2)] = \exp(s\tau)\, E[\exp(-sb_1^{S_2}) \mid S_2 = \tau] \tag{5.2}$$

Hence, for the (∞, N_2) model, substituting $\bar{\Omega}(s) = \exp(-\tau s)$ in (I, 2.26), we obtain

$$\bar{L}_2(s \mid \tau) = \exp[-\{\lambda_1(1 - \bar{b}_1(s))\}\tau] \tag{5.3}$$

where $\bar{b}_1(s)$ is defined by (I, 2.15).

Similarly, for the (N_1, N_2) model we obtain, from (II, 2.42),

$$\bar{L}_2(s \mid \tau) = \frac{\displaystyle\sum_{e=0}^{N_1} \binom{N_1}{e} \frac{\exp(-e\lambda_1\tau)}{\bar{v}_1(e-1, s)}}{\displaystyle\sum_{e=0}^{N_1} \binom{N_1}{e} \frac{1}{\bar{v}_1(e-1, s)}} \tag{5.4}$$

If the busy period is initiated by the arrival of an ordinary unit, the busy-period density will be given by (II, 2.72) for $i = 1$ after substituting $\bar{r}(s \mid \tau)$ by the $\bar{L}_2(s \mid \tau)$ given by (5.3) and (5.4). Similarly, if the busy period is initiated by the arrival of a priority unit, the busy-period density will be given by (II, 2.80) after replacing $\bar{r}(s \mid \tau)$ with $\bar{L}_2(s \mid \tau)$ and $\bar{\Omega}(s)$ by $\bar{b}_1(s)$, the busy period density of the priority units in isolation. Since the first and second type of busy periods are initiated with probabilities $N_2\lambda_2/(\lambda_1^* + N_2\lambda_2)$ and $\lambda_1^*/(\lambda_1^* + N_2\lambda_2)$, respectively, where $\lambda_1^* = \lambda_1$ if the priority source is infinite and $\lambda_1^* = N_1\lambda_1$ if it is finite, we have

$$\bar{\gamma}_2(s) = \frac{N_2\lambda_2}{N_2\lambda_2 + \lambda_1^*} \frac{\displaystyle\sum_{e=0}^{N_2-1} \binom{N_2 - 1}{e} \frac{1}{\bar{h}_2(e\lambda_2 + s)\,\bar{\omega}_2(e-1, s)}}{\displaystyle\sum_{e=0}^{N_2} \binom{N_2}{e} \frac{1}{\bar{h}_2(e\lambda_2 + s)\,\bar{\omega}_2(e-1, s)}}$$

$$+ \frac{\lambda_1^*}{N_2\lambda_2 + \lambda_1^*} \frac{\displaystyle\sum_{e=0}^{N_2} \binom{N_2}{e} \frac{\bar{b}_1(e\lambda_2 + s)}{\bar{h}_2(e\lambda_2 + s)\,\bar{\omega}_2(e-1, s)}}{\displaystyle\sum_{e=0}^{N_2} \binom{N_2}{e} \frac{1}{\bar{h}_2(e\lambda_2 + s)\,\bar{\omega}_2(e-1, s)}} \tag{5.5}$$

where $\bar{\omega}_2(m, s)$ is defined by (II, 2.71) and is given by

$$\begin{aligned} \bar{\omega}_2(m, s) &= \prod_{e=0}^{m} \frac{\bar{h}_2(e\lambda_2 + s)}{1 - \bar{c}_2(e\lambda_2 + s)} && \text{if} \quad m \neq -1 \\ &= 1 && \text{if} \quad m = -1 \end{aligned} \tag{5.6}$$

and $\bar{h}_2(s)$ and $\bar{c}_2(s)$ will be defined below for the (∞, N_2) and (N_1, N_2) models. Finally, the expected length of the busy period duration can be obtained by differentiating (5.5), or directly from (II, 2.78) and (II, 2.84), and is given by

$$E(\gamma_2) = \frac{N_2\lambda_2}{N_2\lambda_2 + \lambda_1^*} E(c_2) \sum_{e=0}^{N_2-1} \binom{N_2 - 1}{e} \frac{1}{\psi_2(e)\,\bar{h}_2(e\lambda_2)}$$

$$+ \frac{\lambda_1^*}{N_2\lambda_2 + \lambda_1^*} \left[E(b_1) + E(c_2) \sum_{e=1}^{N_2} \binom{N_2}{e} \frac{1 - \bar{b}_1(e\lambda_2)}{\psi_2(e-1)\,\bar{h}_2(e\lambda_2)}\right] \tag{5.7}$$

where, as in (II, 2.79), we define

$$\begin{aligned} \psi_2(m) &= \prod_{e=1}^{m} \frac{\bar{h}_2(e\lambda_2)}{1 - \bar{c}_2(e\lambda_2)} && \text{if} \quad m \neq 0 \\ &= 1 && \text{if} \quad m = 0 \end{aligned} \tag{5.8}$$

The values of $\bar{h}_2(s)$ and $\bar{c}_2(s)$ for these models are as follows:

(i) *The* (∞, N_2) *Model*

$$\bar{c}_2(s) = \int_0^\infty S_2(\tau) \exp(-s\tau) \exp\{-[\lambda_1\{1 - \bar{b}_1(s)\}]\tau\} \, d\tau \tag{5.9}$$

$$= \bar{S}_2[\lambda_1\{1 - \bar{b}_1(s)\} + s] \tag{5.10}$$

and

$$\bar{h}_2(s) = \int_0^\infty S_2(\tau) \exp(-s\tau) \exp(\lambda_2\tau) \exp\{-[\lambda_1\{1 - \bar{b}_1(s)\}]\tau\} \, d\tau \tag{5.11}$$

$$= \bar{S}_2[s + \lambda_1\{1 - \bar{b}_1(s)\} - \lambda_2] \tag{5.12}$$

Note that $c_2(t)$, the density of the cycle time in the restoration-time model, is identical to the completion time of the ordinary unit.

Hence, $E(\gamma_2)$ for the (∞, N_2) model is given by

$$E(\gamma_2) = \frac{1}{1 - \rho_1} \frac{1}{N_2\lambda_2 + \lambda_1} \Big[N_2\lambda_2\nu_2 \sum_{e=0}^{N_2-1} \binom{N_2 - 1}{e} \frac{1}{\bar{h}_2(e\lambda_2)\, \psi_2(e)} + \lambda_1\nu_2 \sum_{e=1}^{N_2} \binom{N_2}{e} \frac{1 - \bar{b}_1(e\lambda_2)}{\bar{h}_2(e\lambda_2)\, \psi_2(e - 1)} + \rho_1\Big] \tag{5.13}$$

(ii) *The* (N_1, N_2) *Model.* For this model,

$$\bar{c}_2(s) = \Big[\sum_{e=0}^{N_1} \binom{N_1}{e} \frac{\bar{S}_2(e\lambda_1 + s)}{\bar{v}_1(e - 1, s)}\Big]\Big[\sum_{e=0}^{N_1} \binom{N_1}{e} \frac{1}{\bar{v}_1(e - 1, s)}\Big]^{-1} \tag{5.14}$$

and

$$\bar{h}_2(s) = \Big[\sum_{e=0}^{N_1} \binom{N_1}{e} \frac{[\bar{S}_2(e\lambda_1 - \lambda_2 + s)]}{\bar{v}_1(e - 1, s)}\Big]\Big[\sum_{e=0}^{N_1} \binom{N_1}{e} \frac{1}{\bar{v}_1(e - 1, s)}\Big]^{-1} \tag{5.15}$$

Hence, the expected duration of the busy period for the (N_1, N_2) model is given by

$$E(\gamma_2) = \frac{N_1\lambda_1\nu_1}{N_2\lambda_2 + N_1\lambda_1} \sum_{e=1}^{N_1-1} \binom{N_1 - 1}{e} \frac{1}{\phi_1(e)} + \Big[\nu_2 + \nu_1 \sum_{e=1}^{N_1} \binom{N_1}{e} \frac{1 - \bar{S}_2(e\lambda_1)}{\phi_1(e - 1)}\Big] \times \Big[\frac{N_2\lambda_2}{N_2\lambda_2 + N_1\lambda_1} \sum_{e=0}^{N_2-1} \binom{N_2 - 1}{e} \frac{1}{\psi_2(e)\, \bar{h}_2(e\lambda_2)} + \frac{N_1\lambda_1}{N_2\lambda_2 + N_1\lambda_1} \sum_{e=1}^{N_2} \binom{N_2}{e} \frac{1 - \bar{b}_1(e\lambda_2)}{\psi_2(e - 1)\, \bar{h}_2(e\lambda_2)}\Big] \tag{5.16}$$

5-2. Joint Queue-Length Probabilities

As pointed out in the introduction to this section, the distribution of the number of ordinary units at epochs during which ordinary units enter service in the (∞, N_2) and (N_1, N_2) models can be obtained from the results of the restoration-time model. If $\mathscr{H}(m_2, t)$ denotes the probability that at time t an ordinary unit enters service in the (∞, N_2) and (N_1, N_2) models and leaves behind a queue of $(m_2 - 1)$ ordinary units waiting, we have, using arguments similar to those in Section III, 4 but using (II, 2.76) and (II, 2.81), the following results:

$$\bar{\mathscr{H}}(m_2, s) = \sum_{e=0}^{m_2-1} (-1)^e \binom{N_2 - m_2 + e}{e} \Big[\frac{N_2\lambda_2}{N_2\lambda_2 + \lambda_1^*} \bar{a}_2(N_2 - m_2 + e, s) + \frac{\lambda_1^*}{N_2\lambda_2 + \lambda_1^*} \bar{a}_2^{b_1}(N_2 - m_2 + e, s)\Big] \tag{5.17}$$

where $\bar{a}_2(m, s)$ and $\bar{a}_2^{b_1}(m, s)$ are obtained from (II, 2.73) and (II, 2.83) by using the value of $\bar{c}_2(s)$ and $\bar{h}_2(s)$ obtained above.

Further, let $\mathscr{H}'(m_2, t, Z)\, dZ$ denote the probability that at time t there are m_2 ordinary units in the system and an ordinary unit has departed after being in service for a time between Z and $Z + dZ$. Notice that at such an instant 't' there will be priority units present which have arrived during Z. Because of the equivalence of the priority model with the restoration-time model, we obtain, using (II, 2.77) and (II, 2.82),

$$\begin{aligned}\bar{\mathscr{H}}'(m_2, s, Z) = \sum_{e=0}^{m_2} (-1)^e \binom{N_2 - m_2 + e}{e} \Big[&\frac{N_2\lambda_2}{N_2\lambda_2 + \lambda_1^*} \\ &\times \{\bar{a}_2(N_2 - m_2 + e, s) \exp[-\{(N_2 - m_2 + e)\lambda_2 + s\}Z]S_2(Z) \\ &+ \bar{a}_2(N_2 - m_2 + e - 1, s) \\ &\times \exp[-\{(N_2 - m_2 + e - 1)\lambda_2 + s\}Z]S_2(Z)\} \\ &+ \frac{\lambda_1^*}{N_2\lambda_2 + \lambda_1^*} \{\bar{a}_2^{b_1}(N_2 - m_2 + e, s) \\ &\times \exp[-\{(N_2 - m_2 + e)\lambda_2 + s\}Z]S_2(Z) \\ &+ \bar{a}_2^{b_1}(N_2 - m_2 + e - 1, s) \\ &\times \exp[-\{(N_2 - m_2 + e - 1)\lambda_2 + s\}Z]S_2(Z)\Big]\end{aligned} \tag{5.18}$$

Now, following the method outlined in Section III, 4, we get

$$p(m_1, m_2, t) = \frac{\lambda_1^*}{\lambda_1^* + N_2\lambda_2} \delta(t)$$

$$* \Big[p(m_1, t)\binom{N_2}{m_2} \sum_{e=0}^{m_2} (-1)^e \binom{m_2}{e} \exp[-(N_2 - m_2 + e)\lambda_2 t]\Big]$$

$$+ \sum_{n=0}^{m_2-1} \int_{Z=0}^{\infty} \int_{\tau=0}^{t} \mathscr{H}(m_2 - n, t - \tau, Z)\binom{N_2 - m_2 + n}{n} \sum_{e=0}^{n} (-1)^e \binom{n}{e}$$

$$\times \exp[-(N_2 - m_2 + e)\lambda_2\tau]\, p^I(m_1, \tau \mid Z)\, dZ\, d\tau$$

$$+ \sum_{n=0}^{m_2} \int_{\tau=0}^{t} \int_{Z=0}^{\infty} \mathscr{H}'(m_2 - n, t - \tau + Z, Z)$$

$$\times \binom{N_2 - m_2 + n}{n} \sum_{e=0}^{n} (-1)^e \binom{n}{e}$$

$$\times \exp[-(N_2 - m_2 + e)(\tau - Z)\lambda_2]\, p^L(m_1, \tau \mid Z)\, dZ\, d\tau \tag{5.19}$$

where $\mathscr{H}(m_2, t, Z)\, dZ$ denotes the joint probability that at time t an ordinary unit enters service with $m_2 - 1$ units in the queue and the service time of this unit lies between Z and $Z + dZ$; observe that $\mathscr{H}(m_2, t, Z)$ is related to the $\mathscr{H}(m_2, t)$ given by (5.17) by the simple relation

$$\mathscr{H}(m_2, t, Z) = \mathscr{H}(m_2, t)\, S_2(Z) \tag{5.20}$$

$p^I(m_1, t \mid Z)\, dZ$ and $p^L(m_1, t \mid Z)\, dZ$ are the conditional probabilities associated with the completion-time process of a unit whose service time lies between Z and $Z + dZ$.

Taking the Laplace transform, we get

$$\bar{p}(m_1, m_2, s) = \frac{\lambda_1^*}{\lambda_1^* + N_2\lambda_2} \binom{N_2}{m_2} \sum_{e=0}^{m_2} (-1)^e \binom{m_2}{e} \bar{p}[m_1, s + (N_2 - m_2 + e)\lambda_2]$$

$$+ \int_{Z=0}^{\infty} \Big\{ \sum_{n=0}^{m_2-1} \bar{\mathscr{H}}(m_2 - n, s, Z)\binom{N_2 - m_2 + n}{n} \sum_{e=0}^{n} (-1)^e \binom{n}{e}$$

$$\times \bar{p}^I[m_1, (N_2 - m_2 + e)\lambda_2 + s \mid Z]\Big\}\, dZ$$

$$+ \int_{Z=0}^{\infty} \left\{ \sum_{n=0}^{m_2} \bar{\mathscr{H}}'(m_2 - n, s, Z) \exp(sZ) \binom{N_2 - m_2 + n}{n} \right.$$

$$\times \sum_{e=0}^{n} (-1)^e \binom{n}{e} \exp[(N_2 - m_2 + e) \lambda_2 Z]$$

$$\left. \times \bar{p}^L[m_1, (N_2 - m_2 + e) \lambda_2 + s \mid Z] \right\} dZ \qquad (5.21)$$

Using the results of Appendix I, we obtain, after simplification,

$$\sum_{m_2=0}^{N_2} \alpha_2^{m_2} \bar{p}(m_1, m_2, s)$$

$$= \frac{\lambda_1^*}{(N_2\lambda_2 + \lambda_1^*)} \sum_{m_2=0}^{N_2} \binom{N_2}{m_2} \alpha_2^{N_2-m_2}(1 - \alpha_2)^{m_2} \bar{p}(m_1, m_2\lambda_2 + s)$$

$$+ \sum_{m_2=0}^{N_2-1} \alpha_2^{N_2-m_2}(1 - \alpha_2)^{m_2} \left[\frac{N_2\lambda_2}{\lambda_1^* + N_2\lambda_2} \bar{a}_2(m_2, s) + \frac{\lambda_1^*}{N_2\lambda_2 + \lambda_1^*} \bar{a}_2^{b_1}(m_2, s) \right]$$

$$\times \bar{p}^I(m_1, m_2\lambda_2 + s)$$

$$+ \sum_{m_2=0}^{N_2} \alpha_2^{N_2-m_2}(1 - \alpha_2)^{m_2} \left[\frac{N_2\lambda_2}{N_2\lambda_2 + \lambda_1^*} \left\{ \bar{a}_2(m_2, s) \bar{p}^L(m_1, m_2\lambda_2 + s) \right. \right.$$

$$\left. + \bar{a}_2(m_2 - 1, s) \int_0^{\infty} \bar{p}^L(m_1, m_2\lambda_2 + s \mid Z) \exp(\lambda_2 Z) S_2(Z)\, dZ \right\}$$

$$+ \frac{\lambda_1^*}{N_2\lambda_2 + \lambda_1^*} \left\{ \bar{a}_2^{b_1}(m_2, s) \bar{p}^L(m_1, m_2\lambda_2 + s) \right.$$

$$\left. \left. + \int_0^{\infty} \bar{a}_2^{b_1}(m_2 - 1, s) \exp(\lambda_2 Z) S_2(Z) \bar{p}^L(m_1, m_2\lambda_2 + s \mid Z)\, dZ \right\} \right]$$

$$(5.22)$$

Hence,

$$\sum_{m_2=0}^{N_2} \alpha_2^{m_2} \bar{p}(m_1, m_2, s) = \frac{\lambda_1^*}{N_2\lambda_2 + \lambda_1^*} \sum_{m_2=0}^{N_2} \binom{N_2}{m_2} \alpha_2^{N_2-m_2}(1 - \alpha_2)^{m_2} \bar{p}(m_1, m_2\lambda_2 + s)$$

$$+ \sum_{m_2=0}^{N_2-1} \alpha_2^{N_2-m_2}(1 - \alpha_2)^{m_2} l(m_2, s) \bar{p}^c(m_1, m_2\lambda_2 + s)$$

$$+ \sum_{m_2=0}^{N_2-1} \alpha_2^{N_2-m_2}(1-\alpha_2)^{m_2}\, l(m_2-1, s)$$

$$\times \int_0^\infty \exp(\lambda_2 Z)\, S_2(Z)\, \bar{p}^L(m_1, m_2\lambda_2 + s \mid Z)\, dZ \tag{5.23}$$

where

$$l(m_2, s) = \frac{N_2\lambda_2}{\lambda_1^* + N_2\lambda_2}\, \bar{a}_2(m_2, s) + \frac{\lambda_1^*}{N_2\lambda_2 + \lambda_1^*}\, \bar{a}_2^{b_1}(m_2, s) \tag{5.24}$$

and

$$p^c(m_1, t) = p^I(m_1, t) + p^L(m_1, t)$$

is the probability that there are m_1 units at time t of the completion-time process.

The values of $\bar{p}^I$ and $\bar{p}^L$ can be obtained using (III, 3.1) and (III, 3.2) with (2.1) and (2.2), and using (2.7) and (2.8) for the (∞, N_2) and (N_1, N_2) models, respectively.

Following the method of Section (III, 5), the general-process probabilities are obtained from (5.23) and are given by

$$\sum_{m_2=0}^{N_2} \alpha_2^{m_2}\bar{\bar{p}}(m_1, m_2, s)$$

$$= \bar{e}^{(2)}(s)\Big[1 + \lambda_1^* \sum_{m_2=0}^{N_2} \binom{N_2}{m_2} \alpha_2^{N_2-m_2}(1-\alpha_2)^{m_2}\, \bar{p}(m_1, m_2\lambda_2 + s)$$

$$+ \sum_{m_2=0}^{N_2-1} \alpha_2^{N_2-m_2}(1-\alpha_2)^{m_2}\,(N_2\lambda_2 + \lambda_1^*)\Big\{l(m_2, s)\, \bar{p}^c(m_1, m_2\lambda_2 + s)$$

$$+ l(m_2-1, s) \int_0^\infty \exp(\lambda_2 Z)\, S_2(Z)\, \bar{p}^L(m_1, m_2\lambda_2 + s \mid Z)\, dZ\Big\}\Big] \tag{5.25}$$

where

$$\bar{e}^{(2)}(s) = [s + (N_2\lambda_2 + \lambda_1^*)\, \bar{\gamma}_2(s)]^{-1} \tag{5.26}$$

and $\bar{\gamma}_2(s)$ is given by (5.5).

The steady-state results can be obtained by the usual limiting arguments.

5-3. Occupation Time of the Server

Using the method discussed in Chapter III, we can directly write the double Laplace transform of the transient occupation-time density with respect to the priority units as follows

$$\bar{\mathscr{W}}_1(\theta, s) = \bar{e}^{(2)}(s)\Big[1 + \lambda_1^* \bar{w}_1(\theta, s) + (N_2\lambda_2 + \lambda_1^*) \sum_{m_2=1}^{N_2} \bar{\mathscr{H}}(m_2, s)\, \bar{w}_1{}^c(\theta, s)\Big] \tag{5.27}$$

where $\bar{w}_1{}^c(\theta, t)$ is the Laplace transform of the virtual waiting-time density at time t of the completion-time cycle. Since the completion-time cycle is identical to the initial busy period, we have for the (N_1, N_2) model, following the derivation of the occupation time density during the initial busy period process of Section I, 6 and using $q^\Omega(m, t)$ and $p^\Omega(m, x, t)$ from Section II, 2,

$$\begin{aligned} &\bar{w}_1{}^c(\theta, s) \\ &= \sum_{m_1=0}^{N_1} [\bar{S}_1(\theta)]^{m_1} \binom{N_1}{m_1} \sum_{e=0}^{m_1} (-1)^e \binom{m_1}{e} \frac{\bar{S}_2(\theta) - \bar{S}_2[(N_1 - m_1 + e)\lambda_1 + s]}{(N_1 - m_1 + e)\lambda_1 + s} \\ &\quad + \sum_{m_1=0}^{N_1-1} [\bar{S}_1(\theta)]^{N_1-m_1-1} [1 - \bar{S}_1(\theta)]^{m_1} \bar{a}_1^{S_2}(m_1, s) \frac{\bar{S}_1(m_1\lambda_1 + s) - \bar{S}_1(\theta)}{\theta - m_1\lambda_1 - s} \end{aligned} \tag{5.28}$$

where $\bar{a}_1^{S_2}(m_1, s)$ is defined by (II, 2.45). In addition, $\bar{w}_1(\theta, s)$ is given by (II, 5.2) for $i = 1$ so that

$$\bar{w}_1(\theta, s) = \sum_{m_1=0}^{N_1-1} [\bar{S}_1(\theta)]^{N_1-m_1-1} [1 - \bar{S}_1(\theta)]^{m_1} \bar{a}_1(m_1, s) \frac{\bar{S}_1(m_1\lambda_1 + s) - \bar{S}_1(\theta)}{\theta - m_1\lambda_1 - s} \tag{5.29}$$

where $\bar{a}_1(m_1, s)$ is defined by (II, 2.27). Finally, we can obtain

$$\sum_{m_2=1}^{N_2} \bar{\mathscr{H}}(m_2, s)$$

from (5.17). By substituting all these values in (5.27), we can obtain $\bar{\mathscr{W}}_1(\theta, s)$.

For the occupation-time density with respect to ordinary units, following the method and results of Section III, 7, we obtain

$$\bar{\mathscr{W}}_2(\theta, s) = \bar{e}^{(2)}(s)\Big[1 + \sum_{j=0}^{N_2-1} [\bar{c}_2(\theta)]^{N_2-j-1} [1 - \bar{c}_2(\theta)]^j \times \{N_2\lambda_2\bar{a}_2(j, s) + \lambda_1^*\bar{a}_2^{b_1}(j, s)\} \frac{\bar{c}_2(j\lambda_2 + s) - \bar{c}_2(\theta)}{\theta - s - j\lambda_2}\Big] \quad (5.30)$$

where $\bar{a}_2(j, s)$ and $\bar{a}_2^{b_1}(j, s)$ are obtained from (II, 2.73) and (II, 2.83) by using the values of $\bar{c}_2(s)$ and $\bar{h}_2(s)$ from (5.10) and (5.12) for the (∞, N_2) model and from (5.14) and (5.15) for the (N_1, N_2) model.

6. k-Class Priority Process

Generalization to more than two classes can be done as in Section IV, 7. However, the generalization for the head-of-the-line discipline presents greater algebraic difficulties than that for the preemptive discipline. For the preemptive discipline, the lower priority units do not have any effect on the higher priority units, and, in addition, the completion-time probabilities for the kth-class unit bear a simple relationship with the probabilities of the $(k - 1)$-class priority process. Both these simplifications do not exist for the head-of-the-line discipline, and the generalization is therefore more difficult. In the following, we discuss the k-class priority process assuming all sources to be infinite. In doing so, we will require the results for the jth-class units in the $k, k - 1, \ldots, j$ class priority processes, and since, unlike in the preemptive case, these results depend upon the total number of classes under consideration, we denote the total number of classes as a superscript in parenthesis in the definition of busy-period and occupation-time densities, e.g., $\gamma_j^{(k)}(t)$, $\mathscr{W}_j^{(k)}(t)$ etc. For similar reasons, we write $w_j^{c_k}$ in place of $w_j{}^c$ for the occupation time of the jth-class unit during the completion-time process of a k-class unit. Also, we follow the convention of using $\gamma_j(t)$ for $\gamma_j^{(j)}(t)$.

6-1. Completion Time

The completion time of a jth-class unit in the k-class priority process is initiated by the entry of a jth-class unit into service. After the service of this unit, all units of priority index less than j are serviced. Hence, the duration of the completion time of the jth-class unit is equal to the initial busy period duration for $(j - 1)$ priority classes with the initial occupation time equal to the service time of the jth-class unit; thus,

$$\bar{c}_j(s) = \bar{\gamma}_{j-1}^{S_j}(s) \tag{6.1}$$

where $\bar{\gamma}_{j-1}^{\Omega}(s)$ represents the Laplace transform of the initial busy-period density for the $(j-1)$-class priority process with the initial occupation-time density $\Omega(t)$.

Before proceeding further with the discussion of the completion time, the following may be noted: Consider the initial busy-period process for a j-class priority process with initial occupation time Ω. This process can be regarded as in Fig. V.2. The process starts at

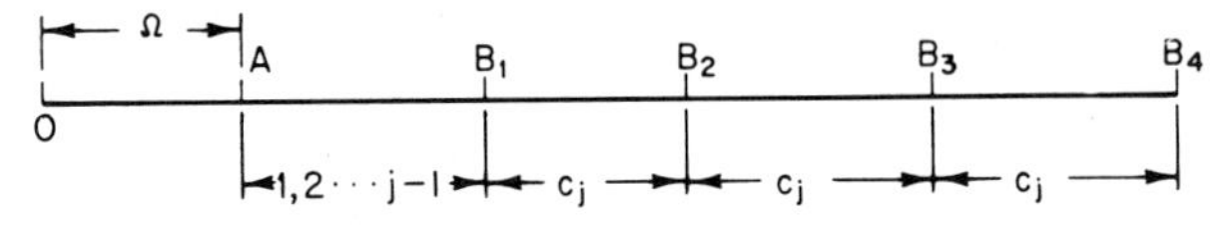

FIG. V.2. Initial busy period of a j-class priority process.

$t = 0$ at O and up to A remains occupied, the density of the length OA being $\Omega(t)$. During AB_1, let the units of class 1 to $j-1$ be serviced, so that at B_1, a jth-class unit if present enters service. From B_1, the process can be described as a sequence of completion times of the jth-class units, ending when there is no jth-class unit present at the termination of a completion time. Hence, whatever the priority discipline may be, we can regard the initial busy-period of the j-class priority process as a basic infinite-source model with parameters (λ_j, c_j) and having the initial occupation time density γ_{j-1}^{Ω}, the initial busy-period density for the $(j-1)$-class process. Hence,

$$\bar{\gamma}_j^{\Omega}(s) = \bar{\gamma}_{j-1}^{\Omega}[s + \lambda_j\{1 - \bar{B}_j(s)\}] \qquad (j \geqslant 2) \tag{6.2}$$

and $\bar{\gamma}_1^{\Omega}(s) = \bar{b}_1^{\Omega}(s)$ is given by (I, 2.26).

From (6.1) and (6.2), we get

$$E(c_j) = E[\gamma_{j-1}^{S_j}] = \frac{E[\gamma_{j-2}^{S_j}]}{1 - \lambda_{j-1}E(c_{j-1})} \tag{6.3}$$

so that, putting $j = 2, 3, \ldots$, we get

$$E(c_2) = E(b_1^{S_2}) = \frac{\nu_2}{1 - \rho_1} \tag{6.4}$$

$$E(c_3) = \frac{E[\gamma_1^{S_3}]}{1 - \lambda_2 E(c_2)} = \frac{\nu_3}{1 - \rho_1 - \rho_2} \tag{6.5}$$

and, in general,

$$E(c_j) = \frac{\nu_j}{1 - \rho_1 - \rho_2 - \cdots - \rho_{j-1}} \qquad (j \geqslant 2) \tag{6.6}$$

Similarly, other moments can be obtained.

6-2. Busy Period

Let us consider $\gamma_k(t)$, the busy-period density for the k-class priority process. Since all the classes are taken into account, we can use the same arguments as in Section IV, 7 for preemptive discipline to obtain $\bar{\gamma}_k(s)$. We have

$$\bar{\gamma}_k(s) = \frac{\lambda_k}{\Lambda_k} \bar{B}_k(s) + \frac{\Lambda_{k-1}}{\Lambda_k} \bar{\gamma}_{k-1}[s + \lambda_k\{1 - \bar{B}_k(s)\}] \tag{6.7}$$

where $\bar{B}_k(s)$ is the root of the equation $\alpha = \bar{c}_k[\lambda_k(1 - \alpha) + s]$ lying inside the unit circle. We use (6.7) to obtain an easier expression for the completion-time density. From (6.2), putting $j = 2$, we get

$$\bar{\gamma}_2^{\Omega}(s) = \bar{b}_1^{\Omega}[s + \lambda_2\{1 - \bar{B}_2(s)\}] \tag{6.8}$$

Using (I, 2.26), we can write (6.8) as

$$\bar{\gamma}_2^{\Omega}(s) = \bar{\Omega}[\lambda_1\{1 - \bar{b}_1[s + \lambda_2(1 - \bar{B}_2(s))]\} + s + \lambda_2\{1 - \bar{B}_2(s)\}] \tag{6.9}$$

so that, using (6.7) for $k = 2$, we get

$$\bar{\gamma}_2^{\Omega}(s) = \bar{\Omega}[s + \lambda_2\{1 - \bar{\gamma}_2(s)\}] \tag{6.10}$$

and, in general,

$$\bar{\gamma}_j^{\Omega}(s) = \bar{\Omega}[s + \Lambda_j\{1 - \bar{\gamma}_j(s)\}] \tag{6.11}$$

Thus, using (6.1), we get

$$\bar{c}_j(s) = \bar{\gamma}_{j-1}^{S_j}(s) = \bar{S}_j[s + \Lambda_{j-1}\{1 - \bar{\gamma}_{j-1}(s)\}] \tag{6.12}$$

the same result as we had for the preemptive resume discipline.

6-3. Joint Queue-Length Probabilities

For the joint queue-length probabilities, while we can write the same results as in (IV, 7.26) and (IV, 7.27), the simple relationship between $\bar{\Pi}^c(\alpha_1, \alpha_2, \ldots, \alpha_k, s)$ and $\bar{\Pi}(\alpha_1, \alpha_2, \ldots, \alpha_{k-1}, s)$ that exists for the preemptive resume discipline and is given by (IV, 7.30) does not exist for the head-of-the-line discipline. The completion-time process for this case can be regarded as an initial busy-period process of the type shown in Fig. V.2 with the following modifications:

(i) The initial occupation time $\Omega = S_k$, the service time of the kth-class unit with whose completion-time process we are concerned.

(ii) During the interval AB_1, units of classes $1, 2, \ldots, k-2$ are serviced.

(iii) The intervals B_1B_2, B_2B_3, ..., have random durations c_{k-1}.

Now, to derive the joint queue-length probabilities during the completion-time process we observe that at any time t from the beginning of the completion-time cycle either (a) no completion-time cycle c_{k-1} has been initiated, i.e., t lies in either OA or AB_1, or (b) a completion-time cycle c_{k-1} has been initiated, in which case t lies in one of the intervals B_1B_2, B_2B_3, ... For case (a), if t is in OA, the service of the kth-class unit is in progress, and units of $1, 2, \ldots, k-1$ classes arrive and wait; if t lies in AB_1, the service of the kth-class unit has been completed and a busy period initiated by units of classes $1, 2, \ldots, k-2$ which arrived during S_k is in progress while units of the $(k-1)$ class accumulate. For case (b), on the other hand, let the current completion-time cycle c_{k-1} be initiated at time $t-\tau$; obviously, at $t-\tau$ there are only units of the $(k-1)$th class, and their distribution is the same as the distribution of the number of units at the service entry points of an initial busy-period process of the basic infinite-source model with parameters (λ_{k-1}, c_{k-1}) and initial occupation time $\gamma_{k-2}^{S_k}$, and will be given by (I, 2.23) with appropriate substitutions. Further, at time t, the completion-time cycle c_{k-1} initiated at $t-\tau$ is in progress, and the units of $(k-1)$th class which arrive in the interval $t-\tau$ and t accumulate. Hence,

$$
\begin{aligned}
&\bar{\Pi}^c(\alpha_1, \alpha_2, \ldots, \alpha_k, s) \\
&\quad = \alpha_k \frac{1 - \bar{S}_k[\lambda_1(1-\alpha_1) + \cdots + \lambda_k(1-\alpha_k) + s]}{\lambda_1(1-\alpha_1) + \cdots + \lambda_k(1-\alpha_k) + s} \\
&\qquad + \bar{\Pi}^{(k-2), S_k}[\alpha_1, \alpha_2, \ldots, \alpha_{k-2}, s + \lambda_{k-1}(1-\alpha_{k-1})] \\
&\qquad + \frac{\bar{\gamma}_{k-2}^{S_k}[s + \lambda_{k-1}(1-\alpha_{k-1})] - \bar{\gamma}_{k-2}^{S_k}[s + \lambda_{k-1}\{1 - \bar{B}_{k-1}(s)\}]}{1 - (1/\alpha_{k-1})\, \bar{c}_{k-1}[s + \lambda_{k-1}(1-\alpha_{k-1})]} \\
&\qquad \times \bar{\Pi}^c[\alpha_1, \alpha_2, \ldots, \alpha_{k-1}, s + \lambda_{k-1}(1-\alpha_{k-1})] \qquad (6.13)
\end{aligned}
$$

where $\bar{\Pi}^{(k-2),S_k}(\alpha_1, ..., \alpha_{k-2}, t)$ denotes the probability generating function of the number of units of type 1 to $k - 2$ present at time t in a $(k - 2)$-class priority process having initially the units of class 1 to $k - 2$ arriving during S_k, the service time of the k-class unit.

Thus, we can, in principle, evaluate $\bar{\Pi}^c$ and use it with (IV, 7.26) and (IV, 7.27) to obtain the joint queue-length probability generating function. However, this would require further investigation into the initial busy-period processes, and the derivation becomes considerably complicated. We may note that through Markov chain analysis, Welch [96] obtained similar recurrence relations for this model. For the finite-source model, recurrence relations have recently been obtained by Hodgson and Hebble [38].

Although general-process probabilities and steady-state results can be obtained, the results are quite complicated, and are not pursued further.

6-4. Occupation Time

The occupation-time density of the server with respect to kth-class units can be obtained in exactly the same way as it was for the preemptive discipline. To obtain the occupation-time density of the server with units of class $\leqslant j \; (j \leqslant k)$ we first obtain following the usual argument, the density during the busy period:

$$\bar{\mathscr{W}}_j^{(k)}(\theta, s) = \frac{\Lambda_{k-1}}{\Lambda_k} \bar{\mathscr{W}}_j^{(k-1)}(\theta, s) + \bar{\mathscr{G}}(1, s)\, \bar{w}_j^{c_k}(\theta, s) \tag{6.14}$$

where $\mathscr{G}(1, t)$ is the probability that at time t a kth-class unit enters service, and $\bar{w}_j^{c_k}(\theta, t)$ represents the Laplace transform of the occupation time density at time t with units of priority index $\leqslant j$ during the completion time of a kth-class unit. Again, we note that the completion-time process of a kth-class unit can be regarded as an initial busy-period process of the $(k - 1)$th-class unit with the service time replaced by completion time, and with the initial occupation-time taken to be the initial busy period of the $(k - 2)$th-class priority process with the initial occupation time as the service time of the kth-class unit.

Hence,

$$\bar{w}_j^{c_k}(\theta, s) = \bar{\mathscr{W}}_j^{(k-2),S_k}(\theta, s) + \frac{\bar{\gamma}_{k-2}^{S_k}(s) - \bar{\gamma}_{k-2}^{S_k}[s + \lambda_{k-1}\{1 - \bar{B}_{k-1}(s)\}]}{1 - \bar{c}_{k-1}(s)} \bar{w}_j^{c_{k-1}}(\theta, s) \quad (j < k - 2) \tag{6.15}$$

where $\mathscr{W}_j^{(k-2),S_k}(\theta, t)$ represents the Laplace transform of the occupation-time density of the server with respect to units of priority $\leqslant j$ at time t in the initial busy period of a $(k-2)$th-class priority process having an initial occupation time S_k. Furthermore,

$$\bar{\mathscr{W}}_j^{(k-2),S_k}(\theta, s) = \bar{\mathscr{W}}_j^{(k-3),S_k}(\theta, s) + \frac{\bar{\gamma}_{k-3}^{S_k}(s) - \bar{\gamma}_{k-3}^{S_k}[s + \lambda_{k-2}\{1 - \bar{B}_{k-2}(s)\}]}{1 - \bar{c}_{k-2}(s)} \times \bar{\mathscr{W}}_j^{c_{k-2}}(\theta, s) \qquad (j < k-2) \tag{6.16}$$

$$\bar{\mathscr{W}}_j^{(j),S_k}(\theta, s) = \frac{\bar{\gamma}_{j-1}^{S_k}[s + \lambda_j\{1 - \bar{B}_j(s)\}] - \bar{\gamma}_{j-1}^{S_k}(\theta)}{\theta - s - \lambda_j + \lambda_j \bar{c}_j(\theta)} \tag{6.17}$$

$$\bar{\mathscr{W}}_j^{c_{j+1}}(\theta, s) = \frac{\bar{\gamma}_{j-1}^{S_{j+1}}[s + \lambda_j\{1 - \bar{B}_j(s)\}] - \bar{\gamma}_{j-1}^{S_{j+1}}(\theta)}{\theta - s - \lambda_j + \lambda_j \bar{c}_j(\theta)} \tag{6.18}$$

The recurrence relation obtained above can be used in principle to obtain $\bar{\mathscr{W}}_j^{(k)}(\theta, s)$. However, the results are quite complicated. We study a very simple particular case of the above results: the case $k = 3$ and $j = 2$.

For this case, we have, from (6.14),

$$\bar{\mathscr{W}}_2^{(3)}(\theta, s) = \frac{\Lambda_2}{\Lambda_3} \bar{\mathscr{W}}_2^{(2)}(\theta, s) + \bar{\mathscr{G}}(1, s)\, \bar{\mathscr{W}}_2^{c_3}(\theta, s) \tag{6.19}$$

Using (6.18), we get

$$\bar{\mathscr{W}}_2^{c_3}(\theta, s) = \frac{\bar{b}_1^{S_3}[s + \lambda_2\{1 - \bar{B}_2(s)\}] - \bar{b}_1^{S_3}(\theta)}{\theta - s - \lambda_2 + \lambda_2 \bar{c}_2(\theta)} \tag{6.20}$$

and, from Section IV, 7, we get for $k = 3$,

$$\bar{\mathscr{G}}(1, s) = \frac{\bar{e}^{(3)}(s) - \bar{e}^{(2)}(s)}{\Lambda_3[1 - \bar{c}_3(s)]\, \bar{e}^{(3)}(s)\, \bar{e}^{(2)}(s)} \tag{6.21}$$

Hence, if $\bar{\mathscr{W}}_2^{(3)}(\theta, t)$ is the Laplace transform of the occupation time density of the server with respect to the first- and second-class units at time t in the general process, we have, using renewal arguments,

$$\bar{\mathscr{W}}_2^{(3)}(\theta, s) = \bar{e}^{(3)}(s)[1 + \Lambda_3 \bar{\mathscr{W}}_2^{(3)}(\theta, s)] \tag{6.22}$$

$$= \frac{\bar{e}^{(3)}(s)}{\bar{e}^{(2)}(s)} \bar{\mathscr{W}}_2^{(2)}(\theta, s) + \left(\frac{\bar{e}^{(3)}(s)}{\bar{e}^{(2)}(s)} - 1\right) \frac{\bar{w}_2^{c_3}(\theta, s)}{1 - \bar{c}_3(s)} \tag{6.23}$$

If $\lambda_3 E(c_3) < 1$, i.e., $\sum_{i=1}^{3} \rho_i < 1$, the limiting occupation-time density exists and its Laplace transform is given by

$$\bar{\mathscr{W}}_2^{(3)}(\theta) = \frac{\hat{e}^{(3)}}{\hat{e}^{(2)}} \bar{\mathscr{W}}_2^{(2)}(\theta) + \left[\frac{\hat{e}^{(3)}}{\hat{e}^{(2)}} - 1\right] \frac{\bar{w}_2^{c_3}(\theta, 0)}{E(c_3)} \tag{6.24}$$

Note that $\bar{\mathscr{W}}_2^{(2)}(\theta)$ for head-of-the-line is the same as $\bar{\mathscr{W}}_2(\theta)$ for preemptive resume discipline and is given by (IV, 3.26). Hence, using (IV, 3.26) and (6.20), we get

$$\bar{\mathscr{W}}_2^{(3)}(\theta) = \frac{\hat{e}^{(3)}[\theta + \lambda_1\{1 - \bar{b}_1(\theta)\}] + \lambda_3[1 - \bar{S}_3\{\theta + \lambda_1[1 - \bar{b}_1(\theta)]\}]}{\theta - \lambda_2 + \lambda_2 \bar{c}_2(\theta)} \tag{6.25}$$

We note that in Chapter IV we derived the steady-state occupation-time density of the server with respect to the jth-class units by identifying the k-class process with a two-class process. For the head-of-the-line case, the steady-state occupation-time density of the server with respect to the jth-class units will be derived below by identifying the k-class process with the three-class process, the results for which were derived above. The k classes can be conceived of as being composed of three groups—the first group consisting of $1, 2, ..., j - 1$ classes, the second of the jth class, and the third of $j + 1, j + 2, ..., k$ classes. The first group can be identified with the first class of the three-class process by putting $\lambda_1 = \Lambda_{j-1} = \sum_{i=1}^{j-1} \lambda_i$ and $b_1 = \gamma_{j-1}$ for the same reasons as given for the preemptive case. The second group is equivalent to the second class if we replace the (λ_2, c_2, S_2) by (λ_j, c_j, S_j). Finally, the third group can be identified with the third class by replacing λ_3 with $\sum_{i=j+1}^{k} \lambda_i$ and $S_3(x)$ with $\sum_{i=j+1}^{k} \lambda_i S_i(x) / \sum_{i=j+1}^{k} \lambda_i$. Hence, from (6.25), we have, by appropriate substitutions, the following:

$$\bar{\mathscr{W}}_j^{(k)}(\theta) = \frac{\hat{e}^{(k)}[\theta + \Lambda_{j-1}\{1 - \bar{\gamma}_{j-1}(\theta)\}] + \sum_{i=j+1}^{k} \lambda_i[1 - \bar{S}_i\{\theta + \Lambda_{j-1}[1 - \bar{\gamma}_{j-1}(\theta)]\}]}{\theta - \lambda_j + \lambda_j \bar{c}_j(\theta)} \tag{6.26}$$

Differentiating (6.26) with respect to θ, we can obtain the moments; e.g.,

$$E(\hat{\mathscr{W}}_j^{(k)}) = \frac{\sum_{i=1}^{k} \lambda_i E(S_i^2)}{2[1 - \sum_{i=1}^{j-1} \rho_i][1 - \sum_{i=1}^{j} \rho_i]} \tag{6.27}$$

$$E[(\hat{\mathscr{W}}_j^{(k)})^2] = \frac{\sum_{i=1}^{k} \lambda_i E(S_i^3)}{3[1 - \sum_{i=1}^{j-1} \rho_i][1 - \sum_{i=1}^{j} \rho_i]} + \frac{\sum_{i=1}^{k} \lambda_i E(S_i^2) \sum_{i=1}^{j} \lambda_i E(S_i^2)}{2[1 - \sum_{i=1}^{j-1} \rho_i]^2[1 - \sum_{i=1}^{j} \rho_i]^2}$$

$$+ \frac{\sum_{i=1}^{k} \lambda_i E(S_i^2) \sum_{i=1}^{j-1} \lambda_i E(S_i^2)}{2[1 - \sum_{i=1}^{j-1} \rho_i]^3[1 - \sum_{i=1}^{j} \rho_i]} \tag{6.28}$$

These results were obtained by Cobham [18]. For an interesting application of the above results to the analysis of some problems associated with a real-time multiprogramming system, the reader may refer to Chang and Wong [17].

The condition under which the above results are derived is $\sum_{i=1}^{k} \rho_i < 1$. However, if $\sum_{i=1}^{k} \rho_i > 1$ but $\sum_{i=1}^{j} \rho_i < 1$ and $\sum_{i=1}^{j+1} \rho_i \geqslant 1$, it can be proved that partial equilibrium exists, i.e., units up to the jth class experience finite delays, while units from $j + 1$ to k classes experience infinite delays. A similar observation regarding partial equilibrium for preemptive discipline was made in Chapter IV. We may note here that partial equilibrium is inherent in all exogenous systems because of the state-independent nature of decision-making with regard to the selection of units for service.

We have not attempted to investigate the system behavior under saturation conditions. A rigorous analysis of the system behavior under saturation conditions has been made by Kesten and Runnenburg [52]. For a treatment of waiting time for a more general priority problem in which the priority index is continuous, the reader is referred to Takács [87]. Generalizations to more than two classes for finite-source models can be attempted in a similar way, but lead to much more complicated results.

7. Optimal Ordering of *k* Priority Classes to Minimize Total Delay Cost

The problem considered in this section is the same as in Section IV, 8. However, the service times of each class are assumed to have arbitrary distribution. Following the same method as in Section IV, 8, we first consider the total delay cost for any ordering, say, 1, 2,..., l, m, n,..., k, and then interchange the priority indices of classes m and n. Note that for the head-of-the-line discipline as well the interchange does not affect the mean delay time of any class other than the classes interchanged. Therefore, the difference in total delay cost under the two orderings is just the difference between the delay costs of classes m and n under the two orderings.

Let $\rho_i = \lambda_i \nu_i$, $\alpha = \sum_{i=1}^{l} \rho_i$ and $\lambda E(S^2) = \sum_{i=1}^{k} \lambda_i E(S_i^2)$, and let K_m and K_n be the costs per unit delay time for classes m and n. Then, if the mth class is assigned higher priority than the nth, we get, from (6.27), by adding the mean service time so as to obtain the mean delay time,

$$T(m, n) = K_m \frac{\lambda_m}{\lambda} \left[\nu_m + \frac{\lambda E(S^2)}{2(1-\alpha)(1-\alpha-\rho_m)}\right] + K_n \frac{\lambda_n}{\lambda} \left[\nu_n + \frac{\lambda E(S^2)}{2(1-\alpha-\rho_m)(1-\alpha-\rho_m-\rho_n)}\right] \tag{7.1}$$

where $T(m, n)$ denotes the contribution to the total delay cost by units of classes m and n and $\lambda = \sum_{i=1}^{l} \lambda_i$.

We now interchange the priorities of class m and n while keeping the priorities of all other classes the same. The contribution to the total delay cost by units of class m and n after interchanging the order becomes

$$T(n, m) = K_n \frac{\lambda_n}{\lambda} \left[\nu_n + \frac{\lambda E(S^2)}{2(1-\alpha)(1-\alpha-\rho_n)}\right] + K_m \frac{\lambda_m}{\lambda} \left[\nu_m + \frac{\lambda E(S^2)}{2(1-\alpha-\rho_n)(1-\alpha-\rho_n-\rho_m)}\right] \tag{7.2}$$

Subtracting the sum of last terms of (7.1) and (7.2) from both $T(m, n)$ and $T(n, m)$ and dividing by $E(S^2)$, we get

$$T_1(m, n) = K_m \lambda_m \left[\frac{1}{2(1-\alpha)(1-\alpha-\rho_m)} - \frac{1}{2(1-\alpha-\rho_n)(1-\alpha-\rho_n-\rho_m)}\right] \tag{7.3}$$

while $T_1(n, m)$ can be obtained from $T_1(m, n)$ by interchanging m and n.

Multiplying $T_1(m, n)$ by the term

$$2(1-\alpha)(1-\alpha-\rho_m)(1-\alpha-\rho_n)(1-\alpha-\rho_m-\rho_n),$$

which is symmetric in m and n, we get

$$T_2(m, n) = K_m\lambda_m[(1 - \alpha - \rho_n)(1 - \alpha - \rho_n - \rho_m) - (1 - \alpha)(1 - \alpha - \rho_m)]$$
$$= -K_m\lambda_m\rho_n[2 - 2\alpha - \rho_m - \rho_n] \tag{7.4}$$

Dividing by $\rho_m\rho_n(2 - 2\alpha - \rho_m - \rho_n)$, we finally get

$$T_3(m, n) = -K_m/\nu_m \tag{7.5}$$

and, by symmetry,

$$T_3(n, m) = -K_n/\nu_n \tag{7.6}$$

Hence, the mth class should be assigned higher priority than n if and only if

$$T_3(m, n) - T_3(n, m) < 0 \qquad \text{or} \quad K_m/\nu_m > K_n/\nu_n \tag{7.7}$$

Thus, the optimal priority assigment is again in descending order of K_i/ν_i. The method that we have followed above is due to Brosh and Naor [13], although the problem has been studied earlier by Cox and Smith [22].

We showed in Chapter IV that for the preemptive resume discipline, the K/ν policy is optimal only if the service-time distributions are exponential, but not for arbitrary distributions, while for the head-of-the-line discipline, the K/ν rule holds good for arbitrary distributions. It can easily be shown that if the service durations of N units are known, the optimal policy to reduce the total delay cost of these N units is to service them in descending order of K/ν. For the head-of-the-line discipline, we use this policy at service entry epochs picking up that unit which has the highest K/ν. However, for preemptive discipline, we may discontinue servicing a lower class unit by a unit of the higher class even if the value $K_i/E(S_i^z)$ for the lower class unit is less than the K/ν value of the new higher priority unit, where $E(S_i^z)$ denotes the expected remaining service time. For exponential service-time distributions, however, the K/ν policy is still optimal, because the future expected service for the unit in service is independent of the elapsed service time. Thus, it appears that we may reduce delay cost if we can keep track of the elapsed service time of the unit currently in service and preempt only if the value of $K_i/E(S_i^z)$ at the time of arrival of a new unit is less than the K/ν for the new arrival. That this is so will be shown in the next chapter, where we study a discretionary priority discipline in which the decision to preempt or to continue the service of a unit in service depends upon the elapsed service time. For discussion of this problem see Fife [101].

8. A Dynamic Programming Approach to Optimum Priority Classification

From the previous section, it is obvious that if the delay costs for different classes of units are equal, the optimum ordering rule will be to assign priorities in ascending order of mean service-time requirements, the highest priority to the class with least mean service time. Thus, if there is only one class of units with parameters (λ, S), then one way of reducing the overall mean delay time is to classify the units into two groups: one consisting of units which require less than or equal to σ units of time of service, and the other requiring more than σ units of time of service. The first group is then given priority over the second. Note that in order for this rule be practicable, the exact service requirement of a unit should be known upon its arrival.

In general, we may pick a sequence $\{\sigma_i\}$ $(i = 1,..., k)$ such that $0 \leqslant \sigma_1 \leqslant \sigma_2 \leqslant \cdots \leqslant \sigma_k \leqslant \infty$, and give priority to customers having service time in the interval $(\sigma_i, \sigma_{i+1}]$ to those in the class $(\sigma_j, \sigma_{j+1}]$ if and only if $i < j$. The question we attempt to answer is: Having decided to have $(k + 1)$ priority classes, what is the choice of $\{\sigma_i\}$ $(i = 1,..., k)$, which minimizes the expected waiting time? The results of this section are based upon a paper by Oliver and Pestalozzi [68]. Note that in this section, we are optimizing the overall expected waiting time rather than the delay cost as in the previous section.

We define α_i, $\rho(\sigma_i)$ and $S_i(x)$ in the following manner:

$$\alpha_i = \alpha(\sigma_{i-1}, \sigma_i) = \int_{\sigma_{i-1}}^{\sigma_i} S(x)\, dx \qquad (i = 1,..., k) \tag{8.1}$$

$$\rho(\sigma_i) = \lambda \int_0^{\sigma_i} xS(x)\, dx \qquad (i = 1,..., k) \tag{8.2}$$

and

$$S_i(x) = \begin{cases} 0 & \text{if } 0 \leqslant x \leqslant \sigma_{i-1} \\ S(x)/\alpha_i & \text{if } \sigma_{i-1} < x \leqslant \sigma_i \\ 0 & \text{if } \sigma_i < x \end{cases} \qquad (i = 1,..., k) \tag{8.3}$$

Clearly, α_i is the fraction of customers belonging to the ith priority class; $\rho(\sigma_i)$ is the utilization factor of all classes up to and including the ith; and $S_i(x)$ is the probability density of the service time for the ith class. From (6.27), the mean waiting time for the jth class is

$$E[\hat{\mathscr{W}}_j^{(k+1)}] = \frac{\lambda E(S^2)}{2[1-\rho(\sigma_{j-1})][1-\rho(\sigma_j)]} \qquad (j = 1, 2,..., (k+1)) \tag{8.4}$$

where $\sigma_0 = 0$ and $\sigma_{k+1} = \infty$. The overall expected waiting time is

$$\begin{aligned} \Xi_{k+1}(\sigma_1, ..., \sigma_k) &= \sum_{j=1}^{k+1} \alpha_j E[\hat{\mathscr{W}}_j^{(k+1)}] \\ &= \frac{\lambda E(S^2)}{2} \sum_{j=1}^{k+1} \frac{\alpha(\sigma_{j-1}, \sigma_j)}{[1-\rho(\sigma_{j-1})][1-\rho(\sigma_j)]} \end{aligned} \tag{8.5}$$

We assume that $\lambda E(S) < 1$, which implies $\rho(\sigma_j) < 1$ for all j. Noting that $\frac{1}{2}\lambda E(S^2)$ is constant with respect to the choice of $(\sigma_1, ..., \sigma_k)$, we want to choose these latter variables so as to minimize

$$\sum_{j=1}^{k+1} \frac{\alpha(\sigma_{j-1}, \sigma_j)}{[1-\rho(\sigma_{j-1})][1-\rho(\sigma_j)]} \tag{8.6}$$

The reason this minimization problem is not trivial is that we have the inequality constraints $0 \leqslant \sigma_1 \leqslant \sigma_2 \leqslant \cdots \leqslant \sigma_k \leqslant \infty$. Thus, except when $k = 1$, we will have to use a more sophisticated optimization technique than the usual calculus method. It turns out that, due to the above special character of the constraint set, dynamic programming is ideal for this problem. If the reader is not familiar with this method he may find it useful to consult either the book by Bellman [7] or by Bellman and Dreyfus [8].

Let us now consider the "general $(k+1)$-class priority problem" defined as follows. For customers with service-time requirements less than or equal to x, find the points $(\sigma_1, ..., \sigma_k)$ such that (i) $0 \leqslant \sigma_1 \leqslant \sigma_2 \leqslant \cdots \leqslant \sigma_k \leqslant x$ and (ii) Eq. (8.6) is minimized, where now the interpretation is that $\sigma_{k+1} = x$ (instead of ∞).

Let $f_{k+1}(x)$ be the minimum value of (8.6). That is,

$$f_{k+1}(x) = \min_{0 \leqslant \sigma_1 \leqslant \cdots \leqslant \sigma_k \leqslant x} \sum_{j=1}^{k+1} \frac{\alpha(\sigma_{j-1}, \sigma_j)}{[1-\rho(\sigma_{j-1})][1-\rho(\sigma_j)]} \tag{8.7}$$

If $\Xi_{k+1}^*(\sigma_1, ..., \sigma_k)$ denotes the minimum value of (8.5), then

$$\Xi_{k+1}^*(\sigma_1, ..., \sigma_k) = \tfrac{1}{2}\lambda E(S^2) f_{k+1}(\infty) \tag{8.8}$$

Observe that $\frac{1}{2}\lambda E(S^2) f_{k+1}(x)$ is the minimum expected waiting time for only those units with a service time requirement less than or equal to x.

Suppose we fix σ_k at $y(0 \leqslant y \leqslant x)$. Then the mean waiting time of the customers in the class $(y, x]$ is

$$E[\hat{\mathscr{W}}_{k+1}^{(k+1)}] = \frac{\lambda E(S^2)}{2[1 - \rho(y)][1 - \rho(x)]} \tag{8.9}$$

Now, we choose $0 \leqslant \sigma_1 \leqslant \sigma_2 \leqslant \cdots \leqslant \sigma_{k-1} \leqslant \sigma_k = y$ so as to minimize the expected waiting time of customers in the class $(0, y]$. By definition, this minimum has the value $\frac{1}{2}\lambda E(S^2) f_k(y)$. Hence, by following the above procedure, i.e., fixing y_k at y and choosing $\sigma_1, ..., \sigma_{k-1}$ optimally, the expected waiting time of all the customers in the class $(0, x]$ is

$$\frac{\lambda E(S^2)}{2} \left\{ f_k(y) + \frac{\alpha(y, x)}{[1 - \rho(y)][1 - \rho(x)]} \right\} \tag{8.10}$$

We now note that $\frac{1}{2}\lambda E(S^2) f_{k+1}(x)$ is the minimum of expression (8.10) over all y in the range $(0, x)$, whence we obtain the functional relationship

$$f_{k+1}(x) = \min_{0 \leqslant y \leqslant x} \left\{ f_k(y) + \frac{\alpha(y, x)}{[1 - \rho(y)][1 - \rho(x)]} \right\} \tag{8.11}$$

This last remark follows from the facts that:

(i) The expected waiting time of the class $(y, x]$ is the same irrespective of the priority classification scheme in $(0, y]$ as long as we have no preemption.

(ii) If $(\sigma_1^*, \sigma_2^*, ..., \sigma_k^*)$ solve the general $(k + 1)$th-class priority problem, then $(\sigma_1^*, \sigma_2^*, ..., \sigma_{k-1}^*)$ solve the general k-class priority problem for $x = \sigma_k^*$. This is the "principle of optimality" typically involved in all dynamic programming solutions.

In particular, for $k = 2$,

$$f_2(x) = \min_{0 \leqslant y \leqslant x} g_1(y, x) = g_1(\sigma_1^*, x) \tag{8.12}$$

where

$$g_1(y, x) = \frac{\alpha(0, y)}{1 - \rho(y)} + \frac{\alpha(y, x)}{[1 - \rho(y)][1 - \rho(x)]}$$

Clearly,

$$f_1(x) \geqslant f_2(x)$$

since

$$g_1(x, x) = f_1(x)$$

Now, if $\int_0^y S(t)\,dt$ and $\int_y^x S(t)\,dt$ are both strictly positive, then it can be shown that $g_1(y, x) < f_1(x)$. Otherwise, $g_1(y, x) = f_1(x)$. Hence, if $\int_0^x S(t)\,dt$ is positive and the service-time distribution is continuous, then σ_1^*, the unconstrained minimum of $g(y, x)$, is assumed to be between 0 and x and is given by

$$\frac{\rho(x)}{\int_0^x S(t)\,dt} = \frac{\lambda\sigma_1^*}{1 + \lambda\sigma_1^* \int_0^{\sigma_1^*} S(t)\,dt - \rho(\sigma_1^*)} \tag{8.13}$$

Let us define

$$u_1(x) = 1 + \lambda x \int_0^x S(t)\,dt - \rho(x) \tag{8.14}$$

and

$$v(x) = \frac{\int_0^x tS(t)\,dt}{\int_0^x S(t)\,dt} = \frac{\rho(x)}{\lambda \int_0^x S(t)\,dt} \tag{8.15}$$

where $v(x)$ is the conditional mean service time of customers having service times in $(0, x)$.

The equation (8.13) defining σ_1^* can now be written as

$$\sigma_1^* = u_1(\sigma_1^*)\, v(x) \tag{8.16}$$

For any given x we can solve (8.16) for σ_1^*, which is the optimum classification point.

For the "general k-class problem," we can write, following our earlier notation, the general functional equation (8.11) as

$$f_{k+1}(x) = \min_{0 \leqslant y \leqslant x} g_k(y, x) \tag{8.17}$$

As before, σ_k^*, the minimizing y, is given by the equation

$$\frac{dg_k(y, x)}{dy} = 0 \tag{8.18}$$

We define $v(y, x)$ such that

$$\frac{d}{dy}\left\{\frac{\alpha(y, x)}{[1 - \rho(y)][1 - \rho(x)]}\right\} = \frac{-S(y)}{[1 - \rho(y)]^2}\, v(y, x) \tag{8.19}$$

Thus,

$$v(y, x) = \frac{1 - \rho(y) - \lambda y \int_y^x S(t)\, dt}{1 - \rho(x)} \tag{8.20}$$

and (8.18) can then be seen to be

$$\frac{df_k(y)}{dy} = \frac{S(y)}{[1 - \rho(y)]^2}\, v(y, x) \tag{8.21}$$

and σ_k^* solves Eq. (8.21).

Now,

$$f_k(x) = f_{k-1}[\sigma_{k-1}^*(x)] + \frac{\alpha[\sigma_{k-1}^*(x), x]}{\{1 - \rho[\sigma_{k-1}^*(x)]\}[1 - \rho(x)]}$$

so that

$$\frac{df_k(x)}{dx} = \frac{\partial}{\partial x}\left\{\frac{\alpha[\sigma_{k-1}^*(x), x]}{[1 - \rho(\sigma_{k-1}^*(x))][1 - \rho(x)]}\right\} = \frac{S(x)}{[1 - \rho(x)]^2}\, v[x, \sigma_{k-1}^*(x)] \tag{8.22}$$

using the fact that $\sigma_{k-1}^*(x)$ solves (8.21) for $(k - 1)$. We have also used the property that for any function $\phi(y, x)$ such that $\phi(y, x) = -\phi(x, y)$,

$$\frac{\partial \phi}{\partial x} = - \left.\frac{\partial \phi}{\partial y}\right|_{(x,y)}$$

Equations (8.21) and (8.22) together imply that σ_k^* is the solution of

$$u_k(y) - v(y, x) = 0 \tag{8.23}$$

where

$$u_k(x) = v[x, \sigma_{k-1}^*(x)] \tag{8.24}$$

Knowing $\sigma_{k-1}^*(x)$ for all x, we can compute the function $u_k(x)$ from (8.24). This in turn specifies the equation (8.23) completely, so that the solution $\sigma_k^*(x)$ can be obtained for all x. Thus, starting from $\sigma_1^*(x)$, which is computed from (8.16), we can find $\sigma_k^*(x)$ for all k and x.

Reference is made to the original paper by Oliver and Pestalozzi [68] if a more rigorous presentation of the preceding results is desired. In that paper, it is further shown that the sequence $\{u_k(x)\}$ is monotonic nonincreasing and is bounded below by 1. The limiting properties as k tends to infinity have also been studied in that work. If $f(x)$ is the limit of $f_k(x)$ as $k \to \infty$, then

$$f(x) = \min_{0 \leqslant y \leqslant x} \left\{ f(y) + \frac{\alpha(y, x)}{[1 - \rho(y)][1 - \rho(x)]} \right\} \tag{8.25}$$

The minimizing y satisfies the equation

$$u(y) - v(y, x) = 0 \tag{8.26}$$

where $u(y) = \lim_{k\to\infty} u_k(y) = 1$ for $y > 0$. Hence, the root of the equation (8.26) is x. In other words, this solution simply says that every time we select for service the customer with the minimum service-time requirement. This latter result has also been obtained by Phipps [72].

Example. Exponential Service Time

Let $S(t) = (1/\nu) \exp(-t/\nu)$ and $\lambda = 1$. This can be done by an appropriate choice of the unit of time. We classify the customers into two groups, one having service time less than or equal to $\phi\nu$, and the other consisting of the rest of the customers. The optimum ϕ is given by

$$\frac{1}{\nu} = 1 + \frac{e^{-\phi}}{\phi - 1}$$

Chapter VI

DISCRETIONARY PRIORITY DISCIPLINE

1. Introduction

We mentioned in Chapter III that a priority discipline is specified by two rules, the first indicating the manner in which a unit is selected for service, and the second, the manner in which the unit is serviced after entering service. The first rule is basic, and leads to exogenous and endogenous disciplines, depending, respectively, on whether it is independent or dependent on the state of the system. However, the second rule may be state-independent or state-dependent. We studied in Chapters IV and V the preemptive and head-of-the-line disciplines, for which the second rule is independent of the state. Consequently, in the preemptive discipline, we may preempt an ordinary unit whose service is almost completed, or, in the head-of-the-line discipline, we may allow a priority unit to wait even if the ordinary unit has just entered service. Obviously, such possibilities can be avoided by making the second rule state-dependent, i.e., by allowing the server to use his discretion to continue or discontinue the service of an ordinary unit. This leads to the "discretionary priority discipline."

Let us consider a two-class priority process. Whenever a priority unit arrives to find an ordinary unit in service, the server uses his discretion in the following manner: If the service time of the ordinary unit is less than a fixed constant z, the preemptive discipline is applied, while if the ordinary unit has received an amount of service greater than or equal to z, the head-of-the-line discipline is adopted. This discipline, called the discretionary priority discipline, was introduced in a paper by Avi-Itzhak *et al.* [3], and has been studied recently by Etschmaier [25].

It will be noted that the implementation of this discipline requires that the amount of service received by an ordinary unit must be constantly recorded, and it is thus more difficult to apply. The decision to implement such a rule will thus have to balance the cost incurred in keeping the extra information against the gain in having less congestion or delay.

Since the discipline is exogenous, the mathematics of Chapter III can be applied as in the previous two chapters. Consequently, we study the completion-time process in detail and use the results of Chapter III to obtain the characteristics of the system. We note that although any preemptive discipline, resume, repeat-identical or repeat-different, may be assumed in our analysis, we derive the results only for an infinite-source preemptive resume—head-of-the-line discretionary model.

2. Completion-Time Process

For the preemptive resume—head-of-the-line discretionary model, the completion-time cycle is shown in Fig. VI.1.

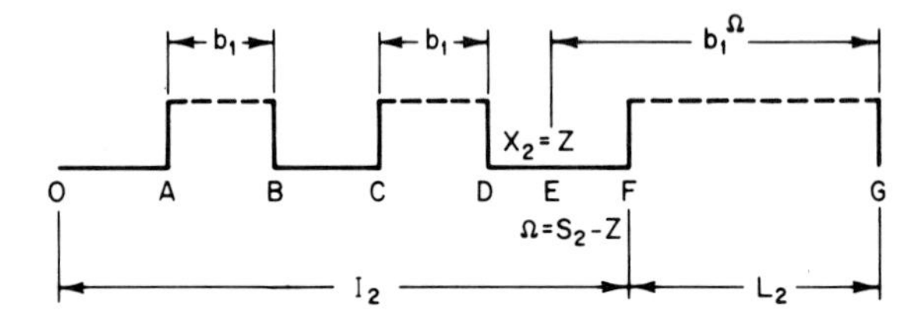

FIG. VI.1. Completion time cycle for the discretionary priority process.

The service of the ordinary unit which is initiated at $t = 0$ is interrupted by the arrival of a priority unit at A. At B, the ordinary unit enters service again and is interrupted at C. This continues until a point E is reached at which the elapsed service time of the ordinary unit is z, after which the service of the ordinary unit is continued to completion even if priority units arrive. Finally, the server starts service on the priority units which accumulate during EF, and, at G, when the server is free to take up the next ordinary unit, the completion time ends. Thus, the completion-time cycle is the same as the cycle under the preemptive resume discipline up to E, and from E on, it is identical to the cycle under the head-of-the-line discipline but with the service time of the ordinary unit $\Omega = S_2 - z$. We can thus obtain the results directly from the results of the completion-time processes studied earlier. However, it would be useful to derive the results from the results of the basic models. Consequently, we define the probability densities $f^I(0, x_2, t)$, $g^I(m_1, x_1, x_2, t)$, $f^{I'}(m_1, x_2, t)$, $g^L(m_1, x_1, t)$, and $c_2(t)$ as in Section III, 3. Note that we have divided the time during which the ordinary unit stays in the system into two parts, I_2 and I_2'.

Equations for the process are

$$\frac{\partial}{\partial t} f^I(0, x_2, t) + \frac{\partial}{\partial x_2} f^I(0, x_2, t + [\lambda_1 + \eta_2(x_2)] f^I(0, x_2, t)$$

$$= \lambda_1 f^I(0, x_2, t) * b_1(t) \qquad (x_2 < z) \tag{2.1}$$

$$g^I(m_1, x_1, x_2, t) = \lambda_1 f^I(0, x_2, t) * p(m_1, x_1, t) \qquad (x_2 < z) \tag{2.2}$$

$$f^{I'}(m_1, x_2, t) = f^I[0, z, t - (x_2 - z)] \frac{[\lambda_1(x_2 - z)]^{m_1}}{m_1!} \exp[-\lambda_1(x_2 - z)]$$

$$\times \frac{\exp[-\int_0^{x_2} \eta_2(x)\, dx]}{F_2{}^c(z)} \tag{2.3}$$

$$g^L(m_1, x_1, t) = f^I(0, z, t) * p^{\Omega}(m_1, x_1, t) \tag{2.4}$$

and

$$c_2(t) = \int_0^z f^I(0, x_2, t)\, S_2(x_2)\, dx_2 + f^I(0, z, t) * b_1{}^{\Omega}(t) \tag{2.5}$$

where

$$\Omega(y) = \frac{S_2(z + y)}{F_2{}^c(z)} \qquad \text{and} \qquad F_2{}^c(z) = \int_z^\infty S_2(x_2)\, dx_2\,.$$

These equations are to be solved subject to the initial condition $f^I(0, x_2, 0) = \delta(x_2)$.

Taking the Laplace transform and solving the above equations, we get

$$f^I(0, x_2, s) = \exp\left[-\{\lambda_1[1 - \bar{b}_1(s)] + s\}\, x_2 - \int_0^{x_2} \eta_2(x)\, dx\right] \qquad (x_2 < z) \tag{2.6}$$

$$\bar{g}^I(m_1, x_1, x_2, s) = \lambda_1 f^I(0, x_2, s)\, \bar{p}(m_1, x_1, s) \qquad (x_2 < z) \tag{2.7}$$

$$f^{I'}(m_1, x_2, s) = \frac{f^I(0, z, s)}{F_2{}^c(z)} \frac{[\lambda_1(x_2 - z)]^{m_1}}{m_1!} \exp[-(\lambda_1 + s)(x_2 - z)]\, F_2{}^c(x_2) \qquad (x_2 \geqslant z) \tag{2.8}$$

$$\bar{g}^L(m_1, x_1, s) = f^I(0, z, s)\, \bar{p}^\Omega[m_1, x_1, s] \tag{2.9}$$

and

$$\bar{c}_2(s) = \int_0^\infty f^I(0, x_2, s)\, S_2(x_2)\, dx_2 + f^I(0, z, s)\, \bar{b}_1{}^\Omega(s) \tag{2.10}$$

Substituting (2.6) in (2.10), we obtain

$$\begin{aligned}\bar{c}_2(s) = \int_0^z &\exp[-\{\lambda_1(1 - \bar{b}_1(s)) + s\}\, x_2]\, S_2(x_2)\, dx_2 \\ &+ \exp[-\{\lambda_1(1 - \bar{b}_1(s)) + s\}\, z]\, F_2{}^c(z) \int_0^\infty \frac{S_2(z + y)}{F_2{}^c(z)} \\ &\times \exp[-\{\lambda_1(1 - \bar{b}_1(s)) + s\}\, y]\, dy\end{aligned} \tag{2.11}$$

so that

$$\bar{c}_2(s) = \bar{S}_2[\lambda_1\{1 - \bar{b}_1(s)\} + s] \tag{2.12}$$

This is the same as for the preemptive resume and head-of-the-line disciplines. This is obviously so because the completion-time density will be the same for any exogenous priority discipline in which the service time of the ordinary unit is not wasted (cf. preemptive repeat).

Defining $p^I(m_1, t)$ and $p^L(m_2, t)$ as in Section III, 3 and using (III, 3.1) and (III, 3.2), we obtain

$$\begin{aligned}\bar{p}^I(m_1, s) = &\left[1 + \lambda_1 \int_0^\infty \bar{p}(m_1, x_1, s)\, dx_1\right] \int_0^z f^I(0, x_2, s)\, dx_2 \\ &+ \frac{f^I(0, z, s)}{F_2{}^c(z)} \int_z^\infty \frac{[\lambda_1(x_2 - z)]^{m_1}}{m_1!} \\ &\times \exp[-(\lambda_1 + s)(x_2 - z)]\, F_2{}^c(x_2)\, dx_2\end{aligned} \tag{2.13}$$

$$\bar{p}^L(m_1, s) = f^I(0, z, s) \int_0^\infty \bar{p}^\Omega(m_1, x_1, s)\, dx_1 \tag{2.14}$$

so that

$$\bar{\Pi}^I(\alpha_1, s)$$

$$= \sum_{m_1=0}^{\infty} \alpha_1^{m_1} \bar{p}^I(m_1, s)$$

$$= [1 + \lambda_1 \bar{\Pi}(\alpha_1, s)] \int_0^z \bar{f}^I(0, x_2, s)\, dx_2$$

$$+ \frac{\bar{f}^I(0, z, s)}{F_2{}^c(z)} \int_z^{\infty} \exp[-\{\lambda_1(1 - \alpha_1) + s\}(x_2 - z)]\, F_2{}^c(x_2)\, dx_2 \qquad (2.15)$$

and, from (I, 2.23), we obtain

$$\bar{\Pi}^L(\alpha_1, s)$$

$$= \bar{f}^I(0, z, s) \frac{[\bar{\Omega}[\lambda_1(1 - \alpha_1) + s] - \bar{\Omega}[\lambda_1\{1 - \bar{b}_1(s)\} + s]][1 - \bar{S}_1\{\lambda_1(1 - \alpha_1) + s\}]}{[1 - (1/\alpha_1)\, \bar{S}_1(\lambda_1(1 - \alpha_1) + s)][\lambda_1(1 - \alpha_1) + s]} \qquad (2.16)$$

so that, from (III, 3.3), we get

$$\bar{\Pi}^c(\alpha_1, \alpha_2, s)$$

$$= \alpha_2[1 + \lambda_1 \bar{\Pi}(\alpha_1, s)] \int_0^z \exp[-\{\lambda_1(1 - \bar{b}_1(s)) + s\}\, x_2]\, F_2{}^c(x_2)\, dx_2$$

$$+ \exp[-\{\lambda_1(1 - \bar{b}_1(s)) + s\}\, z]\, F_2{}^c(z)$$

$$\times \Bigg[\alpha_2 \int_0^{\infty} \exp[-\{\lambda_1(1 - \alpha_1) + s\}\, x_2]\, \frac{F_2{}^c(x_2 + z)\, dx_2}{F_2{}^c(z)}$$

$$+ \frac{\bar{\Omega}[\lambda_1(1 - \alpha_1) + s] - \bar{\Omega}[\lambda_1\{1 - \bar{b}_1(s)\} + s]}{1 - (1/\alpha_1)\, \bar{S}_1[\lambda_1(1 - \alpha_1) + s]}\, \frac{1 - \bar{S}_1[\lambda_1(1 - \alpha_1) + s]}{\lambda_1(1 - \alpha_1) + s}\Bigg] \qquad (2.17)$$

Note that for $z = 0$, the discretionary priority discipline must reduce to the head-of-the-line discipline, and for $z = \infty$, to the preemptive resume discipline. Hence, for $z = 0$ and $z = \infty$, (2.17) reduces to (V, 2.6) and (IV, 2.15), respectively.

3. Evaluation of the System Characteristics

3-1. Busy Period

Since the completion-time density under this discipline is the same as for the preemptive resume discipline or the head-of-the-line discipline, the busy-period distribution is the same for all these disciplines (see Sections IV, 3 and V, 3).

3-2. Joint Queue–Length Probabilities

Substituting (2.17) in (III, 5.4), we obtain the Laplace transform of the transient probability generating function. Then, following the renewal arguments of Section III, 6, we find that if $\lambda_2 E(c_2) < 1$, i.e., if $\rho_1 + \rho_2 < 1$, the steady-state queue-length distribution exists and is obtained from (III, 6.3) by appropriate substitutions. To obtain the mean queue lengths we derive from (2.15) and (2.16) the following results:

$$\bar{\Pi}^I[1, 0] = \nu_2 + \frac{\rho_1}{1-\rho_1} \int_0^z F_2{}^c(x_2)\, dx_2 \tag{3.1}$$

$$\frac{\partial}{\partial \alpha_1} \bar{\Pi}^I[\alpha_1, 0]|_{\alpha_1=1} = \frac{E(\hat{m}_1)}{\hat{e}_1}\left[z - \int_0^z (z - x_2)\, S_2(x_2)\, dx_2\right] + \frac{\lambda_1}{2}\int_z^\infty (x_2 - z)^2\, S_2(x_2)\, dx_2 \tag{3.2}$$

$$\bar{\Pi}^L[\alpha_1, 0]|_{\alpha_1=1} = \frac{\rho_1}{1-\rho_1}\int_z^\infty (x_2 - z)\, S_2(x_2)\, dx_2 \tag{3.3}$$

and

$$\frac{\partial}{\partial \alpha_1} \bar{\Pi}^L[\alpha_1, 0]|_{\alpha_1=1} = \frac{\lambda_1 \rho_1}{2(1-\rho_1)}\int_z^\infty (x_2 - z)^2\, S_2(x_2)\, dx_2 + \frac{E(\hat{m}_1)}{\hat{e}_1}\int_z^\infty (x_2 - z)\, S_2(x_2)\, dx_2 \tag{3.4}$$

where $\rho_1 = \lambda_1 \nu_1$, $\hat{e}_1 = 1 - \rho_1$, and $E(\hat{m}_1)$ defined by (I, 4.8) is given as

$$E(\hat{m}_1) = \rho_1 + \frac{\lambda_1{}^2 E(S_1{}^2)}{2(1-\rho_1)} \tag{3.5}$$

Substituting these in (III, 6.5) and (III, 6.6), we obtain, after simplification, the following results:

$$E(\hat{\mathscr{M}}_1) = \frac{\lambda_1 \lambda_2}{2(1-\rho_1)}\int_z^\infty (x_2 - z)^2\, S_2(x_2)\, dx_2 + \rho_1 + \frac{\lambda_1{}^2 E(S_1{}^2)}{2(1-\rho_1)} \tag{3.6}$$

and

$$E(\hat{\mathscr{M}}_2) = -\frac{\lambda_2 \rho_1}{1-\rho_1}\int_z^\infty (x_2 - z)\, S_2(x_2)\, dx_2 + \frac{\rho_2}{1-\rho_1} + \frac{\lambda_1 \lambda_2}{2}\,\frac{E(S_1{}^2)}{(1-\rho_1)^2} + \frac{\lambda_2{}^2}{2}\,\frac{E(c_2{}^2)}{1-\lambda_2 E(c_2)} \tag{3.7}$$

where $E(c_2)$ and $E(c_2{}^2)$ are given by (IV, 2.7) and (IV, 2.8) respectively. Other moments can be evaluated in a similar way.

3-3. Occupation Time of the Server

To determine the occupation-time density of the server with respect to priority units, let us derive $\bar{w}_1{}^c(\theta, s)$ defined in Section III, 7. We can obtain it by substituting the completion-time process probabilities in (III, 7.2), so that

$$w_1{}^c(\tau, t) = \delta(\tau) \int_{x_2=0}^{z} f^I(0, x_2, t)\, dx_2$$

$$+ \sum_{m_1=1}^{\infty} \int_{x_2=0}^{z} \int_0^{\infty} g^I(m_1, x_1, x_2, t)\, dx_1\, dx_2$$

$$\times \int_{y=0}^{\tau} \frac{S_1(x_1+y)}{1-\int_0^{x_1} S_1(x)\, dx} S_1^{*m_1}(\tau - y)\, dy$$

$$+ \sum_{m_1=0}^{\infty} \int_{x_2=z}^{\infty} f^{I'}(m_1, x_2, t)\, dx_2$$

$$\times \int_{y=0}^{\tau} \frac{S_2(x_2+y)\, dy}{1-\int_0^{x_2} S_2(x)\, dx} S_1^{*m_1-1}(\tau - y)$$

$$+ \sum_{m_1=1}^{\infty} \int_{x_1=0}^{\infty} f^L(m_1, x_1, t)$$

$$\times \int_{y=0}^{\tau} \frac{S_1(x_1+y)}{1-\int_0^{x_1} S_1(x)\, dx} S_1^{*m_1-1}(\tau - y)\, dy\, dx_1 \quad (3.8)$$

Hence, taking Laplace transforms, we obtain, after simplification,

$$\bar{w}_1{}^c(\theta, s) = \int_{x_2=0}^{z} \bar{f}^I(0, x_2, s)\, dx_2\, [1 + \bar{w}_1(\theta, s)] + \bar{f}^I(0, z, s)\, \bar{w}_1{}^{\Omega}(\theta, s) \quad (3.9)$$

Using (3.9) in (III, 7.4), we obtain the double Laplace transform of the occupation-time density of the server with respect to priority units, so that

$$\bar{\bar{\mathscr{W}}}_1(\theta, s) = \frac{\bar{\bar{e}}^{(2)}(s)}{\bar{\bar{e}}_1(s)} \bar{\bar{w}}_1(\theta, s)$$

$$+ \frac{\bar{\bar{e}}_1(s) - \bar{\bar{e}}_2(s)}{[1 - \bar{c}_2(s)]\, \bar{\bar{e}}_1(s)} \left[\frac{\bar{\bar{w}}_1(\theta, s)}{\bar{\bar{e}}_1(s)} \int_0^z \bar{f}^I(0, x_2, s)\, dx_2 + \bar{f}^I(0, z, s)\, \bar{w}_1{}^{\Omega}(\theta, s) \right]$$

$$(3.10)$$

From (3.10), we obtain the Laplace transform of the occupation-time density of the server with respect to priority units; this becomes, after simplification

$$\bar{\hat{\mathscr{W}}}_1(\theta) = \frac{\theta \hat{e}^{(2)} + \lambda_2 \theta \int_0^z F_2{}^c(x_2)\, dx_2 + \lambda_2 F_2{}^c(z)[1 - \bar{\Omega}(\theta)]}{\theta - \lambda_1 + \lambda_1 \bar{S}_1(\theta)} \tag{3.11}$$

where

$$\bar{\Omega}(\theta) = \int_0^\infty e^{-\theta x} \frac{S_2(z + x)}{F_2{}^c(z)}\, dx$$

The moments of the waiting time can be obtained from (3.11) by the usual method of differentiation; e.g., the mean waiting time of a priority unit is given by

$$E(\hat{\mathscr{W}}_1) = \frac{\lambda_1 E(S_1{}^2) + \lambda_2 \int_z^\infty (x_2 - z)^2\, S_2(x_2)\, dx_2}{2(1 - \rho_1)} \tag{3.12}$$

For the ordinary unit, the transient waiting-time density in the queue is given by (III, 7.11) and under steady state by (III, 7.12). The mean waiting time is given by (III, 7.13) and is the same as for the head-of-the-line or preemptive discipline. However, the mean delay time is different, and is obtained by adding the expected duration for which an ordinary unit stays during the completion time to the mean waiting time, so that

$$E(\hat{\mathscr{D}}_2) = \int_0^\infty \Pi^I(1, t)\, dt + \frac{\lambda_2 E(c_2{}^2)}{2[1 - \lambda_2 E(c_2)]} + \frac{1}{2} \lambda_1 \frac{E(b_1{}^2)}{1 + \lambda_1 E(b_1)} \tag{3.13}$$

where $\Pi^I(1, t)$ denotes the probability that at time t the ordinary unit is present during the completion time, so that

$$E(I_2) = \int_0^\infty \Pi^I(1, t)\, dt = \bar{\Pi}^I[1, 0]$$

Thus, using (3.1), we get

$$E(\hat{\mathscr{D}}_2) = \nu_2 + \frac{\rho_1}{1 - \rho_1} \int_0^z F_2{}^c(x_2)\, dx_2 + \frac{\lambda_1 E(S_1{}^2) + \lambda_2 E(S_2{}^2)}{2(1 - \rho_1)(1 - \rho_1 - \rho_2)} \tag{3.14}$$

We have thus evaluated the system characteristics for discretionary priority models in which both priority and ordinary units emanate from infinite sources. The discipline can be extended to study other models, such as the (N_1, ∞), (∞, N_2), and (N_1, N_2) models. It may be pointed out that the last two models will require the results of the restoration-time models, as in Section V, 5. The results will obviously be complicated and will not be derived here. The reader may like to work these models as exercises.

4. Optimal Discretion Point

The point of discretion z can be chosen so as to optimize a given objective function. Consider, for example, the simplest case, in which the objective is to minimize the total delay cost of the priority and ordinary units, assuming the costs to be linear. If $T(z)$ represents the total delay cost for a specified value of z, then

$$T(z) = K_1\lambda_1 E(\hat{\mathscr{D}}_1) + K_2\lambda_2 E(\hat{\mathscr{D}}_2) \tag{4.1}$$

where K_1 and K_2 are the delay costs per unit time. Hence, using (3.12) with the addition of ν_1 and $E(\hat{\mathscr{D}}_2)$, we get

$$T(z) = \frac{K_1\lambda_1\lambda_2}{2(1-\rho_1)} \int_z^\infty (x_2 - z)^2 \, S_2(x_2)\, dx_2 - \frac{K_2\lambda_2\rho_1}{1-\rho_1} \int_z^\infty (x_2 - z)\, S_2(x_2)\, dx_2$$
$$+ K_1\left[\rho_1 + \frac{\lambda_1{}^2 E(S_1{}^2)}{2(1-\rho_1)}\right] + K_2\left[\frac{\rho_2}{1-\rho_2} + \frac{\lambda_1\lambda_2 E(S_1{}^2) + \lambda_2{}^2 E(S_2{}^2)}{2(1-\rho_1-\rho_2)(1-\rho_1)}\right] \tag{4.2}$$

The optimum value z_0 of z is given by

$$\frac{\partial T}{\partial z} = -\frac{K_1\lambda_1\lambda_2}{(1-\rho_1)} \int_{z_0}^\infty (x_2 - z_0)\, S_2(x_2)\, dx_2 + \frac{K_2\lambda_2\rho_1}{(1-\rho_1)} \int_{z_0}^\infty S_2(x_2)\, dx_2 = 0 \tag{4.3}$$

or

$$\frac{K_1}{\nu_1} = \frac{K_2}{E(S_2^{z_0})} \tag{4.4}$$

where

$$E(S_2^{z_0}) = \frac{\int_{z_0}^\infty (x_2 - z_0)\, S_2(x_2)\, dx_2}{\int_{z_0}^\infty S_2(x_2)\, dx_2}$$

is the expected remaining service time of a unit after being in service for a time z_0. However, for z_0 to be minimum, we require that

$$\left.\frac{\partial^2 T}{\partial z^2}\right|_{z=z_0} = \frac{\lambda_1\lambda_2}{1-\rho_1}\left[K_1 \int_{z_0}^{\infty} S_2(x_2)\, dx_2 - K_2\nu_1 S_2(z_0)\right] > 0 \tag{4.5}$$

or

$$\frac{S_2(z_0)}{F_2{}^c(z_0)} < \frac{K_1}{K_2\nu_1} \tag{4.6}$$

Thus, using (4.4), z_0 will be minimum if

$$\frac{S_2(z_0)}{F_2{}^c(z_0)} < \frac{1}{E(S_2^{z_0})} = \frac{F_2{}^c(z_0)}{\int_{z_0}^{\infty} F_2{}^c(x_2)\, dx_2} \tag{4.7}$$

We will show by examples below that this condition is satisfied so that the optimum discretion point is given by (4.4).

The reader will note that if $E(S_2{}^z)$, the expected residual time, is a monotonic decreasing function in z, (4.4) can be interpreted as follows: If $K_2/E(S_2{}^z) < K_1/\nu_1$, the priority unit preempts the ordinary unit; otherwise it does not. The policy will minimize the total delay cost if (4.7) is satisfied. Thus, if the service time of the ordinary unit has a distribution such that the mean residual time is a monotonic decreasing function, we may minimize the delay cost by choosing the above policy. In the examples below, we determine the optimum z_0 when the service-time distribution of the ordinary units is specified as follows:

Example A. k-Erlang Distribution

Equations (4.3) and (4.7) take the form

$$\exp\left[-\frac{kz_0}{\nu_2}\right] \sum_{i=0}^{k-1} \left[K_2 E(S_1) - K_1\nu_2\left(\frac{k-i}{k}\right)\right] \frac{1}{i!}\left(\frac{kz_0}{\nu_2}\right)^i = 0 \tag{4.8}$$

and

$$\left.\frac{\partial^2 T}{\partial z^2}\right|_{z=z_0}$$

$$= \frac{\lambda_1\lambda_2}{1-\rho_1} \exp\left[-\frac{kz_0}{\nu_2}\right]\left\{K_1 \sum_{i=0}^{k-1} \frac{1}{i!}\left(\frac{kz_0}{\nu_2}\right)^i - K_2 E(S_1)\frac{1}{(k-1)!}\frac{k}{\nu_2}\left(\frac{kz_0}{\nu_2}\right)^{k-1}\right\} \tag{4.9}$$

If

$$\frac{1}{k} < \frac{K_2\nu_1}{K_1\nu_2} < 1$$

it can be shown by Decartes' sign rule that a root z_0 of (4.8) exists such that $0 \leqslant z_0 < \infty$, and at this value $\partial^2 T/\partial z^2 > 0$, so that $T(z)$ attains a minimum at z_0. Note that $z_0 = \infty$ satisfies (4.8), but at this point the second and all higher order derivatives vanish; $z_0 = \infty$ corresponds to the preemptive resume case, and the total delay cost function approaches asymptotically to the value for the preemptive resume discipline. The behavior of the normalized total delay cost $T(z)/T(\infty)$ is shown in Fig. VI.2 for different values of k.

Example B. Exponential Distribution

Putting $k = 1$ in the above results, we obtain

$$\frac{\partial T}{\partial z} = -\frac{\lambda_1\lambda_2}{1-\rho_1}[K_1\nu_2 - K_2\nu_1]\, e^{-z/\nu_2} \tag{4.10}$$

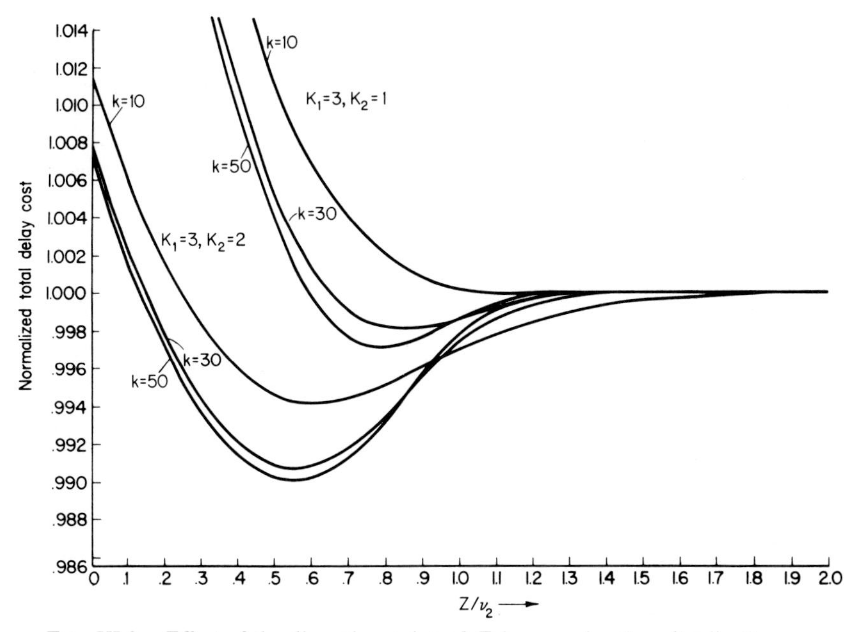

FIG. VI.2. Effect of the discretion point—k-Erlang service time distribution.

and

$$\frac{\partial^2 T}{\partial z^2} = \frac{\lambda_1 \lambda_2}{\nu_2(1 - \rho_1)} [K_1 \nu_2 - K_2 \nu_1] \, e^{-z/\nu_2} \tag{4.11}$$

Thus, if $K_1\nu_2 > K_2\nu_1$, $\partial^2 T/\partial z^2$ is positive and tends to zero as $z \to \infty$, so that, from (4.10), $T(z)$ attains the minimum value at $z = \infty$, i.e., the preemptive resume policy will be optimal. Similarly, if $K_1\nu_2 < K_2\nu_1$, $\partial^2 T/\partial z^2$ is negative and tends to zero as $z \to \infty$, giving a minimum at $z = 0$, i.e., the head-of-the-line policy will be optimal. If $K_1\nu_2 = K_2\nu_1$, the cost is constant over the whole range of z, and thus the discretionary discipline has no significance. These conclusions are depicted graphically in Fig. VI. 3.

Example C. Constant Service Time

Taking $k \to \infty$, we get

$$\frac{\partial T}{\partial z} = \frac{\lambda_1 \lambda_2}{1 - \rho_1} [-K_1(\nu_1 - z) + K_2 \nu_1], \qquad z \leqslant \nu_2 \tag{4.12}$$

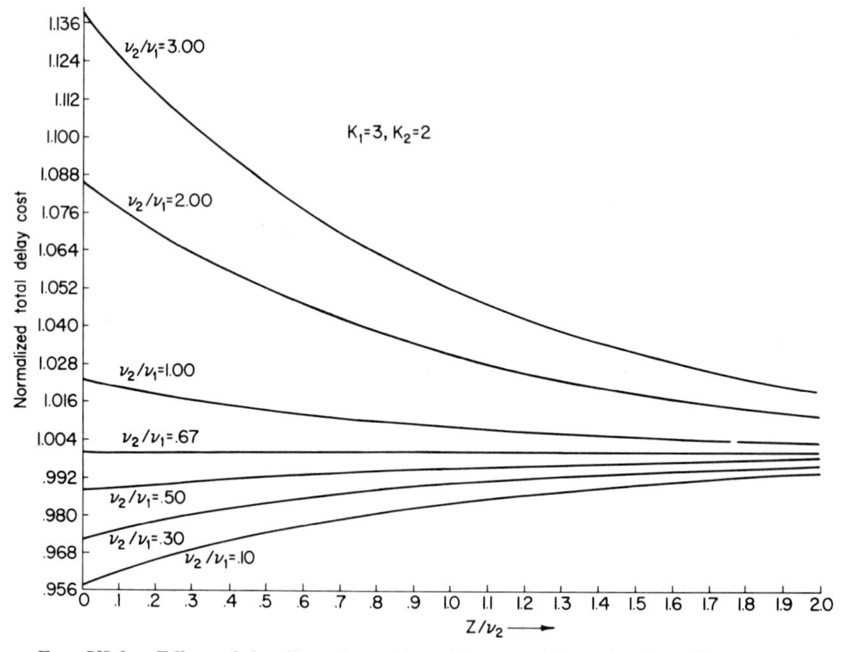

FIG. VI.3. Effect of the discretion point—Exponential service time distribution.

and

$$\frac{\partial^2 T}{\partial z^2} = \frac{\lambda_1 \lambda_2 K_1}{1 - \rho_1} > 0 \tag{4.13}$$

Hence, the optimal value z_0 is given by

$$z_0 = \nu_2 - \frac{K_2}{K_1} \nu_1 \tag{4.14}$$

Example D. Rectangular Distribution

For a rectangular distribution whose density is given by

$$\begin{aligned} S_2(x_2) &= \frac{1}{b - a} \qquad \text{if} \quad a \leqslant x_2 \leqslant b \\ &= 0 \qquad\qquad \text{otherwise} \end{aligned}$$

The optimum value of z is given by

$$z_0 = \frac{b + a}{2} - \frac{K_2}{K_1} \nu_1 \qquad \text{if} \quad b - a < \frac{2K_2}{K_1} \nu_1 \tag{4.15}$$

and

$$z_0 = b - \frac{2K_2}{K_1} \nu_1 \qquad \text{if} \quad b - a > \frac{2K_2}{K_1} \nu_1 \tag{4.16}$$

The above results are due to Etschmaier [25]. The results in example C were obtained earlier by Avi-Itzhak *et al.* [3]. We have restricted ourselves to the simplest assumption about the cost function. However, the cost function need not be linear. It is easy to write the total delay cost function for any other cost structure, but the optimum z need not have a simple relationship. Similarly, we can obtain the optimum discretion point for other models, e.g., the preemptive repeat-different–head-of-the-line or repeat-identical–head-of-the-line models. Although simple discretionary points do not exist for these models even under the linear cost assumption, the optimum value of z can be evaluated numerically.

5. Comparison with Nondiscretionary Disciplines

We close this chapter with a comparison between discretionary disciplines and nondiscretionary disciplines such as the head-of-the-line or preemptive resume disciplines. Consider, for example, the mean delay time under discretionary and nondiscretionary disciplines. From (3.12) and (3.14) we can write

$$E(\hat{\mathscr{D}}_1)|_{\text{Disc.}} - E(\hat{\mathscr{D}}_1)|_{\text{P.Res.}} = \frac{\lambda_2}{2(1-\rho_1)} \int_z^\infty (x-z)^2\, S_2(x)\, dx \tag{5.1}$$

and

$$E(\hat{\mathscr{D}}_2)|_{\text{Disc.}} - E(\hat{\mathscr{D}}_2)|_{\text{H.L.}} = \frac{\rho_1}{1-\rho_1} \int_0^z F_2{}^c(x)\, dx \tag{5.2}$$

Hence, for $0 < z < \infty$,

$$\begin{aligned} E(\hat{\mathscr{D}}_1)|_{\text{P.Res.}} &< E(\hat{\mathscr{D}}_1)|_{\text{Disc.}} < E(\hat{\mathscr{D}}_1)|_{\text{H.L.}} \\ E(\hat{\mathscr{D}}_2)|_{\text{P.Res.}} &> E(\hat{\mathscr{D}}_2)|_{\text{Disc.}} > E(\hat{\mathscr{D}}_2)|_{\text{H.L.}} \end{aligned} \tag{5.3}$$

Thus, if, in place of the preemptive resume discipline we employ the discretionary discipline, this would amount to increasing the mean delay for the priority units and reducing the mean delay for the ordinary units. Just the opposite occurs if we apply discretionary discipline in place of the head-of-the-line discipline. This conclusion may appear obvious, since in any priority discipline, favoring one particular class amounts to disfavoring the other. However, unlike the nondiscretionary disciplines, the amount of favor to a particular class can be controlled by varying z.

One can generalize the concept of discretion to k-class priority processes. Let us define numbers $z_1 = 0, z_2, z_3, \ldots, z_k$ such that the jth-class unit, if in service, will be preempted by the ith-class unit $(i < j)$, if its elapsed service time is less than z_j. If it is more than z_j, the ith class unit has to wait. We do not propose to investigate this process, but conclude this section with the important observation that the k-class discretionary process has $k - 1$ controllable parameters, namely, $z_2, z_3, \ldots, z_k$, which can be suitably fixed to adjust the relative performance of different classes. We will discuss this controllability aspect of priority disciplines further in Chapter VII.

Chapter VII

OTHER PRIORITY DISCIPLINES

1. Introduction

In previous chapters, we studied exogenous priority disciplines in single-server queuing systems with Poisson inputs and arbitrary service-time distributions. The mathematics of exogenous priority models developed in Chapter III can be applied to study several variants of the models discussed. Such variations may occur because of technical restrictions in adopting the priority rules mentioned earlier. For example, the assumption that the units of various classes can be serviced without any loss of time in reorienting the server to take up a unit may not be true. This leads us to consider priority disciplines which include reorientation time. Similarly, a priority or an ordinary unit or both may decide not to join the queue, or, after joining the queue, decide to leave it. To investigate the effect of this behavior, we require the study of priority disciplines to models with balking and reneging (see Section II, 2).

Also, in many situations, the exogenous disciplines, in which the decision to select a unit for service depends only upon the priority class to which a unit belongs, may not be true. For example, if the objective is not to delay any class of unit beyond a certain limit, we have to make our selection-decision rules so as to take into account the waiting time of each unit in the system. Such decision rules, which lead to "endogenous priority disciplines," are more difficult to analyze, but are more important in practice. In most job-shop scheduling or computer operations, one would like to implement an endogenous priority discipline in which the priority of a unit increases as some function of the waiting time so that the more a unit waits, the higher is the chance of its being serviced. Not much has been done so far to study such disciplines.

The aim of this chapter is to account for the work on endogenous priority systems and exogenous systems with structure more complicated than those we have previously discussed. Since we will be mostly reviewing the work on different types of priority models, the reader should not expect the same uniformity of approach that prevailed in earlier chapters.

2. Priorities with Reorientation Time

Situations where the server has to perform an orientation while switching from servicing one type of unit to another typc frequently arise in service systems. As an example, consider a furnace used for processing two types of units requiring different temperature levels, or a machine tool which has to be adjusted each time a different product is produced. In these and similar situations, an orientation or setup time is required whenever the server switches servicing from one type of unit to the other type.

Let us consider the two-class preemptive-resume priority model discussed in Chapter IV under the assumption that the server needs orientation whenever the service is to be switched from one type of unit to the other. Thus, if a priority unit arrives to find an ordinary unit in service, it interrupts the service of the ordinary unit and an orientation from 2 to 1 begins which requires a random time distributed according to the density $S_{21}(t)$. After the orientation is completed, the priority units are serviced. When there is no priority unit left, an orientation of duration S_{12} having density $S_{12}(t)$ is initiated. It may happen that during the reorientation, a priority unit may arrive. In such a case, the server starts a new orientation from 2 to 1 to take up the priority unit, and the amount of time spent on the earlier orientation from 1 to 2 is supposed to go to waste. Thus, an orientation from 1 to 2 is completed under the preemptive repeat policy, while the service discipline of the units is preemptive resume. We study this model due to Gaver [30] to demonstrate the additional complexity in analysis arising from the assumption of reorientation times.

The basic difference produced by the assumption of orientation times is that the idle state can have an orientation either towards a priority unit or towards an ordinary unit, and this information is necessary to determine whether an orientation is needed or not when a unit arrives to initiate the next busy period. Consequently, we have to define idleness probabilities associated with i-type orientation, ($i = 1, 2$), or, in other words, define probabilities of a busy-period termination with a given type of orientation. Before we do this, let us study, as usual, the completion time process.

2-1. Completion Time

Following our definition of completion time, a completion time is initiated when an ordinary unit enters service and ends when the server becomes free to take up the next ordinary unit. This means that at $t = 0$, the server's orientation is 2-type, and, because of preemptive discipline, the completion time ends with the same orientation. The completion-time cycle is represented in Fig. VII.1.

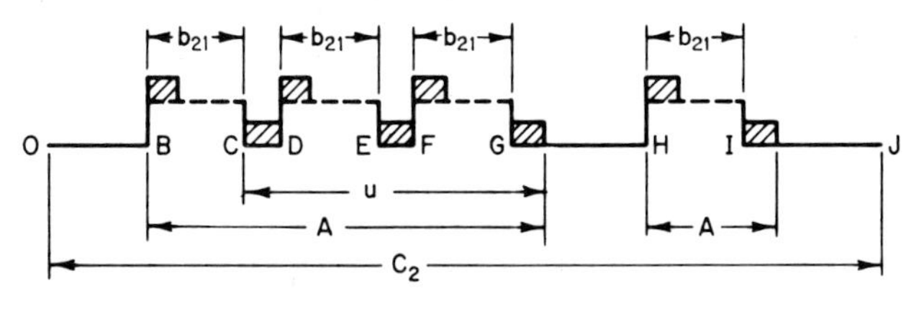

FIG. VII.1. Completion-time cycle.

The shaded areas above the dashed lines denote the time needed for orientation from 2 to 1, while the shaded areas above the solid lines denote the orientation time needed from 1 to 2. The solid lines denote the ordinary unit in service, and the dashed lines denote the priority unit in service. Obviously, the duration of the priority interruptions such as BC, DE, or FG, will be equal to the time needed for the server's reorientation from 2 to 1 plus the time required to completely serve the priority units before orientating from 1 to 2. The duration is thus an initial busy period having the initial occupation time S_{21} but having a unit present at the beginning of the busy period. Thus, it differs from $b_1^{S_{21}}(t)$ defined in Section I, 2. Defining the density of this duration by $b_{21}(t)$, we obtain

$$b_{21}(t) = \sum_{m_1=1}^{\infty} \left[S_{21}(t) \frac{(\lambda_1 t)^{m_1-1}}{(m_1 - 1)!} \exp(-\lambda_1 t)\right] * b_1^{*m_1}(t) \qquad (2.1)$$

Hence, taking the Laplace transform, we get

$$\bar{b}_{21}(s) = \bar{b}_1(s)\,\bar{S}_{21}[\lambda_1\{1 - \bar{b}_1(s)\} + s] \tag{2.2}$$

When the interruption is over, the reorientation of the server from 1 to 2 is initiated, e.g., at C and I. Since, by the assumptions mentioned earlier, the priority units follow a preemptive repeat-identical policy for completing the orientation time, the duration of A_1, the time required to successfully complete an orientation towards the ordinary unit, will have the density $A_1(t)$, and, from (IV, 2.25), is given by

$$\bar{u}(s) = \int_0^\infty \frac{\exp\{-(\lambda_1 + s)\,z\}\,S_{12}(z)\,dz}{1 - \dfrac{\lambda_1}{\lambda_1 + s}\,\bar{b}_{21}(s)[1 - \exp\{-(\lambda_1 + s)\,z\}]} \tag{2.3}$$

Thus, if A is the actual interruption time, i.e., the time between an ordinary unit interruption and its subsequent reentry, its density $A(t)$ is given by

$$A(t) = b_{21}(t) * u(t) \tag{2.4}$$

so that

$$\bar{A}(s) = \bar{b}_{21}(s)\,\bar{u}(s) \tag{2.5}$$

Thus, the completion-time duration in this process is identical to the completion-time duration for the preemptive resume discipline with the interruption duration having density $A(t)$; therefore, from (IV, 2.6), we have

$$\bar{c}_2(s) = \bar{S}_2[\lambda_1\{1 - \bar{A}(s)\} + s] \tag{2.6}$$

2-2. Busy Periods and Renewal Periods

As mentioned earlier, the busy-period duration depends upon the state of orientation during the idle state preceding the busy period. Consequently, instead of studying busy periods, we study the renewal periods τ_i $(i = 1, 2)$, which represent the time from the termination of a busy period with i-type orientation to the termination of the next busy period. Note that τ_i contains an idle period with i-type orientation whose mean duration is $1/(\lambda_1 + \lambda_2)$.

To evaluate τ_2, let us consider, as usual, two cases: (a) the idle state is terminated by the arrival of an ordinary unit, and (b) the idle state is terminated by the arrival of a priority unit. In case (a), the busy period is bound to end with 2-type orientation because of preemptive discipline, but in case (b), the busy period may end with 1-type orientation if no ordinary unit arrives during the busy period. Consequently, we divide (b) into two classes (b1) and (b2) depending upon whether the busy period terminates with 1-type orientation or with 2-type orientation. Let us consider the renewal periods one by one.

(a) The renewal cycle which begins with the termination of a busy period having a 2-type orientation and in which the busy period is initiated by the arrival of an ordinary unit is shown in Fig. VII.2. At

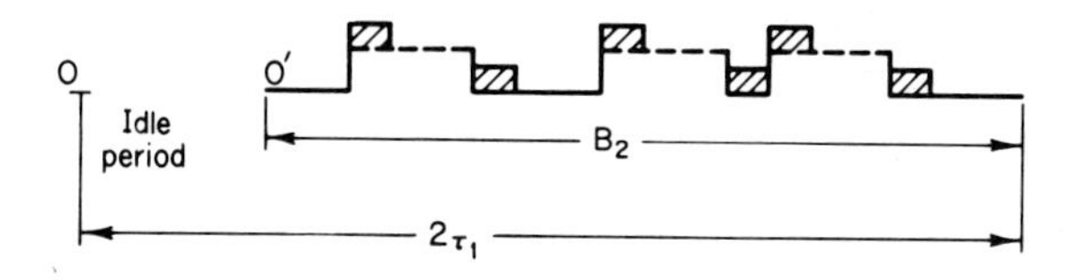

FIG. VII.2. Renewal cycle with 2-type orientation—Case (a).

O′, the ordinary unit arrives, and the duration of the busy period is the same as the busy period of the basic infinite-source model with parameters (λ_2, c_2), where c_2 is the completion time whose density is defined in (2.6) above. Hence, $\bar{B}_2(s)$ is the root of the equation

$$\alpha = \bar{c}_2[\lambda_2(1-\alpha)+s] \tag{2.7}$$

lying inside the unit circle, and if ${}^2\tau_1(t)$ denotes the density that the renewal cycle will end at time t, we have

$${}^2\tau_1(t) = [\lambda_2 \exp(-\lambda_2 t)\exp(-\lambda_1 t)] * B_2(t) \tag{2.8}$$

so that

$${}^2\bar{\tau}_1(s) = \frac{\lambda_2}{\lambda_1+\lambda_2+s}\bar{B}_2(s) \tag{2.9}$$

(b1) Since the busy period terminates with 1-type of orientation, no ordinary unit arrives during the busy period, and the renewal cycle is as shown in Fig. VII.3. If ${}^2\tau_2(t)$ denotes the density of the renewal cycle, we have

$${}^2\tau_2(t) = [\lambda_1 e^{-\lambda_1 t} * b_{21}(t)]\, e^{-\lambda_2 t} \tag{2.10}$$

Hence,

$${}^2\bar{\tau}_2(s) = \frac{\lambda_1}{\lambda_1+\lambda_2+s}\bar{b}_{21}(\lambda_2+s) \tag{2.11}$$

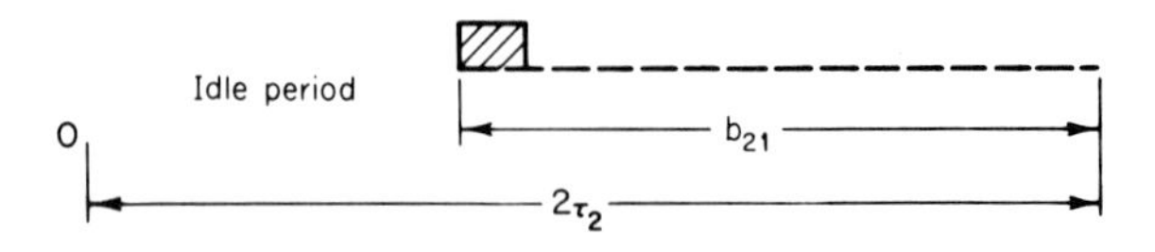

FIG. VII.3. Renewal cycle with 2-type orientation—Case (b1).

(b2) For this case, the renewal cycle is as shown in Fig. VII.4. From the figure, the process can be seen as a busy period of the process with parameters (λ_2, c_2) and with an initial occupation-time density $A(t)$. By taking into consideration the fact that the case where there is no ordinary unit arriving during the first busy period, namely O′B, has been considered in (2a), we have

$$^{2}\tau_3(t) = [\lambda_1 e^{-\lambda_1 t} e^{-\lambda_2 t}] * [B_2{}^A(t) - \{b_{21}(t)\, e^{-\lambda_2 t}\} * B_2{}^u(t)] \tag{2.12}$$

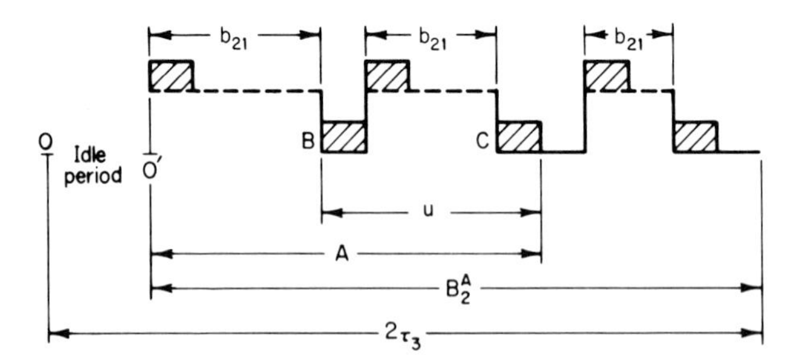

FIG. VII.4. Renewal cycle with 2-type orientation—Case (b2).

The Laplace transform of this is obtained as

$$^{2}\bar{\tau}_3(s) = \frac{\lambda_1}{\lambda_1 + \lambda_2 + s} [\bar{b}_{21}(\lambda_2\{1 - \bar{B}_2(s)\} + s) - \bar{b}_{21}(\lambda_2 + s)]\, \bar{u}(\lambda_2\{1 - \bar{B}_2(s)\} + s) \tag{2.13}$$

Hence, $^{2}\tau(t)$, the density of the renewal cycle which is initiated by the termination of a busy period having orientation of 2-type, is obtained by adding the results (2.9), (2.11), and (2.13), so that

$$^{2}\bar{\tau}(s) = \frac{1}{\lambda_1 + \lambda_2 + s} [\lambda_1 \bar{b}_{21}(\lambda_2 + s) + \lambda_2 \bar{B}_2(s) + \lambda_1 \bar{u}(\lambda_2\{1 - \bar{B}_2(s)\} + s)[\bar{b}_{21}(\lambda_2\{1 - \bar{B}_2(s)\} + s) - \bar{b}_{21}(\lambda_2 + s)]] \tag{2.14}$$

Differentiating (2.14) at $s = 0$, we get, after simplification,

$$E({}^2\tau) = \frac{1 + \lambda_1 E(S_{21}) + \lambda_1 E(u)[1 - \bar{b}_{21}(\lambda_2)][1 - \lambda_1 \nu_1]}{(\lambda_1 + \lambda_2)[\{1 - \lambda_2 E(c_2)\}\{1 - \lambda_1 \nu_1\}]} \tag{2.15}$$

Next, we study the renewal cycles which are initiated by the termination of a busy period at which the server was oriented towards 1-type units. Exactly the same three cases that were discussed above are possible here.

(a) The renewal cycle is initiated by the termination of a busy period and the next busy period is initiated by the arrival of an ordinary unit. The cycle is represented in Fig. VII.5.

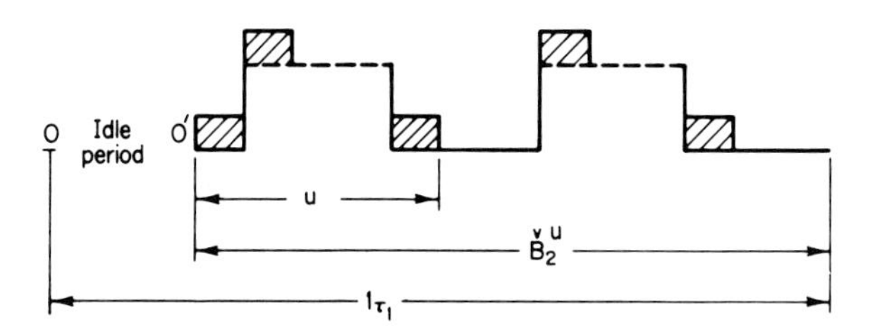

FIG. VII.5. Renewal cycle with 1-type orientation—Case (a).

Hence

$${}^1\tau_1(t) = [\lambda_2 e^{-\lambda_2 t} e^{-\lambda_1 t}] * \check{B}_2{}^u(t) \tag{2.16}$$

where $\check{B}_2{}^u(t)$ denotes the initial busy-period density of the basic infinite-source model with parameters (λ_2, c_2) and an initial occupation-time density $u(t)$, with a unit present at the beginning of the busy period; thus

$${}^1\bar{\tau}_1(s) = \frac{\lambda_2}{\lambda_1 + \lambda_2 + s} \bar{u}[\lambda_2\{1 - \bar{B}_2(s)\} + s]\, \bar{B}_2(s) \tag{2.17}$$

(b1) The case in which no ordinary unit arrives, so that the busy period terminates with a 1-type orientation, is represented in Fig. VII.6. For this case,

$${}^1\tau_2(t) = [\lambda_1 e^{-\lambda_1 t} * b_1(t)]\, e^{-\lambda_2 t} \tag{2.18}$$

so that,

$${}^1\bar{\tau}_2(s) = \frac{\lambda_1}{\lambda_1 + \lambda_2 + s} \bar{b}_1(s + \lambda_2) \tag{2.19}$$

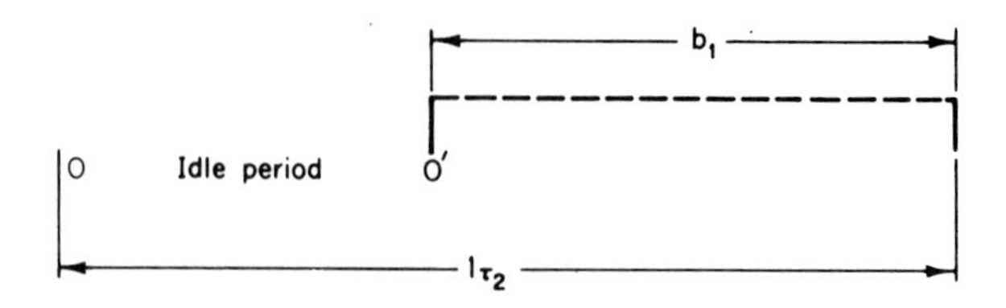

FIG. VII.6. Renewal cycle with 1-type orientation—Case (b1).

(b2) Lastly, the renewal cycle in which the busy period is initiated by the arrival of a priority unit when the server is oriented towards 1-type and ends with a 2-type orientation can be represented as in Fig. VII.7.

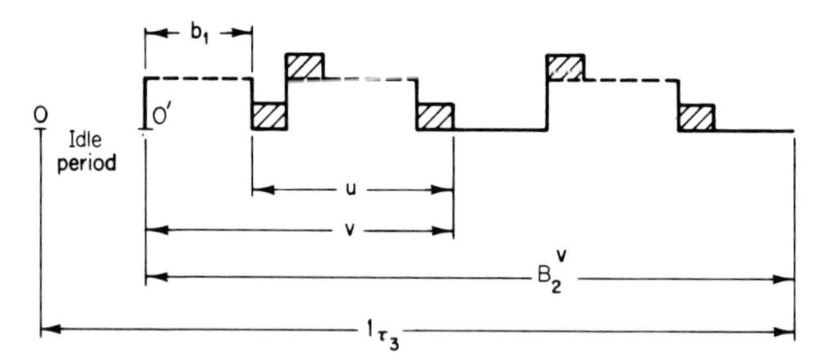

FIG. VII.7. Renewal cycle with 1-type orientation—Case (b2).

For this case,

$$^1\tau_3(t) = [\lambda_1 e^{-\lambda_1 t} e^{-\lambda_2 t}] * [B_2{}^v(t) - \{b_1(t)\, e^{-\lambda_2 t}\} * B_2{}^u(t)] \tag{2.20}$$

where

$$v(t) = b_1(t) * u(t)$$

and the last term arises for the same reasons as in the last case above. Thus,

$$^1\bar{\tau}_3(s) = \frac{\lambda_1}{\lambda_1 + \lambda_2 + s} [\bar{b}_1[\lambda_2\{1 - \bar{B}_2(s)\} + s]\, \bar{u}[\lambda_2\{1 - \bar{B}_2(s)\} + s] - \bar{b}_1(\lambda_2 + s)\, \bar{u}[\lambda_2\{1 - \bar{B}_2(s)\} + s]] \tag{2.21}$$

Adding the three cases, we get the Laplace transform of the renewal density initially having an orientation towards 1-type as

$$^1\bar{\tau}(s) = \frac{1}{\lambda_1 + \lambda_2 + s} [\lambda_1 \bar{b}_1(\lambda_2 + s) + \lambda_1 \bar{u}[\lambda_2\{1 - \bar{B}_2(s)\} + s][\bar{b}_1\{\lambda_2(1 - \bar{B}_2(s)) + s\} - \bar{b}_1(\lambda_2 + s)] + \lambda_2 \bar{B}_2(s)\, \bar{u}[\lambda_2\{1 - \bar{B}_2(s)\} + s]] \tag{2.22}$$

Differentiating (2.22) at $s = 0$, we obtain the mean renewal time $E({}^1\tau)$ as

$$E({}^1\tau) = \frac{1 + E(u)(1 - \lambda_1\nu_1)[\lambda_1 + \lambda_2 - \lambda_1\bar{b}_1(\lambda_2)]}{(\lambda_1 + \lambda_2)[1 - \lambda_1\nu_1][1 - \lambda_2 E(c_2)]} \tag{2.23}$$

From our discussion above, it is obvious that the orientation state at the termination of busy periods constitutes a stationary Markov chain. For this chain, we define Γ_{ij} ($i = 1, 2$ and $j = 1, 2$) as the transition probability that the orientation state at the end of a busy period is j, given that it was i at the end of the previous busy period. To obtain Γ_{21}, for example, we observe that a transition from 2-type orientation to 1-type orientation is possible only in case (b1) above, so that

$$\Gamma_{21} = \int_0^\infty {}^2\tau_2(t)\, dt = {}^2\bar{\tau}_2(0) = \frac{\lambda_1}{\lambda_1 + \lambda_2}\, \bar{b}_1(\lambda_2)\, \bar{S}_{21}[\lambda_1\{1 - \bar{b}_1(\lambda_2)\} + \lambda_2] \tag{2.24}$$

and, obviously, $\Gamma_{22} = 1 - \Gamma_{21}$.

Similarly,

$$\Gamma_{11} = \frac{\lambda_1}{\lambda_1 + \lambda_2}\, \bar{b}_1(\lambda_2) \tag{2.25}$$

and $\Gamma_{12} = 1 - \Gamma_{11}$.

Now, if we define $R_{ij}(t)\, dt$ as the probability that a busy period terminates in the interval $(t, t + dt)$ conditional on being in i- and j-orientations at successive busy period terminations, and $r_{ij}(t)\, dt$ as the joint probability that a busy period terminates in the interval $(t, t + dt)$ and has the j-orientation, given that the previous busy period ended at $t = 0$ with i-orientation, we have

$$r_{ij}(t) = \Gamma_{ij} R_{ij}(t) \qquad (i, j = 1, 2) \tag{2.26}$$

In terms of the probabilities defined above, the results obtained earlier can be expressed as follows:

$${}^i\bar{\tau}(s) = \bar{r}_{ii}(s) + \bar{r}_{ij}(s) \qquad (i \neq j, \quad i, j = 1, 2) \tag{2.27}$$

so that

$$E({}^i\tau) = \Gamma_{ii} E(R_{ii}) + \Gamma_{ij} E(R_{ij}) \qquad (i \neq j, \quad i, j = 1, 2) \tag{2.28}$$

Thus, to summarize we are here dealing with a process in which the orientation of the server at the beginning of a renewal cycle can be either 1 or 2, governed by the transition probability matrix (Γ_{ij}) $(i, j = 1, 2)$. Further, conditional on the orientation being i and j, the time of transition from i-orientation to j-orientation has the density $R_{ij}(t)$. Such a process constitute a 2-state semi-Markov process. The reader is referred to the papers by Pyke [110, 111] for a detailed exposition of such processes. However, since semi-Markov processes of only two states can be dealt easily by renewal-theoretic arguments, we do not propose to go into the details of such processes. We illustate the method by evaluating the servers' idleness probability using the result of renewal theory.

Probability the Server Is Idle

Since the idle state is associated with a certain type of orientation, we define under steady state: ${}^1\hat{e}^{(2)}$, the idleness probability having 1-orientation, and ${}^2\hat{e}^{(2)}$ the idleness probability having 2-orientation.

To obtain these probabilities, we have to study the pattern of renewal points, i.e., the way the renewal points with 1-orientation and 2-orientation are distributed. A renewal point having 1-orientation may be followed by a sequence of renewal points having 2-orientation. If the mean recurrence time between instants at which renewal points terminate with same orientation can be found, the idleness probability can be obtained by using the key renewal theorem (see Section I, 4).

To explain this further, let $f_{ij}(t)\, dt$ denote the joint probability that a busy period ends with j-orientation for the first time in the interval $(t, t + dt)$ given that a busy period terminated with i-orientation at $t = 0$. Then, from Section I.4,

$$
{}^1\hat{e}^{(2)} = \frac{1}{(\lambda_1 + \lambda_2)\, E(f_{11})} \tag{2.29}
$$

and

$$
{}^2\hat{e}^{(2)} = \frac{1}{(\lambda_1 + \lambda_2)\, E(f_{22})} \tag{2.30}
$$

The relations between these first-passage probabilities and $r_{ij}(t)$ defined earlier are obviously as follows:

$$
f_{22}(t) = r_{22}(t) + r_{21}(t) * f_{12}(t) \tag{2.31}
$$

$$
f_{12}(t) = r_{12}(t) + r_{11}(t) * f_{12}(t) \tag{2.32}
$$

Taking the Laplace transform, solving for $\bar{f}_{22}(s)$, and differentiating at $s = 0$, we obtain, after using (2.29) and (2.28),

$$E(f_{22}) = E({}^2\tau) + \frac{\Gamma_{21}}{\Gamma_{12}} E({}^1\tau) \tag{2.33}$$

so that, using (2.15), (2.23), (2.24), and (2.25), we obtain ${}^2\hat{e}^{(2)}$. We can obtain ${}^1\hat{e}^{(2)}$ in a similar way.

Finally, $\hat{e}^{(2)}$, the idleness probability, is obtained as

$$\begin{aligned} \hat{e}^{(2)} &= {}^1\hat{e}^{(2)} + {}^2\hat{e}^{(2)} \\ &= \frac{[(1 - \lambda_1\nu_1)][1 - \lambda_2 E(c_2)][\lambda_1 + \lambda_2 - \lambda_1\bar{b}_1(\lambda_2) + \lambda_1\bar{b}_{21}(\lambda_2)]}{K} \end{aligned} \tag{2.34}$$

where

$$K = [\lambda_1 + \lambda_2 - \lambda_1\bar{b}_1(\lambda_2)][1 - \lambda_1\nu_1][1 + \lambda_1 E(b_1^{S_{21}}) + \lambda_1 E(u)] + \lambda_1\bar{b}_{21}(\lambda_2)$$

The above model can be generalized to k (> 2) classes. An important question that may then arise is to determine the optimal ordering of the k classes so that the total reorientation time is minimized or the idleness probability of the server is maximized. Different assumptions regarding the priority discipline and reorientation policy may be made and their effects on the system behavior studied.

Example

If, in the above model, instead of waiting for a unit to arrive, the server is always oriented towards an ordinary unit at the end of the busy period, it has been shown by Gaver [31] that if $\lambda_1\nu_1 < 1$, $\lambda_2\nu_2 < 1$, and $\bar{S}_{12}(\lambda_1) < \infty$, the steady state exists and the idleness probability is given by

$$\hat{e}^{(2)} = \frac{1 - \lambda_1\nu_1}{[1 + \lambda_1 E(S_{21})]\ \bar{S}_{12}(\lambda_1)} - \lambda_2\nu_2 \tag{2.35}$$

Although other priority disciplines can be studied exactly as above, the case for the head-of-the-line discipline appears to be difficult to analyze. For the head-of-the-line discipline, the completion times need not necessarily terminate with the 2-orientation, as they do for the preemptive discipline, and this presents additional difficulties.

Finally, it is obvious that if the objective happens to increase the idleness probability, which may be a measure indicating the ability of the server to deal with a given traffic input, it may be optimal to assign a priority which minimizes orientations. Hence, the head-of-the-line discipline would be better than the preemptive discipline. Even better would be a discipline in which the server first services one type of units and then, only when there is no unit of that type left, services the other type of units. This discipline is termed an "alternating priority discipline," and will be discussed below in Section VII, 5. However, if the objective function takes into consideration other factors such as cost of waiting, the comparisons are less obvious and can be made numerically.

3. Priorities with Balking and Reneging

We defined balking and reneging behavior in Chapter II, and studied the busy period and the initial busy period of the $M/G/1$ model with balking and reneging. It is conceivable that in situations where more than one class of units are being serviced under a given priority discipline, units of different classes exhibit balking and reneging behavior. Obviously, the lower-priority-class units will be more susceptible to such behavior than the higher-priority-class units.

Let us consider the (∞, ∞) priority model under the assumption that only the ordinary units balk and renege. The balking and reneging behavior is described by the same probability laws as in Section II, 2, i.e., an ordinary unit on finding m_2 units in the system joins the queue with probability $a_{m_2} = 1 - m_2/N_2$ $(m_2 = 0, 1, \ldots, N_2)$ and, after having joined, waits in the queue for a time distributed exponentially with parameter β; after which, if not taken into service, it leaves the system and is lost. We can adopt the same procedure as in the previous chapters to obtain the system characteristics. However, because of the additional assumption of balking and reneging, we need, in place of the results for the busy period and the initial busy period of the $M/G/1$ model, the corresponding results for the $M/G/1$ model with balking and reneging. As noted above, these results are derived in Section II, 2. In the example below, we give some results of the above model under the preemptive-resume priority discipline.

Example. The (∞, ∞) Model under the Preemptive-Resume Priority Discipline with Balking and Reneging

Using (II, 2.92) and (II, 2.103), the busy-period density for this model is given by

$$\bar{\gamma}_2(s) = \left[(\lambda_1 + \lambda_2) \sum_{k=0}^{N_2} \binom{N_2}{k} \frac{(1-a)^k}{\bar{V}_2(k-1, \beta, s)}\right]^{-1}$$

$$\times \left[\lambda_1 \sum_{k=0}^{N_2} \binom{N_2}{k} \frac{(1-a)^k\, \bar{b}_1[k(\lambda_2/N_2 + \beta) + s]}{\bar{V}_2(k-1, \beta, s)}\right.$$

$$+ \lambda_2 \left\{ \sum_{k=0}^{N_2-1} \binom{N_2 - 1}{k} \frac{(1-a)^k}{\bar{V}_2(k-1, \beta, s)}\right.$$

$$\left.\left. - a \sum_{k=1}^{N_2} \binom{N_2 - 1}{k-1} \frac{(1-a)^{k-1}}{\bar{V}_2(k-1, \beta, s)} \right\}\right] \tag{3.1}$$

where $\bar{V}_2(k, \beta, s)$ is obtained from (II, 2.96) after replacing (N, λ, S) by (N_2, λ_2, C_2), and $a = N_2\beta/(N_2\beta + \lambda_2)$.

The expected length of the busy period is therefore given by

$$E(\gamma_2) = \frac{1}{(\lambda_1 + \lambda_2)(1-\rho_1)}$$

$$\times \left[\rho_1 + \lambda_1 \nu_2 \sum_{k=1}^{N_2} \binom{N_2}{k} \frac{(1-a)^k\, [1 - \bar{b}_1[k(\lambda_2/N_2 + \beta)]]}{\Phi_2(k-1, \beta)}\right.$$

$$\left. + \lambda_2 \nu_2 \sum_{k=0}^{N_2-1} \binom{N_2 - 1}{k} \frac{(1-a)^k}{\Phi_2(k, \beta)}\right] \tag{3.2}$$

where $\Phi_2(k, \beta)$ is obtained from (II, 2.98) after replacing (N, λ, S) by (N_2, λ_2, C_2). Finally, the generating function $\Pi(\alpha_1, \alpha_2)$ of the joint queue length probabilities under steady state is given by

$$\hat{\Pi}(\alpha_1, \alpha_2) = \hat{e}^{(2)} \left[1 + \sum_{k=0}^{N_2} (1-\alpha_2)^k\, [a + (1-a)\, \alpha_2]^{N_2-k}\, \lambda_1 \binom{N_2}{k}\right.$$

$$\times (1-a)^k\, \bar{\Pi}[\alpha_1, k(\lambda_2/N_2 + \beta)]$$

$$+ \alpha_2 \sum_{k=0}^{N_2-1} (1-\alpha_2)^k\, [a + (1-a)\, \alpha_2]^{N_2-1-k}$$

$$\left. \times \chi(k, \beta)\, \bar{\Pi}^{I}[\alpha_1, k(\lambda_2/N_2 + \beta)]\right] \tag{3.3}$$

where

$$\bar{\Pi}^{I}(\alpha_1, s) = [1 - \bar{c}_2(s)]\, \tilde{\bar{\Pi}}(\alpha_1, s)$$

$$\chi(k, \beta) = \frac{\Phi_2(k-1, \beta)}{1 - \bar{c}_2[k(\lambda_2/N_2 + \beta)]}$$

$$\times \left[\lambda_1 \sum_{e=k-1}^{N_2} \binom{N_2}{e} \frac{(1-a)^e \{1 - \bar{b}_1[e(\lambda_2/N_2 + \beta)]\}}{\Phi_2(e-1, \beta)}\right.$$

$$\left. + \lambda_2 \sum_{e=k}^{N_2-1} \binom{N_2 - 1}{e} \frac{(1-a)^e}{\Phi_2(e, \beta)}\right]$$

and $\bar{c}_2(s)$ is given by (IV, 2.6). The idleness probability $\hat{e}^{(2)}$ is given by

$$\hat{e}^{(2)} = (1 - \rho_1)\left[1 + \lambda_1 \nu_2 \sum_{k=1}^{N_2} \binom{N_2}{k} \frac{(1-a)^k}{\Phi_2(k-1, \beta)} [1 - \bar{b}_1\{k(\lambda_2/N_2 + \beta)\}]\right.$$

$$\left. + \lambda_2 \nu_2 \sum_{k=0}^{N_2-1} \binom{N_2 - 1}{k} \frac{(1-a)^k}{\Phi_2(k, \beta)}\right]^{-1} \qquad \text{if} \quad \rho_1 < 1$$

$$= 0 \qquad \text{if} \quad \rho_1 \geqslant 1$$

The above results are due to Subba Rao [80]. If $\beta = 0$, the above results with λ_2 replaced by $N_2\lambda_2$ reduce to the results of the (∞, N_2) model obtained in Section IV, 5.

It may be mentioned that the assumption about the balking behavior was made only because it suited the mathematics of the finite-source model developed earlier, but it need not be true in practice. Different assumptions can be made to describe the balking behavior. For example, one can assume constant balking probability [81], or $a_n = \beta/n \ (n > 0)$, $a_0 = 1$. In general, the probability of joining can be any decreasing function of n, the number of units in the system. The study of priorities with such balking behavior involves the solution of basic $M/G/1$ model with the corresponding balking behavior. The solution of the latter models is in general difficult, and much more research effort is needed to describe situations in which the balking as well as the reneging is specified by probability laws, which describe more closely the impatient behavior of the units.

4. Round-Robin Priority Discipline

In Chapters III and IV, we showed that dividing a single class of units into two classes, one having shorter service time than the other, and allotting priority helps in reducing congestion and in minimizing the delay time. However, this requires that either the actual service time of the units be known, or that it at least be possible to divide the units into two classes. However, if such a division is not possible, a possible method is to serve each unit in the system for a specified time in a "round-robin" fashion, i.e., serve each unit for a short specified period, leave it, take the next unit and serve it for the same period, and so on. Thus, the procedure automatically gives priority to those units which have lesser service-time requirements. This is essentially the basis of the round-robin priority discipline.

This concept appears to have arisen from the desire to provide faster responses and minimize delay times for users with short requests in time-sharing computer systems, where a number of users employ the computer simultaneously. Obviously, this helps in jobs such as debugging, short computations, etc. Basically, in a time-sharing system, a request for service is not necessarily processed to completion, but is truncated, the program is transferred into auxiliary storage, and the remaining part of service postponed according to some discipline. Physically, the users communicate with the central processing unit (the computer) through input–output devices located at installations some distance away from the computer. As each user generates a request for service, he enters a queue whose members are serviced in round-robin fashion for not more than a certain specified amount of time, called a "quantum".

To formulate the problem further, let us assume that there are N consoles connected to a single processing unit. As soon as a request for service arises at a console, it is processed immediately if the computer is free; otherwise, it waits in the queue. Let us assume that the time from the instant a console is free to the time it generates a request for service is exponentially distributed with mean $1/\lambda_1$. The computer works on each request (program) for no longer than a "quantum", so that a unit, after having received service once, can be serviced again after the completion of the cycle, i.e., after the computer has finished a quantum of service on each of the waiting units. Note that we assume that there is only one request that can arise in a console at one time.

The reader can now visualize that the model is similar to the finite-source model except that the service discipline is different. This analogy between the round-robin priority model and the finite-source model was pointed out by Greenberger [32]. In order to describe the discipline more fully, let us assume that the actual computer time needed to service a request is z. The request will need $[z/\sigma] + 1$ quantum services in all to be completed, where $[x]$ denotes the greatest integer less than x and σ is the quantum size. A quantum service consists of two parts—(1) the actual operation time x $(0 < x \leqslant \sigma)$, and (2) the swap time τ which is required to bring the program into and out of primary storage; τ is small and is usually assumed to be constant. We make the important assumption that the actual computer time needed to service a request is exponentially distributed with mean ν. Because of the Markovian property of the exponential distribution, it follows that each time a request is processed by the computer, the actual operation time will have the density $S(x)$ given by

$$S(x) = (1/\nu)\, e^{-x/\nu} + \delta(x - \sigma)\, e^{-\sigma/\nu} \qquad (0 < x \leqslant \sigma) \tag{4.1}$$

and this density holds good irrespective of the number of times the request is taken up and processed. Observe that the density is of the mixed type having a mass at the point σ, indicating that each time a request is taken for processing, the operation time either terminates before σ or is taken as terminated at σ.

Thus, the above model is essentially a finite-source model with the following service discipline: A unit is serviced for a random time x having density $S(x)$ given by (4.1), after which, if its service is not completed, it is placed at the end of the queue. The server then spends a restoration time τ, which is constant, before taking the next unit for service. The arrival process is exactly the same as in the basic finite-source model.

This problem was studied by Krishnamoorthi and Wood [57] and Krishnamoorthi [56] through Markov chain analysis and renewal theory. The first reference discusses the stochastic behavior of the number of busy consoles at instants the computer finishes a quantum service, and the second one deals with the stochastic behavior at all time points. Other discussions of this type of model are given by Patel [108], Scherr [76], and Greenberger [32].

It may be pointed out that for a time-sharing system, the objective as we mentioned earlier is to provide rapid response time for short requests. This objective is, however, in opposition to the more general objective of maximizing the total number of requests processed by the computer. Obviously, the second objective can best be attained if we allow minimum wastage of time as swap times, so that the most efficient system satisfying the second objective is the batch-processing system, in which the requests are serviced to completion. Hence, from the point of view of the design of a time-sharing system, one has to balance shorter response for short requests against maximum throughput. The designer can accomplish this balance by studying the effect of the controllable parameters; namely, the number of users in the system and the quantum size. Some interesting numerical results on the effects of these parameters are given in Krishnamoorthi and Wood [57] and Scherr [76].

We assert that the assumption of exponential service-time distribution is a basic one because only this distribution has the characteristic Markovian property such that the same stochastic law for the duration of quantum service holds good irrespective of the number of times this request has been serviced. However, it has been shown by Coffman and Wood [19] that the statistical analysis of the data collected on an actual time-sharing system may not justify the assumption of an exponential distribution. A much more satisfactory approximation is a biphase or triphase hyperexponential distribution.

Several modifications of this model have been suggested in the references cited above, e.g., (i) after each quantum service, the computer chooses a request at random among those present, (ii) the computer moves around the channels giving quantum service to each busy channel just as a patrolling repairman would, and (iii) the processor selects that request which has received the minimum number of quantum services. If there is more than one request which has received the same number of quantum services, the first-come, first-served discipline is adopted.

The last modification mentioned above has been generalized to include the variable quantum size in the following way: Let the requests be arranged in separate queues numbered 1, 2,.... The nth queue consists of those requests which have had access to the processor $n - 1$ times. Each new request enters the first queue and receives a quantum of service σ_1. In general, a unit of the nth queue receives a quantum σ_n. If the service does not get completed, it is placed at the end of the $(n + 1)$th queue, otherwise it leaves the system. The processor always selects the next unit from the lowest-numbered queue, provided it has a request waiting there. This model has been studied by Coffman [99], Schrage [109], and Coffman and Kleinrock [100] assuming that there are an infinite source of consoles and that the interarrival times between requests at the first queue are exponentially distributed.

Further research effort to generalize the above model to a multi-channel model arises from the fact that future time-sharing systems will have more than one processor. In case of more than one processor, one could visualize several configurations in which the processors could be arranged, giving rise to different types of models. For example, the processors could be arranged in parallel, as in Coffman [99], or in series, as in Kleinrock [106]. The reader is referred to a recent review by Estrin and Kleinrock [104] and to Kleinrock [105] for further details regarding priority queuing models applicable to time-sharing systems.

5. Alternating-Priority Discipline

In Section 2 of this chapter, we briefly mentioned this discipline in connection with the reduction of setup times or orientation times. Let us consider a k-class process. Under this discipline, if the server becomes free to take up a unit after completing service on a unit of type i $(1 \leqslant i \leqslant k)$, the next unit to be taken for service will be a i-type if available in the queue. If no i-type unit is available, the server selects the unit with the lowest priority index. Note that this discipline is endogenous in character because the decision to select a unit depends not only on the priority class to which it belongs but also on the type of unit last serviced.

This discipline was introduced in a paper by Avi-Itzhak *et al.* [4] for the case $k = 2$. For this case, the type 1 units will have priority over type 2 if the first arriving unit to start a busy period is a type 1 unit. When all type 1 units have been serviced, the type 2 units get the priority. Hence, the priority alternates from class 1 to class 2, and is therefore called an alternating-priority discipline.

Although the generalization to more than 2 classes seems practicable in many situations, we will mainly study the two-class problem. Examples where such a discipline is followed are given in Section VII, 2. We may note one more pertaining to "traffic flow;" namely, the situation at a controlled traffic intersection where one stream of vehicles is allowed to pass as long as there are vehicles in that stream.

As usual, we study the busy-period process and obtain general process probabilities by using renewal theory. Although, because of the endogenous character of the priority discipline, the busy-period process cannot be further divided into completion-time processes as was possible for exogenous priority disciplines, we can still divide the busy periods into cycles because of the simple character of the endogenous discipline. To illustrate let us study the busy-period cycle in Fig. VII.8, in which the busy period is initiated by the arrival of an ordinary unit.

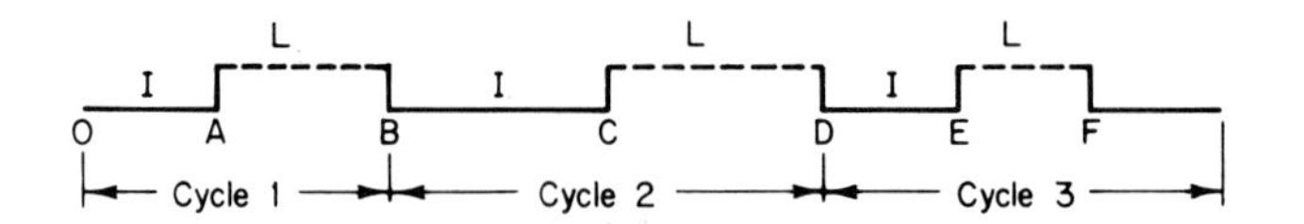

FIG. VII.8. Busy period cycle for the alternating-priority discipline.

Obviously, OA denotes an ordinary busy period for type 2 units. At A, when the busy period ends, a type 1 unit, if present, enters service, and since the priority now switches to type 1, all type 1 units which arrived during OA and those which arrive subsequently are serviced before the server becomes free to take up a type 2 unit at B. The cycle now repeats until the busy period terminates.

It will be noted that each cycle has two phases: phase I, when the type 2 units are being serviced, and phase L, when the type 1 units are being serviced. While one might be tempted to call these cycles "completion-time" cycles with a modified definition, there is an important difference in that the successive cycles are not independent. As a matter of fact, each phase has a stochastic dependence upon the preceding phase.

Let us now consider the ith cycle of the above busy-period process and define the following probabilities at epochs at which the phases are initiated:

(i) $p^I(m_2, t; i)$ $(m_2 > 0, i = 1, 2...)$ the probability that at time t the busy period process which was initiated by the arrival of a type 2 unit enters the I phase of the ith cycle and there are $m_2 > 0$ type 2 units present.

(ii) $p^L(m_1, t; i)$ $(m_1 > 0, i = 1, 2...,)$ the probability that at time t the busy-period process which was initiated by the arrival of a type 2 unit enters the L phase of the ith cycle and there are $m_1 > 0$ type 1 units present.

(iii) $\gamma^I(t; i)$ $(i > 1)$, the probability that the busy period terminates at time t after completing the L phase of the $(i - 1)$th cycle.

(iv) $\gamma^L(t; i)$ $(i \geqslant 1)$, the probability that the busy period terminates at time t after completing the I phase of the ith cycle.

The corresponding equations are:

$$p^I(m_2, t; i) = \sum_{m_1=1}^{\infty} p^L(m_1, t; i-1) * \left[\{b_1^{m_1}(t)\} \frac{(\lambda_2 t)^{m_2}}{m_2!} e^{-\lambda_2 t}\right] \quad (m_2 > 0, \quad i > 1) \tag{5.1}$$

$$\gamma^I(t; i) = \sum_{m_1=1}^{\infty} p^L(m_1, t; i-1) * [\{b_1^{m_1}(t)\} e^{-\lambda_2 t}] \tag{5.2}$$

$$p^L(m_1, t; i) = \sum_{m_2=1}^{\infty} p^I(m_2, t; i) * \left[\{b_2^{m_2}(t)\} \frac{(\lambda_1 t)^{m_1}}{m_1!} e^{-\lambda_1 t}\right] \quad (m_1 > 0, \quad i \geqslant 1) \tag{5.3}$$

$$\gamma^L(t; i) = \sum_{m_2=1}^{\infty} p^I(m_2, t; i) * [\{b_2^{m_2}(t)\} e^{-\lambda_1 t}] \tag{5.4}$$

Let us define the generating function

$$H^L[\alpha_1, t; i] = \sum_{m_1=1}^{\infty} \alpha_1^{m_1} p^L(m_1, t; i)$$

$$H^I[\alpha_2, t; i] = \sum_{m_2=1}^{\infty} \alpha_2^{m_2} p^I(m_2, t; i)$$

so that, taking the Laplace transform and using these generating functions, we get

$$\bar{H}^I[\alpha_2, s; i] + \bar{\gamma}^I(s; i) = \bar{H}^L[\bar{b}_1\{s + \lambda_2(1 - \alpha_2)\}, s; i-1] \quad (i > 1) \tag{5.5}$$

$$\bar{H}^L[\alpha_1, s; i] + \bar{\gamma}^L(s; i) = \bar{H}^I[\bar{b}_2\{s + \lambda_1(1 - \alpha_1)\}, s; i] \quad (i \geqslant 1) \tag{5.6}$$

Also, from (5.2) and (5.4),

$$\bar{\gamma}^I(s; i) = \bar{H}^L[\bar{b}_1(s + \lambda_2), s; i-1] \tag{5.7}$$

$$\bar{\gamma}^L(s; i) = \bar{H}^I[\bar{b}_2(s + \lambda_1), s; i] \tag{5.8}$$

Initially,

$$\bar{H}^I[\alpha_2, s; 1] = \alpha_2$$

and

$$\bar{\gamma}^I(s; 1) = 0$$

Finally, defining

$$\bar{\bar{\Pi}}^I[\alpha_2, s] = \sum_{i=1}^{\infty} \bar{\bar{H}}^I(\alpha_2, s; i) \tag{5.9}$$

$$\bar{\bar{\Pi}}^L[\alpha_1, s] = \sum_{i=1}^{\infty} \bar{\bar{H}}^L(\alpha_1, s; i) \tag{5.10}$$

we obtain

$$\bar{\bar{\Pi}}^I[\alpha_2, s] + \bar{\gamma}^I(s) = \bar{\bar{\Pi}}^L[\bar{b}_1\{s + \lambda_2(1 - \alpha_2)\}, s] + \alpha_2 \tag{5.11}$$

$$\bar{\bar{\Pi}}^L[\alpha_1, s] + \bar{\gamma}^L(s) = \bar{\bar{\Pi}}^I[\bar{b}_2\{s + \lambda_1(1 - \alpha_1)\}, s] \tag{5.12}$$

where

$$\bar{\gamma}^I(s) = \bar{\bar{\Pi}}^L[\bar{b}_1(s + \lambda_2), s] \tag{5.13}$$

$$\bar{\gamma}^L(s) = \bar{\bar{\Pi}}^I[\bar{b}_2(s + \lambda_1), s] \tag{5.14}$$

Equations (5.11)–(5.14) define functional relations between $\bar{\bar{\Pi}}^I$ and $\bar{\bar{\Pi}}^L$. We can discuss the busy-period process initiated by the arrival of a type 1 unit in a similar way. Let us define for this busy-period process G^I and G^L in place of Π^I and Π^L. Note that the relation between G^I and G^L can be obtained by interchanging indices I and L in (5.11) and (5.12). The reader might have observed that our process consists of two cycles, one dependent on the other, and so far we have tried to describe the process only at the beginning of these cycles. The desired characteristics, e.g., the queue length or the waiting time, during a busy period can be evaluated by using these probabilities and convoluting them with the probabilities of the initial busy-period process.

To avoid excessive algebraic work we will demonstrate this by evaluating the waiting-time density of type 1 units. If $\mathscr{W}_1(\tau, t; 2)$ denotes the occupation-time density of the server with respect to the type 1 unit during the busy-period process initiated by the arrival of a type 2 unit, then,

$$\mathscr{W}_1(\tau, t; 2) = \sum_{i=1}^{\infty} \sum_{m_2=1}^{\infty} p^I(m_2, t; i) * w_1^{\Omega}(\tau, t) \tag{5.15}$$

where $\Omega(t)$ denotes the density of the busy period of type 2 units in isolation initiated by m_2 units, i.e., $\Omega(t) = b_2^{m_2}(t)$ and $w_1^{\Omega}(\tau, t)$ is defined by (I, 6.5). The relation (5.15) arises from the fact that if at the beginning of the ith cycle, there are m_2 units of type 2, then the occupation-time density is the same as the occupation-time density for an initial busy-period process having as initial occupation time the busy period of type 2 units with m_2 units initially.

Hence, from (I, 6.5), we get

$$\bar{\mathscr{W}}_1(\theta, s; 2) = \sum_{m_2=1}^{\infty} \sum_{i=1}^{\infty} \bar{p}^I(m_2, s, i) \frac{[\bar{b}_2\{s + \lambda_1(1 - \bar{b}_1(s))\}]^{m_2} - [\bar{b}_2(\theta)]^{m_2}}{\theta - s - \lambda_1 + \lambda_1 \bar{S}_1(\theta)}$$

$$= \frac{\bar{\Pi}^I[\bar{b}_2\{s + \lambda_1(1 - \bar{b}_1(s))\}, s] - \bar{\Pi}^I[\bar{b}_2(\theta), s]}{\theta - s - \lambda_1 + \lambda_1 \bar{S}_1(\theta)} \tag{5.16}$$

In a similar way, we can define $\mathscr{W}_1(\tau, t; 1)$, the occupation-time density of the server with respect to type 1 units during the busy period initiated by the arrival of a type 1 unit and obtain

$$\bar{\mathscr{W}}_1(\theta, s; 1) = \sum_{m_2=1}^{\infty} \sum_{i=1}^{\infty} \bar{q}^I(m_2, s; i)$$

$$\times \frac{[\bar{b}_2\{s + \lambda_1(1 - \bar{b}_1(s))\}]^{m_2} - [\bar{b}_2(\theta)]^{m_2}}{\theta - s - \lambda_1 + \lambda_1 \bar{S}_1(\theta)} + \bar{w}_1(\theta, s) \tag{5.17}$$

the second term arising because the first cycle is not included in the summation and $\bar{q}^I(m_2, s; i)$ is the same as $\bar{p}^I(m_2, s; i)$ but for the busy period initiated by the arrival of a type 1 unit. Hence,

$$\bar{\mathscr{W}}_1(\theta, s; 1) = \bar{w}_1(\theta, s) + \frac{\bar{G}^I[b_2\{s + \lambda_1(1 - \bar{b}_1(s))\}, s] - \bar{G}^I[\bar{b}_2(\theta), s]}{\theta - s - \lambda_1 + \lambda_1 \bar{S}_1(\theta)} \tag{5.18}$$

where

$$\bar{G}^I(\alpha_2, s; i) = \sum_{m_2=1}^{\infty} \alpha_2^{m_2} \bar{q}^I(m_2, s, i)$$

Finally, if $\hat{\bar{\mathscr{W}}}_1(\theta, s)$ represents the Laplace transform of the transient occupation-time density at time t during the general process, we have, following the usual renewal arguments,

$$\hat{\bar{\mathscr{W}}}_1(\theta, s) = \bar{\hat{e}}^{(2)}(s)[1 + \lambda_1 \bar{\mathscr{W}}_1(\theta, s; 1) + \lambda_2 \bar{\mathscr{W}}_1(\theta, s; 2)] \tag{5.19}$$

where $\hat{e}^{(2)}(t)$ is the idleness probability of the server at time t and can be obtained by relating it to the busy-period probabilities.

Because of the functional relationships, these results are difficult to express in any simple explicit form. Consequently, we will obtain the steady-state results. If $\bar{\mathscr{W}}_1(\theta)$ represents the Laplace transform of the steady-state occupation-time density with respect to the priority unit, we have

$$\bar{\mathscr{W}}_1(\theta) = \hat{e}^{(2)}[1 + \lambda_1 \bar{\mathscr{W}}_1(\theta, 0; 1) + \lambda_2 \bar{\mathscr{W}}_1(\theta, 0; 2)] \tag{5.20}$$

We may obtain $\hat{e}^{(2)}$ with the aid of a simple observation, namely, that the value of $\hat{e}^{(2)}$ does not depend upon the priority discipline as long as the server works when units are present and no service time is wasted (cf. the preemptive repeat discipline). The same is true for the busy-period duration. Hence, from the results of Chapter I, we obtain

$$\hat{e}^{(2)} = 1 - \rho \tag{5.21}$$

and

$$E(\gamma_2) = \frac{\rho}{(\lambda_1 + \lambda_2)(1 - \rho)} \tag{5.22}$$

where

$$\rho = \rho_1 + \rho_2 = \lambda_1 \nu_1 + \lambda_2 \nu_2$$

Thus, (5.20) can be written as

$$\bar{\mathscr{W}}_1(\theta) = (1 - \rho) \Big[1 + \lambda_1 \bar{w}_1(\theta, 0) + \lambda_1 \frac{\bar{G}^I(1, 0) - \bar{G}^I[\bar{b}_2(\theta), 0]}{\theta - \lambda_1 + \lambda_1 \bar{S}_1(\theta)} + \lambda_2 \frac{\bar{\Pi}^I(1, 0) - \bar{\Pi}^I[\bar{b}_2(\theta), 0]}{\theta - \lambda_1 + \lambda_1 \bar{S}_1(\theta)}\Big] \tag{5.23}$$

where, from (I, 6.50),

$$\bar{w}_1(\theta, 0) = \frac{1 - \bar{S}_1(\theta)}{\theta - \lambda_1 + \lambda_1 \bar{S}_1(\theta)} \tag{5.24}$$

Hence, (5.23) can be written as

$$\bar{\mathscr{W}}_1(\theta) = \frac{(1 - \rho)[\theta + \lambda_1\{\bar{G}^I(1, 0) - \bar{G}^I[\bar{b}_2(\theta), 0]\} + \lambda_2\{\bar{\Pi}^I(1, 0) - \bar{\Pi}^I[\bar{b}_2(\theta), 0]\}]}{\theta - \lambda_1 + \lambda_1 \bar{S}_1(\theta)} \tag{5.25}$$

The moments can be obtained by differentiating (5.25) at $\theta = 0$ and using (5.11) to (5.14). For example,

$$E(\hat{\mathscr{W}}_1) = \frac{\lambda_1 E(S_1^2)}{2(1 - \rho_1)} + \frac{\lambda_1 \rho_2^2 E(S_1^2) + \lambda_2 (1 - \rho_1)^2 E(S_2^2)}{2(1 - \rho_1)(1 - \rho)(1 - \rho + 2\rho_1\rho_2)} \tag{5.26}$$

The expected waiting time for type 2 units can be obtained from (5.26) by changing the indices, so that

$$E(\hat{\mathscr{W}}_2) = \frac{\lambda_2 E(S_2^2)}{2(1-\rho_2)} + \frac{\lambda_2 \rho_1^2 E(S_2^2) + \lambda_1 (1-\rho_2)^2 E(S_1^2)}{2(1-\rho_2)(1-\rho)(1-\rho+2\rho_1\rho_2)} \tag{5.27}$$

Results for the queue-length distribution can be obtained in a similar way. The expected delay time is obtained by adding ν_1 and ν_2 to (5.26) and (5.27), respectively.

The alternating-priority discipline has also been termed the "zero-switch rule." The results can be used to describe the inventories associated with machines producing more than one item. With two products, no setup times, and exponential service times, the single-machine scheduling problem was studied by Maxwell [60]. The alternating-priority discipline, as noted earlier, is useful for describing the behavior of traffic at intersections and the effect of "red" and "green" phase durations. It is noted that in both the applications cited above, we need to incorporate the reorientation times or setup times in the model discussed above. The problem with reorientation times involves more complicated algebra, and has been studied by Miller [61] and Mevert [59].

We end this section by pointing out that if there are more than two classes, a large number of disciplines can be visualized. It was mentioned in the beginning that if the unit of the type last serviced is not available, the server selects the unit with lowest priority index. However, the selection may be done in a fixed-repeating sequence, from the class which has the maximum queue length, etc. The first selection rule has been studied by Miller [61], who calls it the "strict-rotation" discipline. The reader can visualize several variations of the selection rule to develop new models and apply them to study traffic congestion at road intersections, inventories, etc.

6. Dynamic-Priority Discipline

Like the alternating-priority discipline, the dynamic-priority discipline is endogenous in character, since the order in which an arriving unit will be serviced in relation to those units already waiting is determined not only on the basis of the priority classification, but also upon the length of time which each unit has been waiting. An urgency number is assumed to be associated with each class of unit, and a newly arriving unit takes precedence over a unit in the queue if and only if the urgency number of the latter is numerically superior to that of the former by at least an amount equal to the length of time which the latter has been waiting.

As an example, assume that a unit arrives at time t and has urgency number u. For all units in the queue, we calculate *the amount of time each has already waited at time t*. Call these waiting times $\hat{\mathscr{W}}_i(t)$ and their respective urgency numbers u_i. Then the newly arriving customer takes precedence over all those units j for which $(u_j - u) \geqslant \hat{\mathscr{W}}_j(t)$.

Figure VII.9 illustrates the dynamic-priority concept. Assume that a unit arrived at time t_0 with urgency number u_0, and another unit arrives at t_1. If the second unit's urgency number is u_1, then he takes precedence over the first. If, on the other hand, the second unit's urgency number is u_1', he will not precede the first.

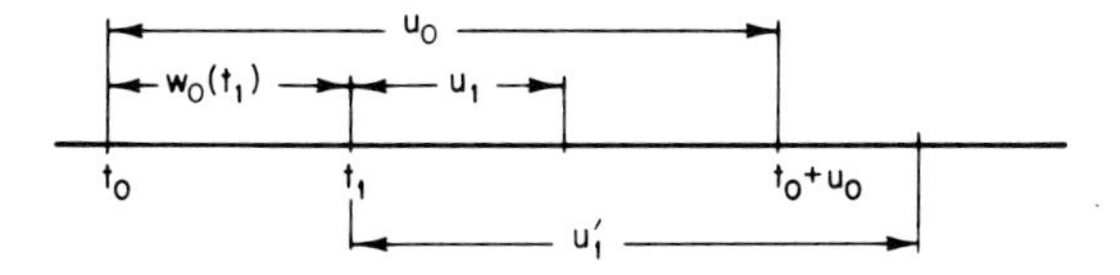

FIG. VII.9. Urgency numbers in dynamic-priority discipline.

It is evident from the above discussion that this dynamic discipline can be used where the management's concern with a unit increases as he waits. If we consider u_i as the scheduled time to completion of the ith unit's service, then this discipline chooses that unit with the earliest scheduled completion date.

This discipline was introduced by Jackson [40–42], and, in spite of its practical significance, it has not been studied much. We summarize primarily the results obtained by Jackson. His work is mostly with discrete time units, presumably to facilitate subsequent simulation experiments. The assumptions made are: (i) Given that a unit is in service, the service will be completed in the next time unit with probability q (ii) a unit enters the system with probability $p < q$; and (iii) π_n is probability that the urgency number is less than or equal to n.

It should be noted that as we let the discrete time unit get arbitrarily small and if p and q are correspondingly small, then this model approximates the $M/M/1$ system. Jackson's results are based on the fact that the first-come, first-served discipline and the head-of-the-line discipline provide convenient bounds for dynamic-priority waiting times.

For convenience, we define the following notation: $\rho = p/q$ is the utilization factor of the server, $\rho_n = \rho\pi_n$ is the utilization factor of the server by units of urgency number $\leqslant n$, $Z = (1 - q)/(1 - p)$, $A = Zp/q$, $R = [(1 - q)/q][\rho/(1 - \rho)]$, and s_k is the steady-state probability that there are k units in the system at the end of a time unit.

We can see that the following equations hold:

$$s_0 = s_0(1 - p) + s_0 pq + s_1(1 - p)\, q \tag{6.1}$$

$$s_k = s_k[(1 - p)(1 - q) + pq] + s_{k+1}[(1 - p)\, q] + s_{k-1}[(1 - q)\, p] \qquad (k = 1, 2 \cdots) \tag{6.2}$$

Note that a unit can enter at the start of a time unit and complete service at the end of the time unit. Iterative solution of these equations yields the generating function

$$\Pi(z) = \frac{1 - A}{1 - Az} \tag{6.3}$$

so that

$$s_k = (1 - A)\, A^k \qquad (k = 0, 1, 2, \cdots)$$

This distribution is true for all three disciplines (first-come, first served; head-of-the-line; and dynamic-priority).

Now, denote by $x_0(t)$ the probability that the total service required by all units present in the system is less than or equal to t; $x_0(t)$ is the cumulative distribution function of the virtual waiting time. Further, let $x_i(t)$ denote the equilibrium probability that after customers who are in the system at a given time have received t units of service, i of them are still in the system; we see that

$$x_0(t) = x_0(t - 1) + qx_1(t - 1) \tag{6.4}$$

$$x_i(t) = (1 - q)\, x_i(t - 1) + qx_{i+1}(t - 1) \qquad (i = 1, 2, \cdots) \tag{6.5}$$

Inductively, we can show that

$$x_i(t) = (1 - A)\, A^i Z^t \qquad (i > 0) \tag{6.6}$$

Then,

$$x_0(t) = 1 - \sum_{i=1}^{\infty} x_i(t)$$

$$= 1 - \rho Z^{t+1} \tag{6.7}$$

We next show that the equilibrium mean waiting time for all urgency classes taken together is given by $E(\hat{\mathscr{W}}) = R$. It is easy to see that $E(\hat{\mathscr{W}})$ is the sum of service times of all units in front of an arriving unit. Given that an arriving unit finds k in the system, the probability that he waits exactly t time units is given by

$$\Pr\{\text{wait} = t \mid k\} = \binom{t-1}{k-1} q^{k-1}(1-q)^{[(t-1)-(k-1)]} \times q \tag{6.8}$$

The unconditional probability of waiting for time t is

$$\Pr\{\text{wait} = t\} = \sum_{k=1}^{t} \binom{t-1}{k-1} q^{k}(1-q)^{t-k} s_k \tag{6.9}$$

Then, the mean waiting time is

$$E(\hat{\mathscr{W}}) = \sum_{t=0}^{\infty} t \Pr\{\text{wait} = t\}$$

and can be shown to be equal to R.

If we let $E(\hat{\mathscr{W}}_j)$ denote the equilibrium mean waiting time for a unit with urgency number j under the head-of-the-line discipline, and $E(\hat{\mathscr{W}}'_j)$ the mean waiting time under the dynamic-priority discipline, the following results can be obtained:

$$E(\hat{\mathscr{W}}_j) = \frac{\rho(1-q)/q}{(1-\rho_{j-1})(1-\rho_j)} \tag{6.10}$$

$$\frac{1-\rho}{1-\rho_j} \leq \frac{E(\hat{\mathscr{W}}'_j)}{E(\hat{\mathscr{W}})} \leq \frac{1}{1-\rho_{j-1}} \tag{6.11}$$

Proofs for these results are given in Jackson [40].

It is also useful to obtain an exact expression for $E(\hat{\mathscr{W}}'_j)$. Let U denote the expected delay of a unit of urgency number j due to units already in the system, and let $d\hat{\mathscr{W}}_t$ be the equilibrium probability that such an arriving unit will wait exactly t time units. Then,

$$\begin{aligned} E(\hat{\mathscr{W}}'_j) &= U + d\hat{\mathscr{W}}_1[\rho_{j-1}] + d\hat{\mathscr{W}}_2[\rho_{j-1} + \rho_{j-2}] + d\hat{\mathscr{W}}_3[\rho_{j-1} + \rho_{j-2} + \rho_{j-3}] + \cdots \\ &= U + \sum_{t=1}^{\infty} d\hat{\mathscr{W}}_t \sum_{i=j-t}^{j-1} \rho_i \end{aligned} \tag{6.12}$$

Some interesting results may be obtained when it is assumed that there is a maximum urgency number J. For this unit, service will never precede service to a unit already in the system. Hence, this unit is thought of as the least important customer. For this unit, it can be shown that

$$E(\hat{\mathscr{W}}'_J) = E(\hat{\mathscr{W}}) + \sum_{i<J} \rho_i[1 - x_0(J - i - 1)]$$

$$= E(\hat{\mathscr{W}}) + E(\hat{\mathscr{W}})(1 - Z) \sum_{i<J} \rho_i Z^{J-i-1} \tag{6.13}$$

where $x_0(t)$ denotes the probability that a unit of class J will wait $\leqslant t$ time units.

Next, assume that there are exactly two urgency classes with urgency numbers 0 and J. It should be noted that the order of service remains the same if we add or subtract a constant from all urgency numbers; only the difference is of importance. Hence, the numbers 0 and J are perfectly general. When $J = 0$, we have a first-come, first-served discipline, and when $J \to \infty$, we have a head-of-the-line discipline. We can see, then, how the two disciplines bound the dynamic priority system. With this two-class system, we can solve for mean waiting times for each class as a function of J. It can be shown that

$$E(\hat{\mathscr{W}}'_J) = E(\hat{\mathscr{W}}) + \rho_0 \left[J - \sum_{t=0}^{J-1} x_0(t)\right] \tag{6.14}$$

and

$$E(\hat{\mathscr{W}}'_0) = E(\hat{\mathscr{W}}) - (\rho - \rho_0) \left[J - \sum_{t=0}^{J-1} x_0(t)\right] \tag{6.15}$$

where $x_0(t)$ is the equilibrium probability that a nonpreferred (i.e., J-class) customer will wait $\leqslant t$.

Preliminary work of Jackson [40] led to two conjectures concerning dynamic-priority systems. These conjectures, discussed below, were tested by simulation techniques and reported in Jackson [41]. It seemed reasonable to assume that if arriving units were sure to wait a "long" time, then an arriving unit with urgency number u would be in about the same statistical situation as a unit with urgency $v > u$ who has already waited $(v - u)$ units of time. This assumption implies that the upper tails of the waiting-time distribution would be similar in shape but displaced by $(v - u)$ units of time.

Let $x_u(t)$ denote the equilibrium probability that a unit of urgency class u will wait $\leqslant t$. For $0 \leqslant f < 1$, define

$$\hat{\mathscr{W}}_u(f) = \inf\{t \mid x_u(t) \geqslant f\} \tag{6.16}$$

This is the fractile f in the cumulative distribution function of waiting time for class u. When the service is governed by first-come, first-served discipline let $x(t)$ be the waiting time distribution function, and then define

$$\hat{\mathscr{W}}(f) = \inf\{t \mid x(t) \geqslant f\} \tag{6.17}$$

The following conjectures are investigated in Jackson [41]: (1) $\hat{\mathscr{W}}_u(f) - \hat{\mathscr{W}}_v(f) \to u - v$ as $f \to 1$; (2) $\hat{\mathscr{W}}_u(f) - \hat{\mathscr{W}}(f) \to u - \bar{u}$ as $f \to 1$, where $\bar{u}$ is approximately the mean of the urgency-number distribution. Simulation results lend statistically significant support to these conjectures.

For further treatment of the dynamic-priority discipline, the reader is referred to the references cited above.

6-1. Instantaneous Priority Index

As mentioned earlier, the dynamic-priority discipline is an endogenous discipline. Inherent in the concept of endogenous disciplines is the assumption of a time-dependent "instantaneous priority index." The instantaneous priority index may be denoted by $\mathscr{I}_j(t)$, which gives the priority index of a jth-class unit at time t. For exogenous priority disciplines, this index remains constant throughout, while for endogenous disciplines, it depends upon the time. For the dynamic-priority discipline, we have

$$\mathscr{I}_j(t) = u_j - \hat{\mathscr{W}}_j(t) \tag{6.18}$$

where u_j is the associated urgency number and $\hat{\mathscr{W}}_j(t)$ is the amount of time the jth-class unit has already waited at time t. Obviously, $0 \leqslant u_1 \leqslant u_2 \cdots \leqslant u_k$, so that if two units arrived at the same instant, the unit with lower priority index will be preferred. Also, as $\hat{\mathscr{W}}_j(t)$ increases, $\mathscr{I}_j(t)$ decreases. Hence, eventually, whatever j may be, $\mathscr{I}_j(t)$ for that unit becomes the smallest among all waiting units.

Apparently, any function which increases with u_j and decreases as $\hat{\mathscr{W}}_j(t)$ increases will achieve the objective of servicing units according to their urgency numbers while giving due consideration to the waiting times of the units. Hence, $\mathscr{I}_j(t)$ may have the following form as well,

$$\mathscr{I}_j(t) = \frac{u_j}{[\hat{\mathscr{W}}_j(t)]^\beta} \qquad (\beta > 0) \tag{6.19}$$

The priority discipline with $\mathscr{I}_j(t)$ as specified by (6.19) has been investigated by Kleinrock and Finkelstein [107]. The particular case $\beta = 1$ was investigated earlier by Kleinrock [54]. Kleinrock called this the "delay-dependent" queue discipline, and later [55], the "lag-priority" discipline. Our definition may look a little different, but is essentially the same. The value of $\mathscr{I}_j(t)$ decreases from ∞ to zero as the waiting time increases, and, since the unit with lowest $\mathscr{I}_j(t)$ is selected for service, the chances of its being selected increases with t.

We may remind the reader that the definition of an endogenous discipline as given in Section III.1 defines only the rule of selecting a unit when the server is free. The decision of "how to serve it," specified as the second rule, may or may not depend on the state of the system. For example, one can associate the non-preemptive or preemptive service rules, provided these are possible, with the endogenous disciplines defined above. In addition, we can conceive of having a partly endogenous discipline for a few classes and an exogenous discipline for the remaining classes in a system. Such models have been studied by Kleinrock [55].

In reference to (6.19), we can see that this is an open area for further work, and a great deal more is required to be done before we can appreciate the effect of endogenous priority disciplines. Further elaboration of this idea is made in Section VIII, 8.

7. Cutoff Priority—Multichannel Priority Models

The cutoff priority has been defined and studied by Benn [10]. Unlike the disciplines discussed so far, this discipline is only defined for multichannel queuing systems. Let us consider $k > 1$ classes of units arriving for service on an N-channel service system, and let us define integers $N_1, N_2, \ldots, N_{k-1}$ such that

$$0 \leqslant N_{k-1} \leqslant \cdots \leqslant N_2 \leqslant N_1 \leqslant N_0 = N$$

The cutoff priority can be defined as follows: Whenever N_{l-1} or more servers are busy, new arrivals from classes l through k are not allowed to begin service, even if some channels are idle. When immediate service is refused to a unit, it may either wait for service or else leave the system. Once a unit enters service, it is not preempted. Also, if $N_i = N_j$, the units of the classes i and j are served according to the head-of-the-line discipline, i having non-preemptive priority over j if $i < j$. Finally, within a class, units queue according to the first-come, first-served discipline. Thus, for a two-class priority process, the cutoff priority discipline can be specified as follows: If fewer than N_1 channels are occupied, any unit whether priority or ordinary will be taken for service. Otherwise, if N_1 or more channels are occupied, only priority units will be taken for service, if possible.

The cutoff priority is obviously useful when it is not possible to preempt the service of a low-priority unit in order to favor a high-priority unit. Such situations often arise with physical systems and most human systems. An example encountered in practice is the so-called combined car-pool problem in which a fixed number N of freight cars is assigned to service k shippers. Each shipper generates a demand for cars and each car of the pool corresponds to a server. The time to deliver the freight from a shipper and its return to the pool is the service time. Values of N_i $(i = 1, 2, \ldots, k - 1)$ are sought which maximize an objective function involving, for example, the cost of waiting or the probabilities of loss or delay.

For the two-class priority processes, we can conceive of four possible models, depending upon whether the priority and ordinary units are assumed lost or delayed when immediate service is not available. Consequently, we define the models given in Table VII.1.

TABLE VII.1

	Assumption made when immediate service is not available	
Model number	Priority unit	Ordinary unit
I	lost	lost
II	delayed	lost
III	lost	delayed
IV	delayed	delayed

We discuss these models assuming that the input process is a Poisson process and service times for all units are distributed according to an exponential distribution with mean $1/\mu$ irrespective of the service channel. The restrictions on the service times assumed above are necessary to make the process Markovian. Any relaxation of this assumption makes the process difficult to analyze (see Section VIII, 2).

Model I

Our objective in this model may be to choose N_1 such that in the long run, the proportion of times units from classes 1 and 2 are lost becomes as close as possible to predetermined levels. To satisfy this objective, we need to determine the steady-state probabilities that a unit from either class is lost as a function of N_1 and N. For the special case when $N_1 = N$, this model was studied by Helly [37], and his work was extended by Burke [14].

Let $\lambda_1 + \lambda_2 = \lambda$, and let $\hat{q}(n)$ $(n > 1)$ denote the steady-state probability that n servers are busy and $\hat{e}^{(2)}$ the probability that all the servers are idle. The appropriate equations for the steady state are

$$-\lambda\hat{e}^{(2)} + \mu\hat{q}(1) = 0 \tag{7.1}$$

$$-(\lambda + n\mu)\,\hat{q}(n) + \lambda\hat{q}(n-1) + (n+1)\,\mu\hat{q}(n+1) = 0 \qquad (0 < n < N_1) \tag{7.2}$$

$$-(\lambda_1 + N_1\mu)\,\hat{q}(N_1) + \lambda\hat{q}(N_1 - 1) + (N_1 + 1)\,\mu\hat{q}(N_1 + 1) = 0 \tag{7.3}$$

$$-(\lambda_1 + n\mu)\,\hat{q}(n) + \lambda_1\hat{q}(n-1) + (n+1)\,\mu\hat{q}(n+1) = 0 \qquad (N_1 < n < N) \tag{7.4}$$

$$-N\mu\hat{q}(N) + \lambda_1\hat{q}(N-1) = 0 \tag{7.5}$$

where $\hat{q}(0) = \hat{e}^{(2)}$.

The solution is given by

$$\hat{q}(n) = \frac{\rho^n}{n!}\,\hat{e}^{(2)} \qquad (0 \leqslant n \leqslant N_1) \tag{7.6}$$

and

$$\hat{q}(n) = \frac{N!}{n!}\,\frac{\hat{q}(N)}{\rho_1^{N-n}} \qquad (N_1 \leqslant n \leqslant N) \tag{7.7}$$

where $\rho = \lambda/\mu$ and $\rho_1 = \lambda_1/\mu$.

Equating the values of $\hat{q}(N_1)$ in (7.6) and (7.7), we get

$$\hat{q}(N) = \frac{\rho^{N_1}\rho_1^{N-N_1}}{N!}\,\hat{e}^{(2)} \tag{7.8}$$

and hence, for $N_1 \leqslant n \leqslant N$,

$$\hat{q}(n) = \frac{\rho^{N_1}\rho_1^{n-N_1}}{n!}\,\hat{e}^{(2)} \tag{7.9}$$

so that $\hat{e}^{(2)}$ is given by

$$\frac{1}{\hat{e}^{(2)}} = \sum_{n=0}^{N_1} \frac{\rho^n}{n!} + \frac{\rho^{N_1}}{\rho_1^{N_1}} \sum_{n=N_1+1}^{N} \frac{\rho_1{}^n}{n!} \tag{7.10}$$

The steady-state probability l_1 that a priority unit is lost is given by the proportion of time N channels are busy, and is therefore given by $\hat{q}(N)$; for an ordinary unit, it becomes

$$l_2 = \sum_{n=N_1}^{N} \hat{q}(n) = \hat{e}^{(2)} \frac{\rho^{N_1}}{\rho_1^{N_1}} \sum_{n=N_1}^{N} \frac{\rho_1{}^n}{n!} \tag{7.11}$$

Model II

The priority units are allowed to queue up while the ordinary units are lost. Let $\hat{q}(n)$ denote the probability that under steady state there are n units, priority or ordinary, in the system. Then, for $n < N$ Eqs. (7.1)–(7.4) hold good, while for $n \geqslant N$, we have

$$0 = -(\lambda_1 + N\mu)\, \hat{q}(n) + \lambda_1 \hat{q}(n-1) + N\mu\hat{q}(n+1) \tag{7.12}$$

The steady-state probabilities are given by

$$\hat{q}(n) = \frac{\rho^n}{n!} \hat{e}^{(2)} \qquad (0 \leqslant n \leqslant N_1) \tag{7.13}$$

$$\hat{q}(n) = \frac{\rho^{N_1} \rho_1^{n-N_1}}{n!} \hat{e}^{(2)} \qquad (N_1 \leqslant n \leqslant N) \tag{7.14}$$

$$\hat{q}(n) = \left(\frac{\rho_1}{N}\right)^{n-N} \frac{\rho^{N_1} \rho_1^{N-N_1}}{N!} \hat{e}^{(2)} \qquad (n \geqslant N) \tag{7.15}$$

and $\hat{e}^{(2)}$ is given by

$$\frac{1}{\hat{e}^{(2)}} = \sum_{n=0}^{N_1} \frac{\rho^n}{n!} + \frac{\rho^{N_1}}{\rho_1^{N_1}} \sum_{n=N_1+1}^{N} \frac{\rho_1{}^n}{n!} + \frac{\rho^{N_1} \rho_1^{N-N_1+1}}{N!(N-\rho_1)} \tag{7.16}$$

Thus, the probability that an ordinary unit is lost is given by

$$l_2 = \sum_{n=N_1}^{\infty} \hat{q}(n) = \hat{e}^{(2)} \left[\frac{\rho^{N_1}}{\rho_1^{N_1}} \sum_{n=N_1}^{N} \frac{\rho_1{}^n}{n!} + \frac{\rho^{N_1} \rho_1^{N-N_1+1}}{N!(N-\rho_1)}\right] \tag{7.17}$$

while $\hat{q}(n)$ the probability that a priority unit waits, is given by

$$\Pr(\hat{\mathscr{W}}_1 > 0) = \frac{\rho^{N_1}\rho_1^{N-N_1}\hat{e}^{(2)}}{(N-1)!\,(N-\rho_1)} \tag{7.18}$$

From these results, other characteristics may easily be evaluated; for example, the expected waiting time for a priority unit is given by

$$E(\hat{\mathscr{W}}_1) = \frac{\rho^{N_1}\rho_1^{N-N_1}[N^2-(N-1)\,\rho_1]\,\hat{e}^{(2)}}{(N-1)!\,(N-\rho_1)^2} \tag{7.19}$$

where $\hat{e}^{(2)}$ given by (7.16).

Model III

In this model, the priority units are assumed lost when all channels are busy. However, the ordinary units wait in queue when they arrive and find N_1 or more channels busy. Thus, to specify the state of the system we will require the number of busy channels and the number of ordinary units waiting in the queue. Let $\hat{q}(m_2, n)$ denote the steady-state probability that there are m_2 ordinary units present in the queue and n channels are busy, and let

$$\hat{q}(\cdot, n) = \sum_{m_2=0}^{\infty} \hat{q}(m_2, n) \tag{7.20}$$

and

$$\hat{q}(m_2, \cdot) = \sum_{n=N_1}^{N} \hat{q}(m_2, n) \qquad (m_2 \geqslant N_1) \tag{7.21}$$

The flow diagram in Fig. VII.10 depicts the transition rates into and out of the states of the system. With the help of this diagram, the difference equations connecting the probabilities defined in (7.20) and (7.21) can be written easily, from which we obtain

$$\hat{q}(0, n) = \frac{\rho^n}{n!}\,\hat{e}^{(2)} \qquad (0 \leqslant n \leqslant N_1) \tag{7.22}$$

$$\hat{q}(\cdot, n) = \frac{N!}{n!}\,\frac{\hat{q}(\cdot, N)}{\rho_1^{N-n}} \qquad (N_1 \leqslant n \leqslant N) \tag{7.23}$$

where $\hat{e}^{(2)} = \hat{q}(0, 0)$ is the probability of all the channels being idle. But, from the flow diagram

$$\lambda_2\hat{q}(m_2, \cdot) = N_1\mu\hat{q}(m_2+1, N_1) \qquad (m_2 \geqslant 0) \tag{7.24}$$

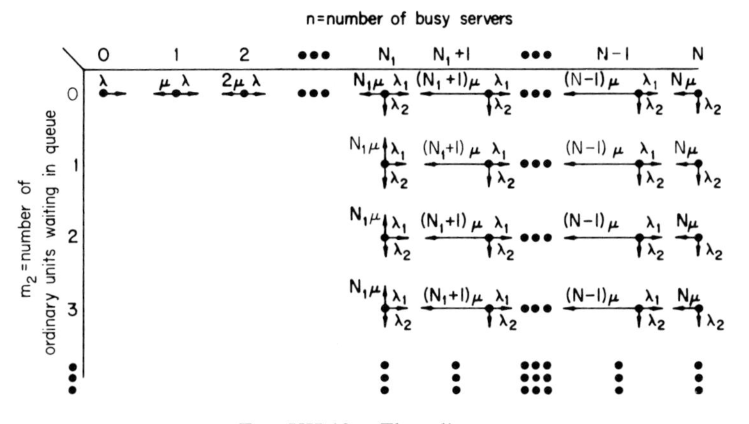

FIG. VII.10. Flow diagram.

Summing (7.24) for all values of m_2, we get

$$\lambda_2 \frac{N!\,\hat{q}(\cdot, N)}{\rho_1{}^N} \sum_{n=N_1}^{N} \frac{\rho_1{}^n}{n!} = N_1\mu \left[\frac{N!\,\hat{q}(\cdot, N)}{N_1!\,\rho_1^{N-N_1}} - \frac{\rho^{N_1}\hat{e}^{(2)}}{N_1!}\right] \tag{7.25}$$

and hence,

$$\hat{q}(\cdot, N) = \frac{-\rho^{N_1}}{\rho_2(N_1 - 1)!} \left\{\frac{(\rho_2 - N_1)}{\rho_2} \frac{N!}{N_1!\,\rho_1^{N-N_1}} + \frac{N!}{\rho_1{}^N} \sum_{n=N_1+1}^{N} \frac{\rho_1{}^n}{n!}\right\}^{-1} \hat{e}^{(2)} \tag{7.26}$$

where

$$\rho_2 = \frac{\lambda_2}{\mu}$$

so that

$$\frac{1}{\hat{e}^{(2)}} = \sum_{n=0}^{N_1-1} \frac{\rho^n}{n!} - \frac{\rho^{N_1}}{(N_1 - 1)!\,\rho_2} \left\{\frac{(\rho_2 - N_1)}{\rho_2} \frac{\rho_1^{N_1}}{N_1!} + \sum_{n=N_1+1}^{N} \frac{\rho_1{}^n}{n!}\right\}^{-1} \sum_{n=N_1}^{N} \frac{\rho_1{}^n}{n!} \tag{7.27}$$

Thus, $\hat{q}(0, n)$ $(0 \leqslant n \leqslant N_1)$ and $\hat{q}(\cdot, n)$ $(N_1 \leqslant n \leqslant N)$ are completely determined.

The proportion of priority units lost is obviously $\hat{q}(\cdot, N)$, and is given by (7.26), and the steady-state probability that an ordinary unit waits is given by

$$\Pr(\mathscr{W}_2 > 0) = \frac{N!}{\rho_1{}^N} \hat{q}(\cdot, N) \sum_{n=N_1}^{N} \frac{\rho_1{}^n}{n!} \tag{7.28}$$

It should be noted that the loss and delay probabilities obtained above have been derived without explicitly obtaining $\hat{q}(m_2, n)$. This was accomplished by judiciously grouping states and then working only with these groups. However, if more detailed knowledge about the system is needed, a procedure similar to the one carried out for the analysis of the next model may be used.

Model IV

For this model, since both types of units can queue up, we denote by $\hat{p}(m_1, m_2, n)$ the steady-state probability that there are m_1 priority and m_2 ordinary units present in the queue and n channels are busy. Assuming $N > N_1 + 1$, the appropriate equations are

$$(\lambda_1 + \lambda_2 + N\mu)\,\hat{q}(m_1, m_2, N) = \lambda_1\hat{q}(m_1 - 1, m_2, N) + \lambda_2\hat{q}(m_1, m_2 - 1, N) + N\mu\hat{q}(m_1 + 1, m_2, N) \qquad (m_1 > 0) \tag{7.29}$$

$$(\lambda_1 + \lambda_2 + N\mu)\,\hat{q}(0, m_2, N) = \lambda_1\hat{q}(0, m_2, N - 1) + \lambda_2\hat{q}(0, m_2 - 1, N) + N\mu\hat{q}(1, m_2, N) \tag{7.30}$$

$$(\lambda_1 + \lambda_2 + n\mu)\,\hat{q}(0, m_2, n) = \lambda_1\hat{q}(0, m_2, n - 1) + \lambda_2\hat{q}(0, m_2 - 1, n) + (n + 1)\,\mu\hat{q}(0, m_2, n + 1) \qquad (N_1 + 1 \leqslant n < N) \tag{7.31}$$

$$(\lambda_1 + \lambda_2 + N_1\mu)\,\hat{q}(0, 0, N_1) = \lambda_1\hat{q}(0, 0, N_1 - 1) + \lambda_2\hat{q}(0, 0, N_1 - 1) + N_1\mu\hat{q}(0, 1, N_1) + (N_1 + 1)\,\mu\hat{q}(0, 0, N_1 + 1) \tag{7.32}$$

$$(\lambda_1 + \lambda_2 + N_1\mu)\,\hat{q}(0, m_2, N_1) = \lambda_2\hat{q}(0, m_2 - 1, N_1) + N_1\mu\hat{q}(0, m_2 + 1, N_1) + (N_1 + 1)\,\mu\hat{q}(0, m_2, N_1 + 1) \qquad (m_2 > 0) \tag{7.33}$$

and

$$(\lambda_1 + \lambda_2 + n\mu)\,\hat{q}(0, 0, n) = \lambda_1\hat{q}(0, 0, n - 1) + \lambda_2\hat{q}(0, 0, n - 1) + (n + 1)\,\mu\hat{q}(0, 0, n + 1) \qquad (0 \leqslant n < N_1) \tag{7.34}$$

Let us define the following generating function:

$$f(m_1, \alpha_2, n) = \sum_{m_2=0}^{\infty} \hat{q}(m_1, m_2, n)\,\alpha_2^{m_2} \tag{7.35}$$

The above equations can be written in terms of this generating function as

$$(\lambda_1 + \lambda_2 + N\mu) f(m_1, \alpha_2, N) = \lambda_1 f(m_1 - 1, \alpha_2, N) + \lambda_2\alpha_2 f(m_1, \alpha_2, N) + N\mu f(m_1 + 1, \alpha_2, N) \qquad (m_1 > 0) \quad (7.36)$$

$$(\lambda_1 + \lambda_2 + N\mu) f(0, \alpha_2, N) = \lambda_1 f(0, \alpha_2, N - 1) + \lambda_2\alpha_2 f(0, \alpha_2, N) + N\mu f(1, \alpha_2, N) \quad (7.37)$$

$$(\lambda_1 + \lambda_2 + n\mu) f(0, \alpha_2, n) = \lambda_1 f(0, \alpha_2, n - 1) + \lambda_2\alpha_2 f(0, \alpha_2, n) + (n + 1)\mu f(0, \alpha_2, n + 1) \qquad (N_1 + 1 \leqslant n < N) \quad (7.38)$$

$$(\lambda_1 + \lambda_2 + N_1\mu) f(0, \alpha_2, N_1) = \lambda_1 f(0, 0, N_1 - 1) + \lambda_2 f(0, 0, N_1 - 1) + \lambda_2\alpha_2 f(0, \alpha_2, N_1) + N_1\mu\bar{\alpha}_2^{1}[f(0, \alpha_2, N_1) - f(0, 0, N_1)] + (N_1 + 1)\mu f(0, \alpha_2, N_1 + 1) \quad (7.39)$$

$$(\lambda_1 + \lambda_2 + n\mu) f(0, 0, n) = \lambda_1 f(0, 0, n - 1) + \lambda_2 f(0, 0, n - 1) + (n + 1)\mu f(0, 0, n + 1) \qquad (n < N_1) \quad (7.40)$$

Equation (7.36) is a difference equation in m_1, and has the solution

$$f(m_1, \alpha_2, N) = f(0, \alpha_2, N)\, w_0^{m_1} \qquad (m_1 \geqslant 0) \quad (7.41)$$

where w_0 is that root of the equation

$$N\mu w^2 - [\lambda_1 + \lambda_2(1 - \alpha_2) + N\mu]\, w + \lambda_1 = 0 \quad (7.42)$$

whose modulus is less than 1. It is easy to show that for $\lambda_1 + \lambda_2 < N\mu$, w_0 is real and $0 < w_0 < 1$. Hence, from (7.37), using (7.41) and the fact that w_0 is the root of (7.42), we get

$$f(0, \alpha_2, N) = f(0, \alpha_2, N - 1)\, w_0 \quad (7.43)$$

To solve (7.38), we use the following discrete transform (see Appendix 1 lemma 3):

$$B(0, \alpha_2, m) = \sum_{n=m}^{N-1} \binom{n}{m} f(0, \alpha_2, n) \quad (7.44)$$

so that (7.38) can be written, after using the results of Appendix I and some simplification, as

$$[\lambda_2(1-\alpha_2)+m\mu]\,B(0,\alpha_2,m)=\lambda_1 B(0,\alpha_2,m-1)$$
$$+\left[\mu w_0\binom{N-1}{m}-\lambda_1\binom{N}{m}\right]f(0,\alpha_2,N-1) \tag{7.45}$$

a difference equation of the same form as studied in Chapter II. Hence, following the method outlined there, we get

$$\frac{B(0,\alpha_2,m)}{X(\alpha_2,m)}=f(0,\alpha_2,N-1)\left\{\sum_{j=m}^{N-1}\frac{1}{X(\alpha_2,j)}\left[-\frac{\mu w_0 N}{\lambda_1}\binom{N-1}{j+1}+\binom{N}{j+1}\right]\right\} \tag{7.46}$$

where

$$X(\alpha_2,m)=\prod_{n=1}^{m}\frac{\lambda_1}{\lambda_2(1-\alpha_2)+\mu n}$$

Using the inversion formula for the transform, we get

$$f(0,\alpha_2,n)=f(0,\alpha_2,N-1)\sum_{m=n}^{N-1}(-1)^{m-n}\binom{m}{n}$$
$$\times\sum_{j=m}^{N-1}\left[-\frac{\mu w_0 N}{\lambda_1}\binom{N-1}{j+1}+\binom{N}{j+1}\right]\frac{X(\alpha_2,m)}{X(\alpha_2,j)}$$
$$(N_1\leqslant n\leqslant N-1) \tag{7.47}$$

Denoting the sum on the right-hand side of (7.47) by $a(\alpha_2, n)$, we can write (7.47) as

$$f(0,\alpha_2,n)=a(\alpha_2,n)f(0,\alpha_2,N-1)\qquad(N_1\leqslant n\leqslant N-1) \tag{7.48}$$

Using (7.48) in (7.39), we obtain

$$\{a(\alpha_2,N_1)[\lambda_1+\lambda_2\{1-\alpha_2\}+N_1\mu\{1-\alpha_2^{-1}\}]$$
$$-a(\alpha_2,N_1+1)(N_1+1)\mu\}f(0,\alpha_2,N-1)$$
$$=(\lambda_1+\lambda_2)f(0,0,N_1-1)-N_1\mu\alpha_2^{-1}f(0,0,N_1) \tag{7.49}$$

Finally, we solve (7.40) by rewriting it in the form

$$(n+1)\mu f(0,0,n+1)-(\lambda_1+\lambda_2)f(0,0,n)$$
$$=n\mu f(0,0,n)-(\lambda_1+\lambda_2)f(0,0,n-1)\qquad(n<N_1) \tag{7.50}$$

Since

$$(\lambda_1 + \lambda_2)\,\hat{e}^{(2)} = \mu\hat{q}(0, 0, 1)$$

we have

$$(\lambda_1 + \lambda_2) f(0, 0, 0) = \mu f(0, 0, 1) \tag{7.51}$$

so that, solving (7.50) recursively and using (7.51), we obtain

$$f(0, 0, n) = \frac{\rho^n}{n!}\,\hat{e}^{(2)} \qquad (n < N_1) \tag{7.52}$$

where $\hat{e}^{(2)} = f\,(0, 0, 0)$ and $\rho = (\lambda_1 + \lambda_2)/\mu$. Hence, from (7.49),

$$f(0, \alpha_2, N-1) = \frac{\dfrac{\rho^{N_1-1}}{(N_1-1)!}\,\hat{e}^{(2)}(1-\alpha_2^{-1})(\lambda_1+\lambda_2)}{a(\alpha_2, N_1)\left[\lambda_1 + \lambda_2\{1-\alpha_2\} + N_1\mu\left(1 - \dfrac{1}{\alpha_2}\right)\right] - (N_1+1)\,\mu a(\alpha_2, N_1+1)} \tag{7.53}$$

Since

$$\hat{e}^{(2)} + \sum_{m_1=0}^{\infty} f(m_1, 1, N) + \sum_{n=N_1}^{N-1} f(0, 1, n) + \sum_{n=1}^{N_1-1} f(0, 0, n) = 1 \tag{7.54}$$

we have

$$\hat{e}^{(2)} \sum_{n=0}^{N_1-1} \frac{\rho^n}{n!} + \left[\frac{w_0}{1-w_0} + \sum_{n=N_1}^{N-1} a(1, n)\right] f(0, 1, N-1) = 1 \tag{7.55}$$

and using, (7.53), we obtain the value of $\hat{e}^{(2)}$. It may be shown by using the combinatorial identity

$$\sum_{j=k}^{N-1} \frac{\rho_1^{N-j-1}}{(N-j-1)!} \sum_{m=0}^{j-k} (-1)^m \frac{\rho_1{}^m}{m!} = 1 \tag{7.56}$$

that

$$a(1, n) = \frac{(N-1)!}{n!\,\rho_1^{N-n-1}}$$

so that L'hospital's rule will have to be applied to evaluate $f\,(0, 1, N-1)$ so that $\hat{e}^{(2)}$ can be found from (7.55).

Finally, the probability that a priority unit waits is given by

$$\Pr(\hat{\mathscr{W}}_1 > 0) = \sum_{m_1=0}^{\infty} \sum_{m_2=0}^{\infty} \hat{q}(m_1, m_2, N) = \sum_{m_1=0}^{\infty} f(m_1, 1, N)$$

$$= \frac{\lambda_1}{N\mu - \lambda_1} f(0, 1, N-1) \tag{7.57}$$

on using the result

$$w_0 \big|_{\alpha_2=1} = \frac{\lambda_1}{N\mu}$$

and the probability that an ordinary unit waits is given by

$$\Pr(\hat{\mathscr{W}}_2 > 0) = 1 - \sum_{n=0}^{N_1-1} \hat{p}^{(2)}(0, 0, n) = 1 - \sum_{n=0}^{N_1-1} \frac{\rho^n}{n!} \hat{e}^{(2)} \tag{7.58}$$

In all the above models, we have considered only two priority classes. Generalization beyond two classes presents additional algebraic complications. For the special case where all N_i $(i = 0, 1, 2,..., k-1)$ are equal to N, the cutoff priority discipline reduces to the head-of-the-line priority discipline which we studied for the case of a single server in Chapter IV. For the multichannel case, this particular case was studied by Cobham [18], who obtained the following result for the expected waiting time for the jth class $(1 \leqslant j \leqslant k)$:

$$E(\hat{\mathscr{W}}_j) = \frac{\dfrac{\Pi}{N\mu}}{\left(1 - \dfrac{1}{N\mu} \sum_{i=1}^{j-1} \lambda_i\right) 1 - \dfrac{1}{N\mu} \sum_{i=1}^{j} \lambda_i\Big)} \tag{7.59}$$

where Π is the probability that all the channels are busy and is given by

$$\Pi = \frac{\rho^N}{N!\left(1 - \dfrac{\lambda}{N\mu}\right)\left[\sum_{j=0}^{N-1} \dfrac{\rho^j}{j!} + \sum_{j=N}^{\infty} \dfrac{\rho^j}{N!\, N^{j-N}}\right]} \tag{7.60}$$

Some recent work on the waiting time distribution for this model has been done by Davis [23].

8. Exogenous versus Endogenous Disciplines

In the present and last four chapters, we discussed several exogenous disciplines as well as a few endogenous disciplines. It was noted that in exogenous disciplines if the system parameters are specified, the performance of each class gets fixed, and thus a system designer has no freedom to adjust the system behavior. An exception to this, however, is the discretionary priority discipline in which we have $k - 1$ controllable parameters for the k-class process. Exogenous disciplines have one advantage, namely, the higher priority classes may have statistical equilibrium even if the system is saturated. Thus, it is possible that units belonging to 1, 2,..., r classes exhibit finite queues and experience finite delays, while units belonging to $(r + 1)$,..., k classes exhibit infinite queues and experience infinite delays. On the other hand, most of the endogenous disciplines have controllable parameters, e.g., u_j $(1 \leqslant j \leqslant k)$ which help in adjusting the relative performance of each class. However, if any class starts experiencing infinite delays, all classes experience infinite delays, and as such partial equilibrium does not exist.

To summarize, the controllability aspect of the discretionary and endogenous priority disciplines offer valuable help in adjusting the system performance, and thus these disciplines are more important than exogenous disciplines (nondiscretionary). However, the advantage of partial equilibrium associated with the latter disciplines is absent in the former.

The reader might have a feeling that the exogenous and endogenous disciplines have little in common. But this appears not to be the case as for a class of exogenous and endogenous disciplines satisfying certain conditions, a conservation law holds good according to which a particular weighted sum of the mean waiting times of units of all classes is constant and is independent of the priority discipline. For the conditions under which this conservation law holds good the reader is referred to Kleinrock [105]. Yet, another observation which lends further insight into the interrelationship between some exgenous and endogenous disciplines is brought out in Section VIII, 7. These observations point to a more inherent interrelationship between exogenous and endogenous disciplines which needs further investigation.

Chapter VIII

AREAS FOR FURTHER WORK

1. Introduction

In this chapter, we discuss those problems that were put aside in earlier chapters as requiring further elaboration. This should help the interested reader to note specific areas where further work is needed. It would be best, therefore, to enumerate such areas and explain the difficulties involved in analyzing each of them. Some of the difficulties are the same as for the classical queuing processes, and will be mentioned in lesser detail. Others are peculiar to priority problems, and are concerned primarily with better decision-making about such questions as "who should be served first" and "how"? Finally, we try to formulate a general decision model. One would hope that by incorporating more system variables into this decision model, one might improve the system behavior in a certain specified sense. However, the models become more difficult to analyze analytically, and so is the implementation. How to improve the priority allocation decision based on the least amount of given system information is what one would like to know in this world of uncertainty.

2. Generalized Inputs and Multichannel Systems

If the assumption of Poisson inputs is relaxed, one finds a non-Markovian stochastic process requiring two or more supplementary variables to make it Markovian. The same is true if we consider multichannel systems with arbitrary service-time distributions. The difficulty is essentially similar as for the basic $M/G/N$ models. To recall the difficulty in studying $M/G/N$ models, we note that since the service-time distribution for each channel is arbitrary, we require N additional supplementary variables to keep complete information about the present history of the system. One is thus confronted with the problem of solving a differential difference equation in $N > 1$ variables—a problem of sufficient complexity even for small values of N. Consequently, much of the work on multichannel priority systems has been confined to exponential service-time distributions, and nothing is known about priority problems with generalized inputs or multichannel systems with arbitrary service-time distribution. A usual procedure is to study the effect of assuming one type of arrival process as Erlangian or a weighted mixture of Erlangian distributions. An attempt in this direction was made by Jaiswal and Thiruvengadam [46], but the mathematics becomes extremely complicated. One would like to see simpler methods for studying such non-Markovian processes which require more than one supplementary variable before trying to generalize the study of priorities for arbitrary inputs and for multichannel systems.

3. Single Finite-Source Models

In previous chapters, we discussed multiple finite-source priority models in which each finite-source generates only one type of input. However, let us consider an operator looking after a set of N machines, each of which can fail because of any of k types of failure. A machine having failed has the probability λ_i/λ of having the ith type of failure, and has repair time density $S_i(x)$. Thus, in such a system at any time there will be n_i machines because of the ith type of failure, so that $\Sigma n_i = n$, the total number of failed machines in the system. It can be seen that, unlike the multiple finite-source priority models, the arrival of ith-class unit (machine with the ith type of failure) affects the arrival rates of all classes. Because of this dependence of arrival rates, these models are more difficult to analyze. The first attempt to study such models was made by Benson and Cox [11] for exponential service-time distributions, two types of failure, and head-of-the-line priority discipline. The model was subsequently generalized by Jaiswal and Thiruvengadam [47] for arbitrary service-time distributions using the supplementary variable method and solving the resulting differential difference equations. The results are, however, obviously complicated, and not much is known about the system behavior.

The model needs to be studied further for different disciplines, e.g., preemptive or discretionary, and a great deal of numerical work is needed to investigate the effect of imposing priorities.

4. Complicated Disciplines and Structures

The priorities can also arise in systems having more complicated service rules or more complicated structures. For example, one can associate priorities with bulk-service queuing systems, processes with batch arrivals, systems in which balking and reneging is permitted, and so on. Attempts to incorporate priorities and study its effect in systems for which the results of the basic models (without priorities) are known, have been started; e.g., we may refer to Subba Rao [80] for studies pertaining to priorities in balking and reneging systems, and to Hawks [33] for systems with batch arrivals.

As an example of priorities in complicated queuing structures, let us consider a network problem. Different types of messages may have to be sent over a given communication network, or different types of jobs processed through assembly lines. Although basic models for network queues have been studied [9, 26], little has been done to study the priority problems in such models analytically. The results for network queues with priorities will be of great practical value and one would like to see more on this aspect. Investigation of the relationship between the capacities, inputs, and outputs at various components of a network will be welcome to design engineers, as it will help in optimizing the efficiency of such systems.

5. Inventory Models with Priorities

The problem of priorities arises also in such related fields as inventory control or reliability. It would be worthwhile to indicate the type of problems involved and point out if the knowledge of priorities in queues could be of use to answer questions in such fields. Consequently, we discuss some inventory models in this section and some reliability models in the next.

Consider the inventory of rental items, e.g., a car pool or skilled laborers. Each item is removed from the inventory by a demand, the distribution of which is assumed to be arbitrary. The inventory has N items. An item once rented returns after a time which is distributed exponentially. If a demand arises when there is no item in the inventory, it is lost. Considered as a queuing model, this is the familiar

$GI/M/N$ situation in which units are lost if all the channels are busy. It can be shown [86] that the queuing model $GI/M/N - 1$ with no queue is identical to the $M/G/1/N$ model. The above model has been studied as an inventory model by Tainiter [83] using the results of the finite-source model, and a modified version of this model has recently been studied by Jain [43].

One can assume two or more types of arrivals in this model and study sales policies which optimize a given objective function.

Above, we assumed that the inventory can be reviewed continuously, and that we can thus use mathematics similar to those used in the study of multichannel priority systems. However, if the inventory is viewed at discrete time points, the investigation of sales policies will be more interesting and of more value. Work in this area has been initiated by Evans [27] and is being continued by Powell [73]. In such discrete-time models, the demands arriving in a time period are accumulated up to the end of the period, and the sales and reorder policies are determined based on the state of the system and relevant cost parameters. It is indeed conceivable that an ordinary customer will be delayed for a certain length of time, even though there may be enough inventory on hand; i.e., the system anticipates a priority customer for whom a shortage (or delay) could produce a higher cost. Analysis of these models have been made using the standard dynamic-programming formulation of multistage inventory theory. Although the convexity of the minimand does not hold in most cases, it is anticipated that efficient search procedures can be developed.

6. Reliability and Maintenance Problems

The problem of finding "measures of reliability" in complex redundant systems subject to stochastic failure and repair laws requires the investigation of certain characteristics (not of direct interest to congestion systems) of the finite-source models. Consider for example a complex system having N identical components. Each component has a failure rate λ and requires a random time for its replacement or repair which is distributed according to an arbitrary distribution. Let us assume that such a system continues to operate until there are $i < N$ components in working condition. The problem of finding the probability that such a system will be operable up to time t is the same as finding the probability that in the finite-source model, the system starting from no queue reaches a queue of

$(N - i + 1)$ units for the first time. The MTSF (mean time to system failure), a parameter of interest to a reliability engineer, is just the mean duration of the first-passage problem of the finite-source model mentioned above.

Let us now consider a complex system having N subsystems, each of which comprises k redundant components. The system continues to operate until at least N different components out of the total Nk components are in operable condition. If the failure and repair rates of the different types of components are different, the problem of finding the rules according to which the components should be assigned priorities in servicing and the way they should be repaired or replaced is essentially a multiple finite-source priority problem. We may repeat that although the stochastic models for the reliability and queuing problems are identical, the characteristics of interest are different. Some work in this direction has recently been completed by Natarajan [61]. We hope that the study of more complex priority models will help in evolving better maintenance procedures for complex equipment so as to optimize system reliability.

7. Discretionary Processes

In Chapter VI, we studied the effect of allowing the server to exercise discretion in exogenous priority systems. We evaluated an optimal choice of z, the "discretion point" between the head-of-the-line and preemptive-resume disciplines. However, discretion can be used in a wider sense. By allowing discretion, one can optimize between various types of exogenous and endogenous systems which may also be helpful in unifying analytical tools for different priority disciplines.

Figure VIII.1 represents a broader classification of discretion in two-class priority processes. The line OA indicates that by using a discretion to partition the service time of the ordinary unit, we can make a transition from the head-of-the-line ($z = 0$) to the preemptive discipline ($z = \infty$). Thus, the discretionary process discussed in Chapter VI helps us in making a continuous transition for the class of exogenous systems from the head-of-the-line discipline to the preemptive disciplines.

One could conceive similiarly of studying the discretion on m_2, the maximum number of ordinary units which may be serviced during the server's orientation towards ordinary units. Obviously, if $m_2 = 1$,

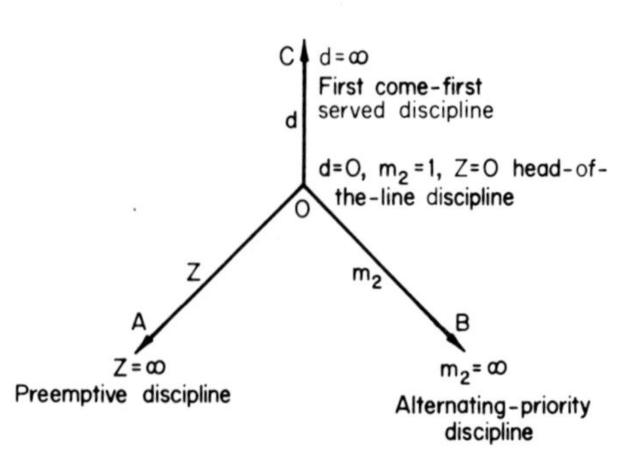

FIG. VIII.1. Classification of discretion in 2-class priority processes.

we get the head-of-the-line priority discipline, while $m_2 = \infty$ corresponds to the alternating-priority discipline. The discretion on m_2 may thus be helpful in optimizing over a broader class of priority disciplines.

Finally, as we noted in Section VII.6, the first-come, first-served and the head-of-the-line disciplines are bounds for dynamic-priority disciplines, since, if we define d as the difference between urgency numbers, we can get to the two bounds by letting d tend to zero and infinity.

Not much appears to have been done using a discretion on m_2 and d. Certainly, further insight into such discretionary processes will help in evolving unifying analytical methods for studying both exogenous and endogenous disciplines.

8. Endogenous Priority Disciplines

It was mentioned in Chapter III that a priority discipline must specify a set of rules by which the server decides which of the units waiting in the system should be taken for service and how it should be serviced. The most crucial of these two is the specification of the first rule. We may define the selection rule based upon the value of a function $D[i, \mathbf{H}_i(t)]$, where i denotes the priority index and $\mathbf{H}_i(t)$ is a vector denoting the characteristics of the ith class as well as the history of the unit at time t, e.g., $\mathbf{H}_i(t)$ may have the elements $\hat{\mathscr{M}}_i(t)$, $\hat{\mathscr{W}}_i(t)$, etc. Note that $\hat{\mathscr{W}}_i(t)$ represents the amount of time the ith class unit under consideration has already waited at time t. The simplest assumption about the form of $D[i, \mathbf{H}_i(t)]$ can be made by considering it to be independent of $\mathbf{H}_i(t)$. Such priority disciplines were called exogenous priority disciplines. Since no information about $\mathbf{H}_i(t)$ is required at the time of decision making, such rules are easy to implement but need not be optimal. What we tried to do was to investigate optimality in the class of exogenous disciplines only and to evolve a few optimal rules.

However, since $D[i, \mathbf{H}_i(t)]$ is independent of $\mathbf{H}_i(t)$, the effect of long waiting lines or the presence of a unit which has been waiting for a long time does not influence the decision making, and hence, in such systems, the priority units get preferential treatment totally at the cost of pushing the lower priority units away from service. This may be against the service system objectives; for example, if each unit is to be serviced before a certain maximum time limit, whatever the priority class may be, the function $D[i, \mathbf{H}_i(t)]$ must be a function of $\mathbf{H}_i(t)$. The $\mathbf{H}_i(t)$ will then be function of the waiting times of the ith class. In general, given a certain objective function, the problem is to determine a suitable decision function $D[i, \mathbf{H}_i(t)]$.

Obviously, the analytic difficulties associated with the study of priority systems with complicated decision functions limit such attempts. Another limiting factor is its implementation. It may be possible to simulate and obtain information about the effect of imposing a certain priority decision rule in specific situations, but much more analytic effort is needed in designing decision rules which may be easier to implement. We may refer to the work of Fine and McIsaac [102], Rothkopf [75], Carroll [15], and Scherr [76] for simulation studies pertaining to job-shop scheduling and time-sharing systems which may be of help in attempts at simulation for priority systems with complicated decision rules.

However, more analytic effort is needed to understand the behavior of complicated systems and thus help in improving the efficiency of real life systems. It is hoped that the present work will help stimulate further effort in this direction.

APPENDIX I

Lemma 1

Consider two sequences $\{a_m\}$ $(m = 1, 2,..., N)$ and $\{b_m\}$ $(m = 0, 1,..., N - 1)$, such that

$$b_m = \sum_{j=m}^{N-1} \binom{j}{m} a_{N-j} \qquad (m = 0, 1,..., N - 1) \tag{1}$$

then,

$$a_r = \sum_{k=0}^{r-1} (-1)^k \binom{N - r + k}{k} b_{N-r+k} \qquad (r = 1, 2,..., N) \tag{2}$$

Proof. Substituting the value of b_m from Eq. (1), the right-hand side of Eq. (2) can be written as

$$\sum_{k=0}^{r-1} (-1)^k \binom{N - r + k}{k} \sum_{j=N-r+k}^{N-1} \binom{j}{N - r + k} a_{N-j}$$

$$= \sum_{j=0}^{r-1} \binom{N - r + j}{j} a_{r-j} \sum_{k=0}^{j} (-1)^k \binom{j}{k} = a_r$$

because

$$\sum_{k=0}^{j} (-1)^k \binom{j}{k} = \begin{matrix} 1 & \text{if } j = 0 \\ 0 & \text{if } j \neq 0 \end{matrix}$$

We define $\{b_m\}$ as a "transformed sequence" of $\{a_m\}$ and the relation (1) as a "discrete transform." We call such relations discrete transforms because of their use in converting differential difference equations into simpler equations, the solution of which can be inverted.

Lemma 2

The generating function $A(\alpha)$ of the sequence $\{a_n\}$ $(n = 1, 2, \ldots, N)$ is given by

$$A(\alpha) = \sum_{m=1}^{N} \alpha^m a_m = \sum_{k=0}^{N-1} \alpha^{N-k}(1-\alpha)^k\, b_k \tag{3}$$

where $\{b_k\}$ is the transformed sequence of $\{a_k\}$.

Proof. Using (2) we get

$$A(\alpha) = \sum_{m=1}^{N} \alpha^m \sum_{e=0}^{m-1} (-1)^e \binom{N-m+e}{e} b_{N-m+e}$$

Setting $N - m + e = k$, we get

$$A(\alpha) = \sum_{m=1}^{N} \alpha^m \sum_{k=N-m}^{N-1} (-1)^{k+m-N} \binom{k}{k+m-N} b_k \tag{4}$$

Changing the order of summation, we can write (4) as

$$A(\alpha) = \sum_{k=0}^{N-1} \alpha^{N-k} b_k \sum_{m=N-k}^{N} (-1)^{k+m-N} \binom{k}{k+m-N} \alpha^{m+k-N}$$

$$= \sum_{k=0}^{N-1} \alpha^{N-k} b_k \sum_{r=0}^{k} (-1)^r \binom{k}{r} \alpha^r$$

$$= \sum_{k=0}^{N-1} \alpha^{N-k}(1-\alpha)^k\, b_k \tag{5}$$

In addition,

$$A(1) = b_0 \tag{6}$$

$$A'(1) = \sum_{m=1}^{N} m a_m = N b_0 - b_1 \tag{7}$$

so that the moments can be calculated directly from the transform.

Lemma 3

Consider the sequences $\{a_m\}$ ($m = 0, 1, \ldots, N-1$) and $\{b_m\}$ ($m = 0, 1, \ldots, N-1$), such that

$$b_m = \sum_{j=m}^{N-1} \binom{j}{m} a_j \qquad (m = 0, 1, \ldots, N-1) \tag{8}$$

Then the inverse relation is given by

$$a_r = \sum_{k=r}^{N-1} (-1)^{k-r} \binom{k}{r} b_r \qquad (r = 0, 1, \ldots, N-1) \tag{9}$$

Proof. The proof of this lemma is as in lemma 1.

Lemma 4

Consider the sequence $\{a_m\}$ ($m = 1, 2, \ldots, N$) and $\{b_m\}$ $m = (0, 1, \ldots, N-1)$, such that

$$b_m = \sum_{j=N-m}^{N} (-\theta)^{j+m-N} \binom{j-1}{j+m-N} \sum_{k=N-j}^{N-1} \binom{k}{N-j} a_{N-k} \tag{10}$$

$$(m = 0, 1, \ldots, N-1)$$

then the inverse relation is given by

$$a_n = \sum_{j=N-n}^{N-1} (-1)^{j+n-N} \binom{j}{j+n-N} \sum_{k=0}^{j} \theta^{j-k} \binom{N-1-k}{j-k} b_k \tag{11}$$

$$(n = 1, 2, \ldots, N)$$

Proof. The proof follows from the observation that (10) consists essentially of two transforms, namely,

$$b'_m = \sum_{k=m}^{N-1} \binom{k}{m} a_{N-k} \qquad (m = 0, 1, \ldots, N-1) \tag{12}$$

and

$$b_m = \sum_{j=N-m}^{N} (-\theta)^{j+m-N} \binom{j-1}{j+m-N} b'_{N-j} \qquad (m = 0, 1, \ldots, N-1) \tag{13}$$

Relation (12) is the same as (1), and the inverse relationship is given by (2). The inverse for (13) is given by

$$b'_m = \sum_{j=0}^{m} \theta^{m-j} \binom{N-1-j}{N-1-m} b_j \tag{14}$$

Using (2) and (14), (11) follows.

Lemma 5

The generating function $A(\alpha)$ of the sequence $\{a_n\}$ defined in lemma 4 is given by

$$A(\alpha) = \alpha \sum_{n=0}^{N-1} (1-\alpha)^n [\theta + (1-\theta)\alpha]^{N-n-1} b_n \tag{15}$$

Proof:

$$A(\alpha) = \sum_{n=1}^{N} \alpha^n a_n$$

$$= \sum_{n=1}^{N} \alpha^n \sum_{N-n}^{N-1} (-1)^{j+n-N} \binom{j}{j+n-N} b'_j$$

$$= \alpha^N \sum_{n=0}^{N-1} \left(\frac{1-\alpha}{\alpha}\right)^n b'_n \tag{16}$$

Using the relation (14), it can be shown in a similar manner that

$$\sum_{n=0}^{N-1} z^n b'_n = \sum_{n=0}^{N-1} z^n (1+\theta z)^{N-n-1} b_n \tag{17}$$

Hence, using the result (17) in (16), (15) follows

Lemma 6

Consider the sequence $\{b_n\}$ $(n = 1, 2, \ldots, N)$ such that

$$b_n = \sum_{k=0}^{n-1} f_{n-k} \binom{N-n+k}{k} \sum_{e=0}^{k} (-1)^e \binom{k}{e} g_{N-n+e} \tag{18}$$

then, the generating function $B(\alpha)$ of this sequence is given by

$$B(\alpha) = \sum_{n=1}^{N} \alpha^n b_n = \sum_{j=0}^{N-1} \alpha^{N-j} (1-\alpha)^j g_j u_j \tag{19}$$

where $\{u_j\}$ is the transformed sequence of $\{f_j\}$ defined as in (1) i.e.,

$$u_j = \sum_{m=j}^{N-1} \binom{m}{j} f_{N-m} \tag{20}$$

Proof. Putting $N - n + e = e'$ in the last summation, (18) can be written as

$$b_n = \sum_{k=0}^{n-1} f_{n-k} \binom{N-n+k}{k} \sum_{e'=N-n}^{N-n+k} (-1)^{e'+n-N} \binom{k}{e' - N + n} g_{e'} \quad (21)$$

and putting $n' = n - k$, we have

$$b_n = \sum_{n'=1}^{n} f_{n'} \binom{N-n'}{n-n'} \sum_{e'=N-n}^{N-n'} (-1)^{e'+n-N} \binom{n-n'}{e' - N + n} g_{e'} \quad (22)$$

Changing the order of summation, we get

$$b_n = \sum_{e'=N-n}^{N-1} (-1)^{e'+n-N} g_{e'}$$

$$\times \sum_{n'=1}^{N-e'} \frac{(N-n')!}{(n-n')!\,(N-n)!} \frac{(n-n')!}{(e'-N+n)!\,(N-e'-n')!} f_{n'} \quad (23)$$

$$= \sum_{e'=N-n}^{N-1} (-1)^{e'+n-N} \binom{e'}{e'+n-N} g_{e'} \sum_{j=e'}^{N-1} \binom{j}{e'} f_{N-j} \quad (24)$$

$$= \sum_{e'=N-n}^{N-1} (-1)^{e'+n-N} \binom{e'}{e'+n-N} g_{e'} u_{e'} \quad (25)$$

where $u_{e'}$ is given by (20).

Using (4) of lemma 2, the result follows.

APPENDIX II

In Appendix I, we defined those discrete transforms which we have mainly used in this book. The discrete transform method is, however, quite general and for a given set of differential difference equations, suitable discrete transform can be defined by following a systematic procedure which we discuss below:

Let $\mathbf{X}$ and $\mathbf{C}$ be $(N \times 1)$ column vectors and $\mathbf{P}$ a $(N \times N)$ matrix. Consider the matrix equation

$$(\theta \mathbf{I} - \mathbf{P})\,\mathbf{X} = \mathbf{C} \tag{1}$$

where θ is a scalar and $\mathbf{I}$ is the identity matrix.

Then if $\mathbf{P}$ can be reduced to diagonal form, say $\mathbf{P} = \mathbf{Q}^{-1}\mathbf{\Lambda}\mathbf{Q}$ where $\mathbf{\Lambda}$ is a diagonal matrix, the Eq. (1) on premutiplying by $\mathbf{Q}$ becomes

$$(\theta \mathbf{I} - \mathbf{\Lambda})\,\mathbf{Y} = \mathbf{D} \tag{2}$$

where

$$\mathbf{Y} = \mathbf{QX} \tag{3}$$

and

$$\mathbf{D} = \mathbf{QC} \tag{4}$$

Now, $\mathbf{Q}$ is the transformation matrix which transforms $\mathbf{X}$ to $\mathbf{Y}$ and vector $\mathbf{Y}$ defines the required discrete transform of vector $\mathbf{X}$.

GLOSSARY OF SYMBOLS

Only those symbols which have been used consistently are listed below. Since, throughout this book, the density function of a random variable f has been denoted by $f(t)$, only the density functions are listed below, since it would be redundant to list both the random variables and the density functions.

$b^i(t)$	Busy-period density initiated by $i > 0$ units for the basic infinite or finite-source models.
$b^{\Omega}(t)$	Initial busy-period density with the initial occupation-time density $\Omega(t)$ for the basic infinite or finite-source models.
$B_j(t)$	Busy-period density of the jth-class ($j > 1$) unit in isolation with the service time replaced by completion time.
$\gamma_k(t)$	Busy-period density for the k-class priority process.
$\gamma_j^{(k)}(t)$	Density of the busy-period duration for units with priority index $\leqslant j$ for the k-class priority process.
$\gamma_k{}^{\Omega}(t)$	Initial busy period for the k-class priority process with initial occupation-time density $\Omega(t)$.
$c_j(t)$	Completion-time density of the jth-class unit.
$\hat{d}(t)$	Delay-time density for a unit in the basic infinite or finite-source models.
$DM_i^{(k)}$	Design measure of the ith-class units in a k-class priority process.
$\hat{\mathscr{D}}_j(t)$	Delay-time density for the jth-class unit in a priority process.
$\hat{e}^i(t)$	Probability that the server is idle at time t for the basic infinite and finite-source models given that the process started with $i \geqslant 0$ units at $t = 0$.
$\hat{e}^{(k)}(t)$	Probability that the server is idle at time t for the k-class priority process given that the server is in the idle state at $t = 0$.

$f^I(\cdots)$, $g^I(\cdots)$	Probability densities associated with the part I_k of the completion time c_k.
$g^L(\cdots)$	Probability density associated with part L_k of the completion time c_k.
$\mathscr{G}(\alpha_k, t)$	$= \sum \alpha_k^{m_k} \mathscr{H}(m_k, t)$.
$\mathscr{H}(m_k, t)$	Probability that at time t a kth-class unit enters service leaving behind a queue of $m_k - 1$ units of the kth class during a busy period of a k-class priority process.
I_j	Part of the completion time of the jth-class unit when the jth-class unit is present.
$\mathscr{I}_j(t)$	Instantaneous priority index of the jth class unit at time t.
k	Total number of priority classes.
K_j	Delay cost per unit time for the jth-class unit.
L_j	That part of the completion time of the jth class unit when the jth class unit has left and units of 1, 2,..., $j - 1$ classes are present.
λ_j	Mean arrival rate of the jth-class unit.
$m(t)$, $\hat{m}(t)$	Number of units waiting or being serviced at time t during the busy period and the general process, respectively, of the basic infinite or finite-source models.
$m_j^c(t)$	Number of units of the jth class waiting or being serviced at time t during the completion-time process.
$\mathscr{M}_j(t)$, $\hat{\mathscr{M}}_j(t)$	Number of the jth-class units waiting or being serviced at time t during the busy period and the general processes, respectively, for the priority models.
N_j	Size of the jth source.
ν_j	Mean service time of the jth class unit.
$p(\cdots)$, $q(\cdots)$	Queue length probabilities associated with the busy-period process.
$\hat{p}(\cdots)$, $\hat{q}(\cdots)$	Queue length probabilities associated with the general process.
$p^\Omega(\cdots)$, $q^\Omega(\cdots)$	Queue length probabilities associated with the initial busy-period process.
$p^I(\cdots)$, $p^L(\cdots)$, $p^c(\cdots)$	Queue length probabilities associated with the completion-time process.
$p_e(m, t)$	Probability that at time t a unit enters service leaving behind a queue of $m - 1$ units during a busy period of the basic infinite or finite-source models.
$\Pi(\cdots)$, $\hat{\Pi}(\cdots)$, $\Pi^c(\cdots)$	Generating functions of the queue length probabilities for the busy-period, general, and completion-time processes, respectively.

$S_j(x)$	Service-time density of the jth-class unit.
$\xi^i(t)$, $\hat{\xi}^i(t)$	Occupation time of the server at time t during the busy-period and the general processes, respectively, for the basic infinite or finite-source models initiated with i units at $t = 0$.
$\chi_j(t)$, $\hat{\chi}_j(t)$	Occupation time of the server with respect to the jth-class unit during the busy-period and the general process, respectively, of a priority model.
$\hat{w}(\tau)$	Steady-state occupation-time density of the server for the infinite or finite-source models.
$w(\tau, t)$, $\hat{w}(\tau, t)$	Occupation-time density of the server at time t during the busy-period and the general processes, respectively, of the basic infinite or finite-source models.
$\mathscr{W}_j(\tau, t)$, $\hat{\mathscr{W}}_j(\tau, t)$	Occupation-time density of the server at time t with respect to the jth-class unit during the busy-period and the general processes, respectively, for the priority model.
$\hat{\mathscr{W}}_j(\tau)$	Steady-state occupation-time density for the jth-class unit for the priority model.
$w^{\Omega}(\tau, t)$	Occupation-time density of the server at time t during the initial busy-period process with initial occupation-time density $\Omega(t)$ for the basic infinite or finite-source models.
$w_j{}^c(\tau, t)$	Occupation time of the server at time t with respect to the jth-class unit during the completion-time process.
z	Elapsed service time of a unit.
$\tilde{z}$	Service time of a preempted unit.
(I, 2.7)	Eq. (2.7) of Chapter I.
(2.7)	Eq. (2.7) of the same chapter where the cross-reference is made.
Section I, 4	Section 4 of Chapter I.

REFERENCES

1. H. Ashcroft, The productivity of several machines under the care of one operator, *J. Roy. Stat. Soc.*, Series B **12**, 145–151 (1950).
2. B. Avi-Itzhak, Preemptive repeat priority queues as a special case of the multipurpose server problem, Parts I and II, *Operations Res.* **11**, 597–609, 610–619 (1963).
3. B. Avi-Itzhak, I. Brosh, and P. Naor, On discretionary priority queueing, *Z. Angew. Math. Mech.* **6**, 235–242 (1964).
4. B. Avi-Itzhak, W. L. Maxwell, and L. W. Miller, Queuing with alternating priorities, *Operations Res.* **13**, 306–318 (1965).
5. B. Avi-Itzhak and P. Naor, On a problem of preemptive priority queuing, *Operations Res.* **9**, 664–672 (1961).
6. B. Avi-Itzhak and P. Naor, Some queuing problems with the service station subject to breakdown, *Operations Res.* **11**, 303–320 (1963).
7. R. Bellman, "Dynamic Programming." Princeton Univ. Press, Princeton, New Jersey, 1957.
8. R. Bellman and S. E. Dreyfus, "Applied Dynamic Programming." Princeton Univ. Press, Princeton, New Jersey, 1962.
9. V. E. Beneš, "Mathematical Theory of Connecting Networks and Telephone Traffic" (Mathematics in Science and Engineering Series). Academic Press, New York, 1965.
10. B. A. Benn, Hierarchical Car Pool Systems in Railroad Transportation, Ph.D. Thesis, Case Institute of Technology, Cleveland, Ohio (1966).
11. F. Benson and D. R. Cox, The productivity of machines requiring attention at random intervals, *J. Roy. Stat. Soc.*, Series B **13**, 65–82 (1951).
12. G. Blom, Some contribution to the theory of machine interference, *Biometrika* **50**, 135–143 (1963).
13. I. Brosh and P. Naor, On optimal disciplines in priority queuing, *Bull. Inst. Internat. Statist.* **40**, 593–609 (1963).
14. P. J. Burke, Priority traffic with at most one queuing class, *Operations Res.* **10**, 567–569 (1962).

15. D. C. Carroll, Heuristic Sequencing of Single and Multiple Component Jobs, Ph.D. Thesis, Alfred P. Sloan School of Management, Mass. Inst. Tech., Cambridge, Massachusetts (1965).
16. Wei Chang, Preemptive priority queues, *Operations Res.* **13**, 820–827 (1965).
17. Wei Chang and Donald J. Wong, Analysis of real time multiprogramming, *J. Assoc. Comput. Mach.* **12**, 581–588 (1965).
18. A. Cobham, Priority assignment in waiting line problems, *Operations Res.* **2**, 70–76 (1954).
19. E. G. Coffman, Jr. and R. C. Wood, Interarrival statistics for time sharing systems, *Comm. ACM* **9**, 500–503 (1966).
20. D. R. Cox, The analysis of non-Markovian stochastic processes by the inclusion of supplementary variables, *Proc. Cambridge Philos. Soc.* **51**, 433–441 (1955).
21. D. R. Cox, "Renewal Theory." Methuen, London, 1962.
22. D. R. Cox and W. L. Smith, "Queues." Methuen, London, 1961.
23. R. H. Davis, Waiting-time distribution of a multiserver, priority queuing system, *Operations Res.* **14**, 133–136 (1966).
24. S. A. Dressin and E. Reich, Priority assignment on a waiting line, *Quart. Appl. Math.* **15**, 208–211 (1957).
25. M. Etschmaier, Discretionary Priority Processes, M.S. Thesis, Case Institute of Technology, Cleveland, Ohio (1966).
26. R. V. Evans, "Network Queuing Theory" (*Proceedings of the Short Course on Recent Developments in Operations Research*). Operations Research Group, Case Institute of Technology, Cleveland, Ohio, 1966.
27. R. V. Evans, Sales and restocking policies in a single item inventory system, Tech. Memo **55**, Case Institute of Technology, Cleveland, Ohio (1966).
28. D. P. Gaver, Jr., Imbedded Markov chain analysis of a waiting-line process in continuous time, *Ann. Math. Stat.* **30**, 698–720 (1959).
29. D. P. Gaver, Jr., A waiting line with interrupted service, including priorities, *J. Roy. Stat. Soc.*, Series B **24**, 73–90 (1962).
30. D. P. Gaver, Jr., Competitive queuing: idleness probabilities under priority disciplines, *J. Roy. Stat. Soc.*, Series B **25**, 489–499 (1963).
31. D. P. Gaver, Jr., A comparison of queue disciplines when service orientation times occur, *Nav. Res. Logistics Quart.* **10**, 219–235 (1963).
32. M. Greenberger, The priority problem and computer time sharing, *Management Sci.* **12**, 888–906 (1966).
33. A. G. Hawks, Time-dependent solution of a priority queue with bulk arrival, *Operations Res.* **14**, 586–595 (1966).
34. C. R. Heathcote, The time-dependent problem for a queue with preemptive priorities, *Operations Res.* **7**, 670–680 (1959).
35. C. R. Heathcote, A single queue with several preemptive priority classes, *Operations Res.* **8**, 630–638 (1960).
36. C. R. Heathcote, Preemptive priority queuing, *Biometrika* **48**, 57–63 (1961).
37. W. Helley, Two doctrines for the handling of two priority traffic by a group of *N* servers, *Operations Res.* **10**, 268–269 (1962).
38. V. Hodgson and T. L. Hebble, Non-Preemptive Priorities in Machine Interference, Statistics, Report **M90**, Florida State Univ. Tallahassee, Florida (1965).
39. J. L. Holley, Waiting line subject to priorities, *Operations Res.* **2**, 341–343 (1954).

40. J. R. Jackson, Some problems in queuing with dynamic priorities, *Nav. Res. Logistics Quart.* **7**, 235–249 (1960).
41. J. R. Jackson, Queues with dynamic priority discipline, *Manag. Sci.* **8**, 18–34 (1961).
42. J. R. Jackson, Waiting-time distributions for queues with dynamic priorities, *Nav. Res. Log. Quart.* **9**, 31–36 (1962).
43. H. C. Jain, An inventory problem applied to a rental situation, *Australian J. Statist.* **8**, 154–162 (1966).
44. N. K. Jaiswal, Preemptive resume priority queue, *Operations Res.* **9**, 732–742 (1961).
45. N. K. Jaiswal, Time-dependent solution of the head-of-the-line priority queue, *J. Roy. Stat. Soc.*, Series B **24**, 91–101 (1962).
46. N. K. Jaiswal and K. Thiruvengadam, Preemptive resume priority queue with Erlangian inputs, *Indian J. Math.* **4**, 53–70 (1962).
47. N. K. Jaiswal and K. Thiruvengadam, Simple machine interference with two types of failures, *Operations Res.* **11**, 624–636 (1963).
48. N. K. Jaiswal and K. Thiruvengadam, Finite-source priority queues, Tech. Memo. **49**, Case Institute of Technology, Cleveland, Ohio (1966) (to appear in *SIAM J. Appl. Math.*).
49. J. Keilson, Queues subject to service interruption, *Ann. Math. Statist.* **33**, 1314–1322 (1962).
50. D. G. Kendall, Some problems in the theory of queues, *J. Roy. Stat. Soc.*, Series B **13**, 151–185 (1951).
51. D. G. Kendall, Stochastic processes occurring in the theory of queues and their analysis by the method of imbedded Markov chain, *Ann. Math. Statist.* **24**, 338–354 (1953).
52. H. Kesten and J. Th. Runnenberg, Priority in waiting-line problems I and II, *Nederl. Akad. Wetensch. Proc.*, Series A. **60**, 312–324, 325–336 (1957).
53. A. Ya. Khintchine, Über die mittlere Dauer des Stillstandes von Maschinen, *Mat. Sbornik* **40**, 119–123 (1933).
54. L. Kleinrock, A delay dependent queue discipline, *Nav. Res. Log. Quart.* **11**, 329–341 (1964).
55. L. Kleinrock, Queuing with strict and lag priority mixtures, *Proc. 4th Intern. Conf. Operational Res.* Boston, Massachusetts (1966).
56. B. Krishnamoorthi, The stationary behavior of a time-sharing system under Poisson assumptions, *OPSEARCH* (*India*) **3**, 101–117 (1966).
57. B. Krishnamoorthi and R. C. Wood, Time shared computer operations with interarrival and service times exponential, *J. Assoc. Comput. Mach.* **13**, 317–338 (1966).
58. J. D. C. Little, A proof for the queuing formula $L = \lambda W$, *Operations Res.* **9**, 383–387 (1961).
59. P. Mevert, The alternating queuing process with setup times, Tech. Memo **63**, Case Institute of Technology, Cleveland, Ohio (1966).
60. W. L. Maxwell, An Investigation of Multi-Product, Single-Machine Scheduling and Inventory Problems, Ph.D. Thesis, Cornell University, Ithaca, New York (1961).
61. L. W. Miller, Alternating Priorities in Multi-Class Queues, Ph.D. Thesis, Cornell University, Ithaca, New York (1964).

62. R. G. Miller, Priority queues, *Ann. Math. Statist.* **31**, 86–103 (1960).
63. P. M. Morse, "Queues, Inventories, and Maintenance." Wiley, New York, 1958.
64. P. Naor, On machine interference, *J. Roy. Stat. Soc.*, Series B **18**, 280–287 (1956).
65. P. Naor, Normal approximation to machine interference with many repair men, *J. Roy. Stat. Soc.*, Series B **19**, 334–341 (1957).
66. P. Naor, Some problems of machine interference, *Proc. First Intern. Conf. Operations Res.* 147–164 (1957). English Univ. Press, Oxford.
67. R. Natarajan, Assignment of priority in improving system reliability, to appear in *IEEE Trans. Reliability*. **R-16**, (1967).
68. R. M. Oliver and G. Pestalozzi, On a problem of optimum priority classification, *J. Soc. Indust. Appl. Math.* **13**, 890–901 (1965).
69. C. Palm, Arbtskvaftnes Ferdelning Vid Beljening ar Autom Matmaskener, *Ind. Norden* **75**, 75–80, 90–94, 119–123 (1947).
70. C. Palm, The assignment of operators to servicing automatic machines, *J. Indust. Eng.* **6**, 28–42 (1955).
71. E. Parzen, "Stochastic Processes." Holden-Day, San Francisco, California, 1962.
72. T. E. Phipps, Jr., Machine repair as a priority waiting-line problem, *Operations Res.* **4**, 76–85 (1956).
73. B. A. Powell, Priority Problems in Inventory Control, Ph.D. Thesis (to be submitted), Case Institute of Technology, Cleveland, Ohio (1967).
74. N. U. Prabhu, "Stochastic Processes," Macmillan, New York, 1965.
75. M. Rothkoff, Scheduling Independent Tasks on One or More Processors, Interim Techn. Report **2**, Operations Research Center, Mass. Inst. Tech., Cambridge, Massachusetts (1964).
76. A. L. Scherr, An Analysis of Time-Shared Computer Systems, Ph.D. Thesis, Project MAC-TR-18, Mass. Inst. Tech., Cambridge, Massachusetts (1965).
77. L. E. Scharge and L. W. Miller, The queue $M/G/1$ with the shortest remaining processing time discipline, *Operations Res.* **14**, 670–684 (1966).
78. L. Schwartz, Théorie des Distributions, I, II. Hermann, Paris, 1950.
79. W. L. Smith, Asymptotic renewal theorems, *Proc. Roy. Soc. (Edinburgh)* **64**, 9–48 (1954).
80. S. Subba Rao, Balking and Reneging in Waiting Line Systems, Ph.D. Thesis, University of Delhi, Delhi, India (1966).
81. S. Subba Rao, The effect of postponable interruptions on a $M/G/1$ system with impatient customers, *Austral. J. Statist.* **9**, 16–34 (1967).
82. F. F. Stephan, Two queues under preemptive priority with Poisson arrival and service rates, *Operations Res.* **6**, 399–418 (1958).
83. M. Tainiter, Some stochastic inventory models for rental situations, *Manag. Sci.* **11**, 316–326 (1964).
84. L. Takács, Probabilistic treatment of the simultaneous stoppage of machines with consideration of the waiting times, *Magyar Tud. Akad. Mat. Fiz. Oszt. Közl.* **1**, 228–234 (1951).
85. L. Takács, On the limiting distribution of the number of coincidences concerning telephone traffic, *Ann. Math. Statist.* **30**, 134–142 (1959).
86. L. Takács, "Introduction to the Theory of Queues." Oxford Univ. Press, New York, 1962.
87. L. Takács, Priority queues, *Operations Res.* **12**, 63–74 (1964).

88. K. Thiruvengadam, Queuing with breakdowns, *Operations Res.* **11**, 62–71 (1963).
89. K. Thiruvengadam, A generalization of queuing with breakdowns, *Defence Sci. J.* (*India*) **14**, 1–16 (1964).
90. K. Thiruvengadam, Machine interference problem with limited server's availability, *OPSEARCH* (*India*) **2**, 65–84 (1965).
91. K. Thiruvengadam, Studies in Waiting Line Problems, Ph.D. Thesis, University of Delhi, Delhi, India (1965).
92. K. Thiruvengadam and N. K. Jaiswal, The stochastic law of busy periods for the simple machine interference problem, *Defence Sci. J.* (*India*) **13**, 263–270 (1963).
93. K. Thiruvengadam and N. K. Jaiswal, Application of discrete transforms to a queuing process of servicing machines, *OPSEARCH* (*India*) **1**, 87–105 (1964).
94. K. Thiruvengadam, A priority assignment in machine interference problem, *OPSEARCH* (*India*) **1**, 197–216 (1964).
95. R. E. Thomas, Discussion on the Paper of D. P. Gaver, Jr., *in* "Proceedings of the Symposium on Congestion Theory" (Univ. North Carolina Monograph Series in Probability and Statistics), 241–244, 1965.
96. P. D. Welch, Some Contribution to the Theory of Priority Queues, Ph.D. Thesis, Columbia University, New York (1963).
97. P. D. Welch, On preemptive resume priority queues, *Ann. Math. Statist.* **35**, 600–612 (1964).
98. H. White and L. S. Christie, Queuing with preemptive priorities or with breakdown, *Operations Res.* **6**, 79–95 (1958).
99. E. G. Coffman, Stochastic Models of Multiple and Time-Shared Computer Operations, Department of Engineering Report No. 66-38, Univ. California, Los Angeles, California (1966).
100. E. G. Coffman and L. Kleinrock, Some feedback queuing models for time-shared systems (to be published).
101. D. W. Fife, Scheduling with random arrivals and linear loss functions, *Management Sci.* **11**, 429–437 (1965).
102. G. H. Fine and P. V. McIsaac, Simulation of a Time-Sharing System, System Development Corporation Report No. SP-1909, Santa Monica, California (1964).
103. A. J. Fabens, The solution of queuing and inventory models by semi-Markov processes, *J. Roy. Stat. Soc., Series B* **23**, 113–127 (1961).
104. G. Estrin and L. Kleinrock, Measures, Models and Measurements for Time-Shared Computer Utilities, Department of Engineering Internal Memorandum No. 51, Univ. California, Los Angeles, California (1967).
105. L. Kleinrock, "Communication Nets; Stochastic Message Flow and Delay." McGraw-Hill, New York, 1964.
106. L. Kleinrock, Sequential processing machines (S.P.M.) analyzed with a queuing theory model, *J. Assoc. Comput. Mach.* **13**, 179–193 (1966).
107. L. Kleinrock and Roy P. Finkelstein, Time dependent priority queues, *Operations Res.* **15**, 104–116 (1967).
108. N. R. Patel, A Mathematical Analysis of Computer Time-Sharing Systems, M.S. Thesis, Department of Electrical Engineering, Mass. Inst. Tech., Cambridge, Massachusetts (1964).

109. L. E. Schrage, The queue $M/G/1$ with feedback to lower priority queues, *Management Sci.* **13**, 466–474 (1967).
110. R. Pyke, Markov renewal processes: Definitions and preliminary properties, *Ann. Math. Statist.* **32**, 1231–1242 (1961).
111. R. Pyke, Markov renewal processes with finitely many states, *Ann. Math. Statist.* **32**, 1243–1259 (1961).

SUBJECT INDEX

Mathematics in Science and Engineering

A Series of Monographs and Textbooks

Edited by RICHARD BELLMAN, *University of Southern California*

1. Tracy Y. Thomas. Concepts from Tensor Analysis and Differential Geometry. Second Edition. 1965
2. Tracy Y. Thomas. Plastic Flow and Fracture in Solids. 1961
3. Rutherford Aris. The Optimal Design of Chemical Reactors: A Study in Dynamic Programming. 1961
4. Joseph LaSalle and Solomon Lefschetz. Stability by Liapunov's Direct Method with Applications. 1961
5. George Leitmann (ed.). Optimization Techniques: With Applications to Aerospace Systems. 1962
6. Richard Bellman and Kenneth L. Cooke. Differential-Difference Equations. 1963
7. Frank A. Haight. Mathematical Theories of Traffic Flow. 1963
8. F. V. Atkinson. Discrete and Continuous Boundary Problems. 1964
9. A. Jeffrey and T. Taniuti. Non-Linear Wave Propagation: With Applications to Physics and Magnetohydrodynamics. 1964
10. Julius T. Tou. Optimum Design of Digital Control Systems. 1963
11. Harley Flanders. Differential Forms: With Applications to the Physical Sciences. 1963
12. Sanford M. Roberts. Dynamic Programming in Chemical Engineering and Process Control. 1964
13. Solomon Lefschetz. Stability of Nonlinear Control Systems. 1965
14. Dimitris N. Chorafas. Systems and Simulation. 1965
15. A. A. Pervozvanskii. Random Processes in Nonlinear Control Systems. 1965
16. Marshall C. Pease, III. Methods of Matrix Algebra. 1965
17. V. E. Benes. Mathematical Theory of Connecting Networks and Telephone Traffic. 1965
18. William F. Ames. Nonlinear Partial Differential Equations in Engineering. 1965
19. J. Aczel. Lectures on Functional Equations and Their Applications. 1966
20. R. E. Murphy. Adaptive Processes in Economic Systems. 1965
21. S. E. Dreyfus. Dynamic Programming and the Calculus of Variations. 1965
22. A. A. Fel'dbaum. Optimal Control Systems. 1965
23. A. Halanay. Differential Equations: Stability, Oscillations, Time Lags. 1966
24. M. Namik Oguztoreli. Time-Lag Control Systems. 1966
25. David Sworder. Optimal Adaptive Control Systems. 1966
26. Milton Ash. Optimal Shutdown Control of Nuclear Reactors. 1966
27. Dimitris N. Chorafas. Control System Functions and Programming Approaches (In Two Volumes). 1966
28. N. P. Erugin. Linear Systems of Ordinary Differential Equations. 1966
29. Solomon Marcus. Algebraic Linguistics; Analytical Models. 1967
30. A. M. Liapunov. Stability of Motion. 1966

31. George Leitmann (ed.). Topics in Optimization. 1967
32. Masanao Aoki. Optimization of Stochastic Systems. 1967
33. Harold J. Kushner. Stochastic Stability and Control. 1967
34. Minoru Urabe. Nonlinear Autonomous Oscillations. 1967
35. F. Calogero. Variable Phase Approach to Potential Scattering. 1967
36. A. Kaufmann. Graphs, Dynamic Programming, and Finite Games. 1967
37. A. Kaufmann and R. Cruon. Dynamic Programming: Sequential Scientific Management. 1967
38. J. H. Ahlberg, E. N. Nilson, and J. L. Walsh. The Theory of Splines and Their Applications. 1967
39. Y. Sawaragi, Y. Sunahara, and T. Nakamizo. Statistical Decision Theory in Adaptive Control Systems. 1967
40. Richard Bellman. Introduction to the Mathematical Theory of Control Processes Volume I. 1967 (Volumes II and III in preparation)
41. E. Stanley Lee. Quasilinearization and Invariant Imbedding. 1968
42. William Ames. Nonlinear Ordinary Differential Equations in Transport Processes. 1968
43. Willard Miller, Jr. Lie Theory and Special Functions. 1968
44. Paul B. Bailey, Lawrence F. Shampine, and Paul E. Waltman. Nonlinear Two Point Boundary Value Problems. 1968
45. Iu. P. Petrov. Variational Methods in Optimum Control Theory. 1968
46. O. A. Ladyzhenskaya and N. N. Ural'tseva. Linear and Quasilinear Elliptic Equations. 1968
47. A. Kaufmann and R. Faure. Introduction to Operations Research. 1968
48. C. A. Swanson. Comparison and Oscillation Theory of Linear Differential Equations. 1968
49. Robert Hermann. Differential Geometry and the Calculus of Variations. 1968
50. N. K. Jaiswal. Priority Queues. 1968

In preparation

Robert P. Gilbert. Function Theoretic Methods in the Theory of Partial Differential Equations

Yudell Luke. The Special Functions and Their Approximations (In Two Volumes)

Hukukane Nikaido. Convex Structures and Economic Theory

V. Lakshmikantham and S. Leela. Differential and Integral Inequalities

King-sun Fu. Sequential Methods in Pattern Recognition and Machine Learning

Masao Iri. Network Flow, Transportation, and Scheduling: Theory and Algorithms